A MESSAGE FROM

Independence Blue Cross

and

Pennsylvania Blue Shield

**Independence
Blue Cross
Pennsylvania
Blue Shield**

With the increasing public interest in health care, Independence Blue Cross and Pennsylvania Blue Shield are pleased to join PHILADELPHIA Magazine in the publication of the *PHILADELPHIA Magazine Guide to Good Health.*

Enthusiasm for last year's Guide was most gratifying; it was a big hit with the Magazine's readers, our customers, and the general public. This is why 1994 marks the second straight year of our involvement.

Our co-sponsorship of this publication is not based on public acceptance alone, however. It's also because the Guide is a direct extension of our 'lean on us' corporate philosophy.

Every day of the year our customers lean on us for quality services, and the kind of innovative health insurance products and managed care benefit designs that only Independence Blue Cross, Pennsylvania Blue Shield and our subsidiaries can provide.

As providers of access to health care services for more than 2 million people in this region, we are situated at the very center of the region's health care delivery system. This vantage point gives us an understanding for what people want and need to know about healthy lifestyles, and about the hospitals, the physicians, and the resources comprising the system itself.

Filling the health information gap is only part of what we do for our customers and for the community. With health care reform so much in the news, it's noteworthy that The Blues have been doing for years much of what's being recommended.

We are the region's insurer of last resort, serving several hundred thousand people who would have no coverage otherwise. We do not medically underwrite, nor do we cancel because of costly illnesses.

Independence Blue Cross is financially strong, and our administrative costs are among the lowest in the nation. In addition, we offer a comprehensive range of products encompassing traditional indemnity coverage, as well as managed care programs which emphasize provider networks and preventive care.

Perhaps it's because of our interest in preventive care and healthy lifestyles that we applaud the Guide to Good Health for organizing and localizing so much of what's new, and not-so-new, on today's health care scene.

Independence Blue Cross, Pennsylvania Blue Shield and Philadelphia Magazine are pleased to make the Guide available. We hope you use it well, and often.

And if you need to "lean on us" in some specific way, please turn the page to find out how.

Independence Blue Cross Pennsylvania Blue Shield

Lean on us.

INDEPENDENCE BLUE CROSS

General Offices

215-241-2400

Group Sales

215-241-3400

CUSTOMER SERVICE

Direct Pay - 215-568-8204

Small Group - 215-568-3800

Large Group - 215-567-5959

National Group - 215-567-5667

Caring Program for Children - 1-800-464-KIDS

Personal Choice - 1-800-626-8144

Keystone Health Plan East - 215-241-2001

Corporate Communications - 215-241-3131

Hearing Impaired - 215-241-2944 (TDD)

Spanish Language Line (Se Habla Español) - 215-241-2949

Philadelphia
MAGAZINE

Guide to Good Health

by Carol Saline

Researched by Michelle J. Felzer

Guide to Good Health, produced by *Philadelphia Magazine.*

EDITOR, *Carol Saline;* CHIEF RESEARCHER, *Michelle J. Felzer;* RESEARCH ASSISTANT, *Susan Kirschbaum;* BOOK DESIGNER, *Paradigm:design;* ILLUSTRATOR, *Jenny Lynn;* CHIEF COPY EDITOR, *Robert Huber;* TYPESETTER, *Timothy Haas;* CONTRIBUTING WRITERS, *Pamela Albert, Marta McCave, Margaret Pantridge, Ronnie Polaneczky;* PUBLICATION MANAGER, *Jodie Green*

DIRECTOR OF ADVERTISING/SPECIAL PROJECTS, *Carmen N. Hist;* ASSISTANT TO THE DIRECTOR, *Meredith D. Bass;* SENIOR ACCOUNT EXECUTIVES, *Deborah K. Long, Michele S. Freiberg, Amy Huskey Marrone;* ACCOUNT EXECUTIVES, *Amy Freedman Goldberg, Deborah S. Hoxter, Joseph T. Sosnowski, Elizabeth Segal;* ADVERTISING SALES ASSISTANT, *Cara I. Meyers;* PRODUCTION MANAGER, *Deborah A. Cassell;* ASSISTANT PRODUCTION MANAGER, *Michele Murati;* ADVERTISING DESIGNER, *Carla Coutts-Miners;* ASSISTANT ADVERTISING DESIGNER, *Lori Sabatini;* DIRECTOR OF MARKETING, *Stephanie LaFair Smith;* PROMOTION DIRECTOR, *Sherry L. Litwer;* CIRCULATION MANAGER, *A. Carmen Colavita;* MANAGER OF INFORMATION SYSTEMS, *Daniel J. Shimberg;* CONTROLLER, *Mary F. Gruszka;* CREDIT MANAGER, *Pat John Romanelli*

CHAIRMAN, *D. Herbert Lipson;* PRESIDENT AND PUBLISHER, *David H. Lipson Jr.;* EDITOR, *Eliot Kaplan;* VP/TREASURER, *Frederick B. Waechter Jr.;* ASSOCIATE PUBLISHER/DIRECTOR OF ADVERTISING, *Marian Hettel*

Table of Contents

4

SECTION FIVE
The Healthy Woman

SECTION SIX
Mind Over Matter

SECTION SEVEN
Wisdom for the Aging

SECTION EIGHT
For Your Information

Philadelphia Magazine's Guide to Good Health (ISBN 0-9635666-2-8) is published at 1818
Market Street, Philadelphia, PA 19103-3682; 215-564-7700. All contents of this guide are
copyrighted 1994 by *Philadelphia Magazine* and Metro Health, division of METROCORP™.

Three Solid Reasons Why More Than Two Million People...
Lean On Us.

1. Traditional Blue Cross & Blue Shield

Traditional Independence Blue Cross and Pennsylvania Blue Shield coverage comes with a broad, comprehensive benefit package and great freedom of choice. In fact, you are able to use virtually any doctor, specialist or hospital you want for care-with all the dependability you've come to expect from 56 years of healthcare expertise.

2. Personal Choice ℠

With Personal Choice, there's no need to enroll with a Primary Care Physician, and you don't need a referral to see a specialist. Best of all, with Personal Choice, you get the economy of an HMO with the flexibility of Traditional coverage-featuring a network of more than 60 area hospitals and over 5,000 physicians and specialists.

3. Keystone Health Plan East

Only Keystone offers all the benefits of an HMO backed by Independence Blue Cross and Pennsylvania Blue Shield. The area's fastest growing HMO, Keystone combines excellent coverage with superior managed care through 63 of the area's finest hospitals and over 5,500 physicians and specialists.

More and more Delaware Valley residents are **Leaning On Us** for their healthcare needs. Reason? It's because we have health plans to fit everyone's needs. From Traditional, to Personal Choice, to Keystone-we have it all! To find out how you can lean on us, call (215) 241-3400.

Lean On Us.
SM Service mark of Independence Blue Cross & Blue Shield.

Independence Blue Cross Pennsylvania Blue Shield

® Registered marks of the Blue Cross & Blue Shield Association.

1

Prevention Is the Best Medicine

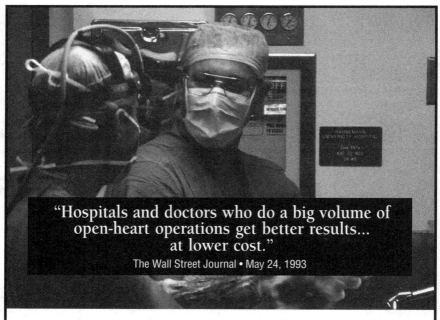

"Hospitals and doctors who do a big volume of open-heart operations get better results... at lower cost."

The Wall Street Journal • May 24, 1993

It makes us better.

IN CARDIAC CARE, EXPERIENCE IS EVERYTHING. ■ And in Philadelphia, no one is more experienced than The Heart Hospital at Hahnemann University. ■ The first modern heart surgery in America was performed by a Hahnemann doctor. Today, there are more cardiac surgical procedures performed here than at any other Philadelphia hospital. ■ And with expertise in every aspect of cardiac care—such as catheterization, echocardiography, and electrophysiology—we're leading the way in treating heart disease. ■ Experience doesn't just make us bigger...it makes us better.

For information about cardiac care call 215-762-3627.

THE HEART HOSPITAL
— *at* —
Hahnemann
University™

Philadelphia's First Team in Cardiac Care

BROAD & VINE • PHILADELPHIA

CHAPTER 1

Testing, Testing . . .

. . . and more testing. Billions of dollars' worth of medical tests may be unnecessary. And that includes the all-purpose annual physical

Just try to remember the last time you visited a doctor and didn't wind up having some kind of medical test. Feeling tired? Let's do a complete blood workup for $300. Complaining of headaches? Go get a CAT scan for $846. Just a routine checkup? At the least you'll have a urinalysis and a chest X-ray—$60 for the basic front view, $157 for a four-sided picture. And heaven forbid you've got some tightness in your chest, because you'll probably need an EKG for $121, a stress test for $400 and maybe even a heart catheterization for a whopping $3,900.

Okay, I'm exaggerating—but only slightly. The point is, patients have come to expect, even request, excessive testing, in part because their insurance foots the bill. Granted, the doctor's arsenal of 1,500 available medical tests has removed a lot of the guesswork from health care. But it seems the over-reliance on testing has burgeoned into too much of a good thing, in part because tests are sometimes used to produce income or avoid lawsuits rather than to obtain information.

"No one would suggest that there is anything wrong with a diagnostic test when symptoms indicate a need, but otherwise these tests are just money-makers," says Dr. Edward Pinckney, a California internist and author of *A Patient's Guide to Medical Tests.* Pinckney believes too many tests are fishing expeditions used by doctors in lieu of careful examinations of patients. That's akin to the view of Dr. John Eisenberg, chairman of the department of medicine at Georgetown Medical Center: "More important than an EKG in your pocket," he says, "is developing a relationship with a doctor who knows you, your lifestyle and your family history, and counsels you according to your risks."

Dr. Katalin Roth, vice chairman for general medicine at Pennsylvania Hospital, points out: "Third-party payers [insurance companies] do not reimburse doctors for ten minutes of health counseling. But you get paid $100 for doing an EKG and as much as $250 for a flexible sigmoidoscopy. The way health care is financed, there's little incentive for doctors to spend time talking about important areas like prevention." And as for whether Americans need all the tests they get, according to former Secretary of Health and Human Services Louis Sullivan, "Increasingly we're finding that a substantial portion of the care that's being . . . billed for is of unproven medical necessity and effectiveness."

What drives excess testing

We asked Dr. Arnold Relman, former editor of the *New England Journal of Medicine*, why American doctors do so much testing. One of his explanations was exactly what we'd expected: the profit motive. But the whole answer goes much deeper. An enormous amount of unnecessary testing is motivated by a fear of malpractice litigation. Just in case something goes wrong with a patient, doctors can't afford to be held liable for insufficient diagnostic studies. They engage in exhaustive testing to avoid being accused of negligence. The doctor who does 20 tests on somebody and misses a diagnosis is less likely to lose a lawsuit than the doctor who did only a handful. This self-protection often gets carried to extremes. A local physician told us he overheard a conversation in which a nervous gynecologist mused that maybe he should introduce ultrasound screenings as part of a woman's annual checkup. It seems a colleague of his had been sued for missing an ovarian cancer at a stage when it was too early to be detected by manual probing.

In addition, the inclination to overtest is fueled by our obsession with expert opinions. "Americans with health insurance love to see specialists," Dr. Relman says. "In this country, 75 percent of physicians are specialists who, by their very nature, are trained to do special tests. An awful lot of headaches and chest pains could be handled for far less money by general practitioners." That's precisely the goal of the Clinton health plan and one of the reasons it's expected to lower costs.

Then there is the problem of what Dr. Relman calls "technology assessment." "We've got all this high-tech screening available," he says, "yet we don't know exactly what works and what doesn't. That creates a lot of uncertainty, and as a result we spend an enormous amount on services which haven't been fully evaluated." This is especially true, he explains, when a doctor is in doubt. Doctors have a do-something mentality. Because they want to know all they can, doctors engage in diagnostic overkill, opting for actions that will yield every possible shred of information. For example: While MRIs are superb vehicles for imaging neurological conditions, the machine tends to be used for a raft of other problems that a less expensive CAT scan would reveal just as well.

Tests that are increasingly being viewed as a waste of money for healthy people are:

chest X-rays: should only be done in the presence of symptoms.

electrocardiograms: many people have irregular heartbeats, so without other symptoms or family risks, the results can be misleading; more important, a normal

EKG does not rule out disease in a high-risk patient.

....

stress tests: can be too unpredictable to forecast heart problems.

....

False negatives; false positives

Indeed, many medical tests are highly inaccurate. Some of the most common screenings are riddled with false-positive or false-negative results. "What does it mean psychologically to be called hypercholesterolemic [suffering from abnormally high cholesterol] when you're perfectly healthy, or to suffer through the false-positive of a mammography?" asks Harvard Medical School's Dr. Robert Lawrence. Lawrence chaired the government's Preventive Services Task Force, which questioned the validity of a plethora of routine tests. "This kind of thing does real damage to people. We in modern medicine find great comfort in doing lab tests and concluding things that may not be valid. The measurable tends to drive out the important, and the behavioral issues threatening health [things like smoking, drinking and diet] get ignored because they aren't quantifiable."

A short list of common tests with a significant level of unreliability would include the test for chlamydia, the most common sexually transmitted disease. Its false-positive rate is 10 to 20 percent; the false-negative rate as high as 30 percent. The Lyme disease test is notoriously unreliable. Cholesterol tests from a good laboratory have just a 5 percent inaccuracy rate, but the popular rapid screenings done at health fairs with a finger stick are often inaccurate. If the results are abnormal, have them corroborated before getting nervous. Blood tests for mononucleosis tend to run up to 15 percent false-negative in adults and as high as 50 percent in young children. Today, Pap smears are less likely than before to have a false-negative rate. However, false positives are fairly common and should always be confirmed by retesting.

Probably the biggest offender when it comes to inaccuracy is the routine blood test. Because of the way the machinery for assessing blood is designed, it takes as much time and money for a technician to do one test as it takes to do dozens. So instead of a simple red cell/white cell count, doctors go for the package. This detailed multiphasic blood profile typically contains an alarming false positive in some category—and that opens a Pandora's box. Dr. Marie Savard, a local internist, tells us "it's common, for instance, for a blood test to show an elevated liver enzyme, which usually pans out to be nothing, but it forces the doctor to check on it with lots of expensive tests. Calcium often comes back borderline-high, also requiring expensive testing to rule out problems that never existed in the first place."

Frequently improper readings are the fault of the laboratory, although that has improved since government regulations now mandate inspections at some 300,000 laboratories. Just as problematic is how to interpret what's normal. It's quite common for someone to fall outside the so-called normal range and yet be perfectly healthy. "We do so much blood testing," explains Dr. Savard, "because it's an inexpensive screening that occasionally picks up kidney disease or diabetes, or liver problems that indicate alcoholism. What's being asked in this era of cost containment is whether those few that are helped by an unexpected finding offset the expense and worry for the far greater numbers who are wrongly diagnosed."

Is this test necessary?

What can you do to break the overused test pattern? The People's Medical Society advises asking your doctor why a test has been requested. Is it because you're a high-risk patient? If not, why bother? What is the test supposed to reveal? How reliable is the lab where the test will be processed, and what's the margin of error for the results? Are there risks? If so, are there safer alternatives that will yield comparable information?

Finally, if something wrong *is* discovered, can it be treated? A friend of ours learned through a routine blood test that she had a very low white-cell count. In an effort to find the cause, she underwent an exhaustive battery of tests; every one came back normal. Though the doctor was convinced she had a nonthreatening abnormality, as a last resort he suggested a bone marrow tap—a fairly radical and painful procedure. "What will it tell me?" she asked. The answer was: nothing that would lead to medical treatment. "Then what's the purpose of going through it?" she pressed. "There really isn't any," the doctor admitted. Together they decided to stop testing. The next time your doctor recommends some kind of medical test, be a partner in the decision.

If there is one trend in testing you want to seriously reconsider, it's the idea of an unnecessary annual physical. Many, many people see a doctor every year even though they're perfectly healthy. They're like the 60-year-old friend of mine who was telling me he had just gotten the results of his yearly checkup and happily, he was in A-okay shape for another year. I asked him if he'd gone to the doctor because something was wrong. "Nope," he replied. "I feel great, and getting checked every year gives me the peace of mind that I'm as healthy as I think I am."

That kind of reassurance may be the *only* reason for healthy people to have an annual checkup. Major studies and reams of research indicate that this staple of American health care may have outlived its usefulness as a general rule. The head-to-toe yearly physical, first introduced in 1914 by the Metropolitan Life Insurance Company for its employees and policyholders, may, like the appendix, have become an anachronism.

The truth about routine exams

That doesn't mean people should see a doctor only if they're sick. But the all-inclusive, expensive ($400 to $500) routine exam no longer makes either medical or economic sense. "The word *routine* checkup implies nonthinking," says Georgetown Medical Center's Dr. Eisenberg. "It's a tragedy that people so often get the tests they don't need, but they don't get the tests they do need. The traditional knee-jerk evaluation without regard to risk factors is bad medicine."

Instead, what doctors and their patients ought to be practicing is an individualized approach to health care based on something called risk assessment.

Using a variety of criteria, doctors today can place patients in high- or low-risk categories; those labels in turn will dictate who needs to be examined for what problems. As Dr. Savard explains, "Today we evaluate patients by looking at their family history, their lifestyle—do they smoke or drink?—various genetic and environmental factors, even their emotional makeup. Then we decide how often to see them and what tests they need. For somebody who has no risks and no symptoms, there are just a few basic areas that need occasional checking. Beyond that, risk factors should be used to determine precisely what needs periodic monitoring." One category of high-risk patient is the person with a family history of a particular disease. In that case you'd want to discuss with your doctor the following tests: for colon cancer, fecal occult blood, sigmoidoscopy or colonoscopy; for diabetes, a fasting plasma glucose; for heart disease, an electrocardiogram; for osteoporosis, a bone mineral content.

Test cases: Mammography and prostate

The question of when to begin mammographies and how often to get them is currently under hot debate. Using the high-risk/low-risk model, a woman whose mother or sister had breast cancer would fall into a high-risk category, requiring annual mammograms as early as age 35. Yet a woman with no family history of breast cancer would fall in a low-risk group and could postpone her first mammography until she's well over 40. Currently the A.C.S. and the N.C.I. recommend mammograms every one or two years for women between 40 and 49. But new studies have challenged whether this frequency is actually useful, and the guidelines are currently being reviewed. Simultaneously, there are other experts claiming that women between 40 and 49 should have yearly mammograms because cancers grow faster in younger women. Let your risk factors be your guide, and when you do have a mammogram, choose a facility accredited by the American College of Radiology.

The PSA blood test for prostate cancer is similarly confusing. It's recommended for men over 50 by the A.C.S., because it ferrets out prostate cancer among high-risk men better than the old digital rectal exam. But the test isn't cheap—$30 to $70—and it's difficult to interpret because it gives misleading signals. So aggressive use among low-risk men is not only wasteful but may lead to rounds of more tests and uncalled-for treatment. *The Philadelphia Inquirer* reported that some doctors think the number of patients who actually live longer as a result of early treatment may be smaller than those unnecessarily harmed.

The value of seeing a family doctor once a year for a pre-set battery of tests first came into question over a decade ago with a landmark report issued for the Canadian National Health Service. Another study in London compared 3,292

patients who'd had regular health checkups with 3,132 who hadn't; the results
showed no appreciable difference in the health of one group compared to the other.
But the strongest argument against routine physicals rose from an exhaustive
research project undertaken from 1984 to 1989 by the United States Preventive
Services Task Force. After collating and reviewing some 2,400 worldwide studies of
the screening and monitoring tests commonly used by doctors—things like X-rays,
blood work, EKGs—it concluded that a vast majority are a waste of time and
money. Simply stated in *The Annals of Internal Medicine:* For the nonpregnant
adult without any symptoms of illness, no evidence supports the need for a complete physical examination as it's usually defined.

The task force found a surprising number of medical staples to be ineffec-
tive—or even useless. Into the don't-bother basket went such customary procedures
as taking the temperature and pulse and breathing rates, chest X-rays and resting
EKGs for patients without any signs of heart disease. The 300-page report contained
a long list of diseases and conditions that could be eliminated from routine screening unless indicated. By contrast, there was a rather short list of mandatory age- and
gender-related evaluations suggested for healthy adults in the average or low-risk
categories. In general, upon reaching the ripe old age of 20 everybody should visit
the dentist annually and get a one-time full-body examination for moles that might
develop into melanoma, the deadliest of skin cancers. Anyone found at risk should
thereafter be checked annually.

The bare essentials

Based on the task-force recommendations, here's a checklist of sensible tests and
screenings for healthy men and women throughout their adult life.

AGE 19-39	*Every 5 years* **Discuss with doctor:** diet, physical activity, drug/alcohol/tobacco use, sexual practices; have a blood pressure screening, a height and weight check, a nonfasting total blood cholesterol. **For women:** a Pap smear
AGE 40-64	*Every 1-3 years* **Discuss with doctor:** diet, physical activity, drug/alcohol/tobacco use, sexual practices; have a blood pressure screening, a height and weight check, a non-fasting total blood cholesterol. **For women:** a Pap smear **For men over 50:** a PSA (prostate screening) every year **For women:** a clinical breast exam, a mammo-gram (bi-annually before age 50)

Age 65 and Over	*Every year* **Discuss with doctor:** diet, physical activity, alcohol/drug/tobacco use, any symptoms related to transient strokes (e.g., weakness, blackouts), functional abilities; test for height and weight, blood pressure, visual acuity, hearing and hearing aids, glaucoma, non-fasting total blood cholesterol, dipstick urinalysis; immunize against influenza and pneumonia. **For women:** clinical breast exam, mammogram, thyroid function **For men:** PSA (prostate screening)

Be wise and immunize

Dr. Katalin Roth includes certain inoculations as part of her recommendations for routine health care: a tetanus booster every ten years after age 20, a flu and pneumonia vaccine after 65 and a revaccination for rubella (measles) for anyone born after 1956. (The vaccine that was first introduced in 1957 and administered until 1965 doesn't give complete protection.) Roth, an advocate of preventive medicine, sums up the attitude among enlightened doctors toward the old-fashioned routine checkup: "I think if an individual has had a blood pressure reading, a cholesterol check and a good family history to assess risks and everything is normal, that person does not need a complete physical with lab tests every year. Those executive physicals are unnecessary. It is useful for everybody to check in occasionally with a doctor who knows them, and a woman should see a gynecologist annually who can manage the rest of her general health care."

Can we talk?

When patients do visit the doctor, it would be valuable if, in addition to poking and prodding, physicians increased their talking and listening. The task force strongly urged family doctors to spend less of their average 12-minute visits with patients on tests and pulse-taking and more on counseling, particularly in those areas where behavioral changes can really modify risks. These include discussions about diet, aerobic exercise, tobacco and drugs, using seat belts, practicing safe sex and buying smoke detectors. Rather than taking chest X-rays, doctors should be advising patients to stop smoking.

Critics of the task force's strong pro-counseling position complained that the government spent money in studying preventive health measures only to conclude that doctors ought to spend more time advising patients about diet and wearing seat belts. Dr. Lawrence's retort: "If we did more of that we'd have a healthier nation and wouldn't need to do all this screening in the first place."

The doctors and scientists at the University of Pennsylvania Medical Center are committed to improving patient care by making new discoveries and developing new treatments. As researchers and educators, we've published more medical articles than the doctors from all other Delaware Valley medical centers combined.

Our patients benefit first from these advances, even before the articles are published. Because we make sure our results move rapidly from the laboratory to the place that matters most: patient care.

If you want to receive the most advanced care, you can wait till others read about it tomorrow. Or you can call the University of Pennsylvania Medical Center for an appointment today.

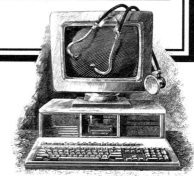

Most doctors learn about advances in medicine from reading journal articles. Our doctors write the articles.

1-800-789-PENN

UNIVERSITY OF
PENNSYLVANIA
MEDICAL CENTER

The future of medicine.℠

The University of Pennsylvania Health System

CHAPTER 2

Barbells Are Not for Dumbbells

If you want to live longer and better, start exercising

Attention couch potatoes! The evidence is in, and it's incontestable: Regular exercise is essential to good health and a longer life. The reason you can't climb a flight of stairs without puffing, can't lift a bag of groceries without straining your back, can't make it through the day without a nap isn't that you're getting older. It's that you're inactive. Many of the physiological changes we normally attribute to getting older—loss of muscle tone, agility, coordination, flexibility and endurance—aren't caused by aging, but by sitting around and channel surfing instead of swimming.

"Over the past five to ten years a wealth of scientific data has shown not only the positive effects of exercise and an active lifestyle but the negative effects of sedentary living as well," says Dr. Nicholas DiNubile, chief of orthopedic surgery at Delaware County Memorial Hospital and special adviser to the President's Council on Physical Fitness. "To put it simply, inactivity is a killer."

The Centers for Disease Control says lack of exercise is the second leading cause of death related to heart disease and a higher risk factor than obesity, smoking or high blood pressure. And other research links inactivity to a variety of problems from stroke to some kinds of cancer. Yet, DiNubile says, as a nation we are less fit and less active than ever before at every age level. "Our children are slower, fatter and weaker than two decades ago. Forty percent of them have at least one major coronary risk factor and 15 to 20 percent are considered obese." Adults don't fare much better.

Better than a magic pill

The benefits of exercise affect virtually every part of the human body. Exercise improves circulation, makes the heart pump more efficiently, strengthens bones and reduces calcium loss. It reduces many kinds of pain and boosts the mood of the depressed and anxious. A variety of studies, including one that followed thousands of Swedish men for many years and one that examined a large group of Harvard alumni, found an increase in colon cancer among men with sedentary jobs. This latter study led the Harvard Medical Letter to conclude that "sitting on one's duff increases the risk of colon cancer by about 50 percent for both men and women."

The role of exercise in preventing heart disease is quite specific. As we age, our maximal heart rate drops anywhere from 3 to 8 percent per decade. Exercise can compensate for this decline by increasing the capacity of the heart to pump blood—and a heart accustomed to pumping at a higher level has less trouble performing on demand. That's what gives an 80-year-old marathon runner the endurance to finish a race, even though it may take him an hour longer than when he was 35. And because aerobic exercise maintains maximum cardiac output, somebody who plays tennis can climb three flights of stairs without puffing, while a bridge player may have trouble going up to his bedroom. And don't kid yourself that the benefits of being a youthful athlete will hang around and help you fight the sloth of a desk job. The data show that prior training adds almost nothing to endurance capacity in later life unless some kind of rigorous activity is continued.

Exercise not only builds endurance, it is a critical aid to dieting. Aging means an inevitable loss of muscle and bone and an addition of fat. A normal, healthy, lean 20-year-old male has about 12 percent body fat, while his 50-plus counterpart has closer to 30 percent. Muscle strength peaks around age 30 and declines at a rate of 1 percent annually, eventually becoming one of the primary reasons that older people fall and injure themselves. A good ratio of strong muscles to fat not only prevents weakness, but also boosts your slowing metabolism. "The more muscle you have, the more calories you burn in any activity, including sleeping," explains Dr. Mona Shangold, director of the Sports Gynecology and Women's Life Cycle Center at Hahnemann University Hospital. Exercises that build muscle also increase bone density, which is particularly important in combating osteoporosis, a serious problem for women.

Just the facts, ma'am

Hypertension: A study of 15,000 men between 35 and 74 found that those who didn't engage in strenuous sports had a 35 percent greater risk of developing hypertension than those who did.

Diabetes: The ability of insulin to regulate sugar levels declines with age, causing adult-onset diabetes to be a problem for one in five older Americans. Consistent, demanding exercise seems to restore normal glucose tolerance.

Incontinence: Some women have found relief from incontinence with a form of weight training that uses very tiny weights inserted in the vagina to build up the muscles that support the bladder.

Arthritis: Dr. Ralph Schumacher, a rheumatologist at the Hospital of the University of Pennsylvania, studied research on the use of isokinetic weight-bearing exercise to strengthen the leg muscles of patients with arthritic knees. "Results show that people with arthritis can do more exercise that previously thought possible without injuring their joints," he says, "showing we can be a lot more aggressive in using exercise with arthritic patients."

Mental function: Anybody who's seen George Burns on television these days can't help but notice that although he's as sharp as he ever was, he seems to respond more slowly. Psychologist Ted Bashore wondered whether a sluggish reaction time was inevitable or preventable. He studied very active older people and found that those who engaged in demanding sports like racquetball and singles tennis hadn't slowed down one bit mentally. The correlation between physical and mental agility was corroborated in further studies showing that very active older people can actually process information faster than sedentary young adults.

Drug addiction: A citywide program called Time Out helps adults of all ages stay clean and sober by using the model of physical accomplishment to develop emotional strength. Exercise is particularly appealing to addicts because it provides instant gratification. Performing two push-ups one day, three the next and five the next helps give addicts the sense of achievement they need to develop self-esteem.

Gain without pain

The good news is that you don't have to be an aerobics junkie or a mountain climber to get the benefits of exercise. The no-pain, no-gain approach to exercise preached over the past two decades is no longer advocated. Optimal intensity depends on your goal. Any activity—walking, running, cycling—that raises your heart rate and makes you perspire is just fine. "Vigorous exercise certainly improves your body, but it isn't necessary for health protection," says DiNubile.

The revised recommendations of the American College of Sports Medicine suggest 30 minutes of moderate physical activity most days of the week. That does not necessarily mean pumping iron at the gym. Gardening and walking to work qualify. "If you like to sit, just stand," DiNubile suggests. "And don't stand still. Walk. Get in the habit of taking stairs instead of escalators, and park your car at the far end of the mall. Look for exercise opportunities in your daily life."

Reasonable exercise not only improves the quality of life, it actually prolongs it. The Aerobics Research Center in Dallas followed 10,000 men and 3,000 women for 12 years and found that those with low levels of physical fitness were more likely to die from a variety of causes than those in the moderately or highly fit categories. It's worth noting that there was a far higher death-rate variation between the low and moderate groups than between the moderate and high groups.

It's never too late to start

Perhaps the most exciting finding on the exercise front is the mounting evidence that no matter how old you are, you can begin even the mildest exercise program and not only slow, but actually reverse, the aging process. Moreover, vigorous exercise can produce remarkable benefits even in older people who never exercised at all when they were young. We used to believe that beginning exercise in later life was dangerous. We also used to believe that smoking was safe.

The research proving that exercise can keep people vital into their 80s and beyond has changed the focus of geriatrics. Not so long ago, this specialty focused on making people comfortable until they died. Now the goal is optimal aging. "People always wanted to age well, but they didn't think they had much choice," says Medical College of Pennsylvania gerontologist Dr. Joel Posner. "Now it's clear they do."

When a study looked at some 10,000 Harvard graduates, it found that their activity levels affected their mortality. It was no surprise that the more active grads lived longer. "The question," says Dr. Vincent Cristofalo, director of the Center for Gerontological Research at the Medical College of Pennsylvania, "is whether they're more healthy because they're more active or more active because they're more healthy. The indication is the former. Regular exercise, along with proper nutrition, is probably the most important thing that older people can do for themselves to amplify and maintain good health as they age."

Weights are the measure

Aerobic workouts are an excellent place to begin, but a balanced exercise program must include some kind of weight training—the very stuff that sculpted Arnold Schwarzenegger. And some fascinating studies have shown that weight training can be introduced at any age with surprising results. In one, a small group of frail nursing-home residents ages 90 to 96 put on an eight-week high-intensity weight-training program showed dramatic gains in muscle strength, ranging from 61 to 374 percent! By the end of the study, two could again walk without canes and one no longer had to use her arms to rise from a chair.

Studies like this have made strengthening exercises the hottest trend among the 50-plus set—those very folks doctors traditionally cautioned "Don't lift or strain." The axiom "use it or lose it" has a new twist: With exercise, you can get it back. "The difference between young and old is muscle," says MCP's Posner. "While cardiovascular fitness is important, you must add specific muscle strengthening if you want to prevent the ravages of aging."

Posner's concept of a complete fitness package for people over 55 is one that burns fat, builds endurance through aerobics and develops strength and flexibility with power lifting and stretching. That's exactly the kind of program he offers at the Center for Continuing Health on City Line Avenue and at a satellite in Center City. On an average afternoon, one might find a 60ish advertising executive walking the treadmill to the rhythm of soft rock music next to an 85-year-old gent who came to the center because he didn't like the way his belly hung over his bathing suit. Within months, the executive was able to last 25 minutes on the treadmill at a three-mile-an-hour pace, his cholesterol dropped from 236 to 198, and he lost 20 pounds to boot.

So we've sold you the program. Great. Before you go out and buy your jogging shoes, it's wise to see your doctor. Don't quit just because you feel sore in the beginning. That's to be expected. And need we remind you that whatever your age, the easiest part of any exercise program is starting? The hardest part is keeping it up.

For Your Information

The Center for Continuing Health, an outpatient division of the geriatric medicine department at MCP, is a first-rate facility for medically supervised exercise programs for those over 55. Located at Presidential City, Monroe Office Center, City Avenue and Presidential Boulevard (878-1234) and in Center City at the Sidney Hillman Center, 2116 Chestnut Street (568-4080). It provides all kinds of equipment, from stationary bikes to treadmills to resistance machines. Each client undergoes an extensive medical workup before being given an individual exercise prescription, which is then monitored by the highly trained staff for an unbelievably low charge of $20 a month.

Graduate Hospital's Human Performance and Sports Medicine Center, 200 West Lancaster Avenue, Wayne (688-6767), works with physicians to design personal fitness regimens.

For information about any of the Time Out exercise programs for people in recovery, call 985-2928.

CHAPTER 3

Smoking Is Stupid

How to give up the world's nastiest habit

Smoking is the most preventable cause of death in our society. While the number of smokers in our country has certainly decreased, one wonders why there are any left at all given how horrifying the statistics are. It's been 30 years since the surgeon general first warned us about the hazards of smoking, yet tobacco products still kill more than 420,000 Americans each year. The American Lung Association (ALA) estimates one in every five deaths is related to smoking. Puffing on tobacco products is responsible for 87 percent of lung cancers and 30 percent of all cancer deaths.

Even if you've never smoked, you may still be in danger. The American Cancer Society (ACS) estimates environmental tobacco smoke causes over 50,000 deaths annually from heart disease and lung cancer. Children who live with a smoker—there are 9 million of them under the age of five, according to the ALA— have increased risks of respiratory illnesses and infections, impaired development of lung function and middle-ear infections simply from being exposed to secondhand smoke. If you're still a smoker, consider the damage you may be doing to your loved ones.

The good news is that it's never too late to quit. The surgeon general says that people who quit live longer than people who continue to smoke regardless of when they stop. Even better, smokers who quit before age 50 have half the risk of dying in the next 15 years compared with those who continue to smoke. And it's obvious that if you stop smoking you reduce the risk of coronary heart disease, cardiovascular disease and lung and other cancers.

One of the biggest impediments to giving up cigarettes is the difficulty of physical withdrawal. Nicotine is America's number-one addictive drug. A major step forward in handling withdrawal has been the availability of nicotine replacement therapy—otherwise known as "the patch." Nicotine transdermal systems ease withdrawal symptoms by delivering a diminishing supply of nicotine to your body through a small patch applied daily to your skin, for a maximum of three months. You can get the patch only by prescription from your doctor, who will determine if you are a good candidate. Nicotine replacement therapy should be used in conjunction with a smoking-cessation program that includes behavior modification, and you can't start until you've given up the weed.

Have we convinced you it's worth the effort to give it try? Well, don't tough it out alone. Here are some programs to help you. Many are covered by insurance—check with your carrier.

Smoking Cessation and Treatment Programs

American Lung Association
825-3443

Learn how to deal with your cravings to smoke and get the support you need to quit for good. $100 for an eight-week program. Call for schedule and locations.

Associates for Health and Guidance
473-8900

Learn to hypnotize yourself, practice methods of behavior modification, try electro-acupuncture and acupressure, or use nicotine replacement therapy. The staff here will even make you a personalized relaxation tape. Call for an appointment.

Free and Clear
1-800-292-2336

A personalized smoking cessation program designed to the participant's schedule and needs. Includes contact with an assigned specialist five times throughout the year. The toll-free Quitline offers additional guidance and support. $145 for a one-year program.

FreshStart
665-2925

A "straightforward, no-nonsense, quit smoking program" run by the American Cancer Society. Prices vary according to location. Call for schedule.

Quit Smoking Anonymous
887-1765

Twelve-step program based on the AA model. Donations requested.

Smart Move
665-2925

A single-session, action-oriented program run by the American Cancer Society to help smokers examine their habit and their readiness to quit. Free. Call for dates and locations.

Smoke Enders
332-8813

A learning technique based on behavior modification, taking into consideration weight control, physical withdrawal symptoms, etc., with the object of reaching complete "freedom" from the smoking habit. $325 for six-week seminar. Self-study Learn-to-Quit Kit is $125. Discounts for corporate seminars. Call for schedule and locations.

Smoke Stoppers
1-800-843-6247

A national organization offering three treatment options. 1. Group Program: Maximum interaction with an instructor, group support and intensive behavior modification and lifestyle management. $100-$165 for eight sessions. 2. Staying-Stopped Program: Support program with a flexible format that gives the participant the "how tos" of smoking cessation. Ideal for those thinking about quitting, ready to quit or relapsing. $75-$125 for five sessions. 3. Self-Help Program/Kit: A 26-day program designed for self study, including: behavior modification, relapse prevention and lifestyle management development. Participants have access to a toll-free telephone support service. $49-$69. Call for information, locations and schedules.

Smokers Anonymous
468-0932

Twelve-step program based on the AA model. Donations requested.

TAO-Eager to Quit
241-4709

A four-week program offering varied treatment methods: not ready (readiness preparation), gradual withdrawal, withdrawal with a nicotine replacement product and "cold turkey." $150 for four sessions. Call for schedule and locations.

Dr. Steven Rosenberg
ELKINS SQUARE MALL, STE. 206, OLD YORK AND CHURCH ROADS, ELKINS PARK; 782-8414

A psychologist and hypnotherapist who has used hypnotism to help hundreds of people stop smoking. In addition, he gives his patients a "smoke-breaker" kit with herbal tablets he's developed to ease nicotine withdrawal.

For additional listings of the many smoking cessation programs held at area hospitals, see Chapter 12.

Stick it to me

For reasons not well understood, acupuncture can be dramatically successful getting motivated people to kick the habit. In a short time it suppresses the urge to smoke and eliminates physical withdrawal symptoms. Acupuncture treatments may be combined with hypnosis, acupressure and herbal medicines. The following acupuncturists all have experience in using acupuncture to stop smoking.

....

Ghodratolla Heidary, M.D.
LANKENAU HOSPITAL, 100 LANCASTER AVENUE,
WYNNEWOOD, PA; 649-7135 OR 645-2142

Unlimited treatment for six weeks: $585.

....

Steven King, M.D.
THE PAIN CENTER, THOMAS JEFFERSON UNIVERSITY
HOSPITAL, BEN FRANKLIN HOUSE, 834 CHESTNUT
STREET, SUITE T150, PHILADELPHIA, PA 19107; 955-
PAIN

One-hour visit: $300. (Follow-up visit, if necessary: $150)

Fastest growing eye center in the Delaware Valley

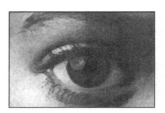

Retina and Diabetic Eye Institute

of Mercy Haverford Hospital

Ophthalmologists/surgeons recruited from Harvard, Joslin Diabetes Center and University of Pennsylvania offer a unique team approach.

As leaders in the field, we are committed to caring for you and your eyesight in a sensitive way. Prevention, early diagnosis and the most advanced laser and surgical treatments are the emphasis of the Eye Institute.

MACULAR DEGENERATION
First in the Delaware Valley to provide the most sophisticated diagnostic technique, ICG

DIABETIC EYE DISEASE
Comprehensive treatment including education and support from the largest staff of certified diabetic educators in Pennsylvania.

Mercy Haverford Hospital
2000 Old West Chester Pike, Havertown, PA
Conveniently located just off Exit 4 of Route 476 (The Blue Route)

Physicians' offices also in:
Abington Memorial Hospital
Crozer-Chester Medical Center
Fitzgerald Mercy Hospital

WE ACCEPT MOST TYPES OF INSURANCE COVERAGE.
We welcome your questions...call **(610)449-0400**

CHAPTER 4

Why Fat Makes You Fat

And why there's only one real way to get thin

I f you are a devotee of diet books, you might just as well read nursery rhymes. The latest research on the diet front suggests that the secret to staying thin comes from none other than Jack Sprat—the skinny little man who ate no fat. The belief that weight control is strictly a matter of cutting calories has been declared obsolete, and it now appears that all calories are not alike. Calories derived from fatty foods are actually more fattening.

Conventional dietary wisdom counts calories on the assumption that 100 calories of apples are the same as 100 calories of cheese, even though fat is denser and on a weight-per-weight basis has a higher caloric content. (One gram of fat has nine calories, while one gram of protein or carbohydrate has only four.) But the numbers game is only part of the whole picture. The equally important component is the way we metabolize those calories. It's been found that when we eat protein and carbohydrates the body works mightily to burn them up, but it puts forth very little effort converting fat into energy. As a result, the quantity of fat in our diet becomes as critical to weight loss as the number of calories we eat in a day.

Each of us uses a given number of calories daily just to keep our body machine running and our weight in neutral. Caloric requirements vary from individual to individual and are based on things like height, weight, activity and genes. (The rule of thumb for determining your 24-hour base caloric need is as follows: body weight multiplied by 12 for sedentary women, by 14 for sedentary men, by 15 for moderately active women, by 17 for moderately active men, by 18 for active women and by 20 for active men.) Weight gain was heretofore considered a function of taking in more calories than the body required for daily maintenance. But now that simple equation—too many calories equals too many pounds—no longer computes.

For example, the Chinese eat 20 percent more calories per unit of body weight than Americans, but they have practically no obesity. That's because they live on a plant-based diet heavy in vegetables and grains but light on fat—only 15 percent. Compare that to the average American diet—40 percent fat, and loaded with dairy and oils. To determine the role of fatty foods in diet control, the Lipid Nutrition Laboratory in Washington, D.C., did a study in which 28 women of average weight cut the fat intake of their diets from 40 percent to 20 percent without lowering the number of calories they took in daily. After nine months they lost an average of 1 percent body fat. Another study at Stanford examining the daily dietary patterns of obese men found the heftiest of the lot ate the fattiest foods, but didn't necessarily down the most calories. Even laboratory rats put on low-fat diets gain less weight than rats on an equal-calorie high-fat diet.

From the lips to the hips

The human body is amazingly efficient at changing the fat from food directly into body fat. When you slather 100 calories of butter on a baked potato, the body expends a mere three calories of energy to metabolize the butter, leaving 97 calories of fat for that storage bin in your thighs. On the other hand, it takes 23 calories to metabolize 100 calories of a carbohydrate. What's worse, once the body is into a low-work fat mode, it tends to stay there. Fat-laden diets make the body more sluggish, while the extra effort required to convert carbohydrates raises the overall metabolic rate. In a 24-hour period of gorging on pasta and veggies your metabolism will be more active than if you overload on cheese snacks and fried chicken.

There's even more good news about carbohydrates. The energy they supply almost never turns into body fat. First of all, carbohydrates don't go from the lips to the hips. Small quantities settle in the muscles and the liver in the form of glycogen, a sugar the body uses as a primary energy source. Second, while the body can sock away huge amounts of fat, its capacity for storing glycogen is quite limited.

The scientific term for the energy expended converting food into energy is *thermogenesis*, and as you might have expected, this scientific principle has already been translated into a new diet fad. The truth is that trimming the amount of fat in your diet can make a difference, but it depends entirely on how much fat you're consuming these days. Don't expect miracles unless you're up there in the 30 to 40 percent bracket.

Fake fats

Modern science has partially solved the fat problem with "fake fats." Several large food companies market substitutes for cooking oils and spreads (products like Simplesse and Olestra) that have the flavor of fat but don't get converted *into* fat.

What attracts us to fat is not just the taste—fat is also filling. Dr. Steven Peiken, head of the division of gastroenterology and liver diseases at Cooper Hospital University Medical Center in Camden, explains in his first book, *The Feel Full Diet*, that fat releases a hormone initiating a chain reaction that ends with the brain getting the message that you've eaten enough. Studies show that fat craving is highest when people are most hungry and lowest after they've eaten. It's no accident that sweets (the sugary carbohydrates) come at the end of the meal rather than the beginning. If you want to lower your appetite and the amount you eat at mealtime, Peiken recommends a high-satiety snack of a bowl of hot soup or a tablespoon of peanut butter on a celery stick 20 minutes before sitting down at the table. Your brain will think you're full and you'll put less on your plate.

Fats are unhealthy

Not only do fats create unwelcome bulges, too much fatty food is also a health hazard. In his recent book *Gastrointestinal Health,* Dr. Peiken says, "Reducing fat in the diet relieves heartburn, prevents gallbladder attacks and aids pancreatitis. It also helps prevent colon cancer and the development of kidney stones in people with Crohn's disease. In addition, high-fat diets have been associated with breast cancer and heart disease."

The study of fat has produced some bad news for chronic dieters: Dieting itself may be fattening. The yo-yo syndrome—gaining/losing/gaining/losing—may ultimately *add* to your fat content. Weight loss is a loss of a combination of fat and muscle. Say you lose 20 pounds on a diet: 15 of them will be fat and five muscle. But when you regain those 20 pounds, 17 will be fat and only three muscle. You will weigh the same as before but your body composition will have more fat. Not only is fat harder to take off than muscle, but as mentioned earlier, the higher the ratio of fat to muscle, the lower your metabolic rate and the less you can eat just to keep your weight the same. In addition, the new fat may settle in a different place and cause another set of problems. Dr. Kelly Brownell, formerly of the Obesity Research Group at the University of Pennsylvania, has done studies indicating that upper-body fat puts people at a higher risk for heart attacks and diabetes than lower-body fat. A pot belly is a greater health hazard than thunder thighs.

The best way to dissolve body fat is through exercise. But just as all calories are not alike, neither are all exercises. Stop-and-start exercises that require spurts of energy, such as racquet sports, calisthenics and weight-lifting, burn more of the fuel stored in muscles than in fat cells. Continuous aerobic activities, such as walking and jogging, use more of the energy deposited in the fat bank. Exercise also has a positive effect on boosting the body's metabolic rate—the dieter's greatest ally. Stanford University conducted a study in which 32 sedentary middle-aged men embarked on a yearlong running program without going on a low-cal diet. The more they ran, the more fat they lost—even when they increased their calorie intake.

The big sucking sound

Some people lose weight and exercise regularly but are still stuck with flabby tummies, saddlebags and saggy bottoms. For them the answer to eliminating these pockets of genetically or hormonally derived fat may be liposuction. Except for massive weight gains of 80 pounds or more, it appears that our total number of fat cells is fixed by adolescence. A fat cell has the expandability of a balloon; gaining or losing weight merely increases or decreases the size. Only liposuction can permanently reduce the number. "Liposuction works best on people who are already slender but can't get rid of bulges," says Dr. Leonard Dzubow, assistant professor of dermatology at the Hospital of the University of Pennsylvania. "It's a fallacy that liposuction is an alternative to diet. It should not be used for weight reduction. It's a procedure to change and reshape the contour of the body by removing the fat that lies right under the skin."

When first popularized in the late '70s, liposuction developed a reputation for being a dangerous procedure. Removing large amounts of fat from several different body parts under general anesthesia sometimes resulted in serious complications, from shock to infection, when too much body fluid was sucked out along with the fat. Today the procedures have been refined to a point where liposuction is one of the most frequently performed cosmetic surgeries, and it's quite safe when done by experienced hands.

How to read a food label

If we all ate nothing but fresh fruit, vegetables, chicken and fish, it would be easy to maintain a low-fat diet. But we live in a world of packaged foods, and if you're serious about cutting the fat content of what you eat, you need to know how to read a food label. Until recently, deciphering the information on food labels was as confusing as trying to follow the instructions on how to program your VCR. Now the government has issued clear, standardized guidelines, which appear on all packages under the words "Nutrition Facts."

When you're checking a label, be aware that fat content varies considerably within a particular classification of food. Take frozen diet dinners. A Weight Watchers Chicken a la King meal contains 29 percent fat, while an Armour Dinner Classics Lite Chicken Breast Marsala has only 18 percent fat. Grains are tricky too, because some breakfast cereals are made with coconut and palm oil: Shredded Wheat is 10 percent fat, but Grape Nuts has no fat at all. The traditional diet snack cracker can also be fat-saturated. If you rub a cracker with a napkin and there's a grease ring, it's got too much fat. The same goes for packaged microwave popcorn. Made in an air-popper, corn is a great low-fat snack. Popped in the packet, it may be as much as 50 percent fat. And don't be taken in by milk that's 1 or 2 percent fat. Milk has only 4 percent fat to begin with, so only skim milk is truly fat-free.

Here are the terms you'll find under "Nutrition Facts" and what they mean:

Total Fat: This is the stuff everybody's interested in. Although the American Heart Association recommends a total fat intake of less than 30 percent of your daily calories, more stringent dietary programs recommend a daily fat intake of under 10 percent.

Saturated Fat: This is the fat most likely to raise blood cholesterol and, with it, your risk of heart disease.

Cholesterol: Too much cholesterol—second only to fat—can lead to heart disease. Limit yourself to less than 300 mg. each day.

Sodium: Keep sodium intake below 2400 mg. daily, because salt intake is related to high blood pressure.

Total Carbohydrates: This category is composed of dietary fiber and sugars. Dietary fiber is the stuff your grandmother called roughage; it includes beans, whole grains, fruits and vegetables. Eat as much of this good stuff as possible! Sugars add calories and flavor, but have no nutritional value.

Protein: Most Americans eat more than enough animal protein—fish, poultry, meat and dairy—and not enough vegetable protein—beans and whole grains.

Vitamins and Minerals: The government says most Americans can fulfill the daily recommended requirements through the foods they eat. But given the unbalanced dietary habits of the people I know, it's not a bad idea to pop a multivitamin every day.

Daily Value: This little portion of the label sets the goal for what you should get from the combined foods in your diet. It's based on 2,000 to 2,500 calories per day. In my opinion, you'd need a calculator every time you sit at the table to make any sense of it.

Ingredients: These are listed in descending order of weight and also broken down into content. For example, if one of the ingredients in the package is cheddar cheese, the label will state what is in cheddar cheese (milk, cheese culture, salt, enzyme). It's wise to read this section if you're trying to avoid certain foods, especially if you have an allergy.

What does "all-natural" really mean?

Food marketing is a highly competitive business, and manufacturers have learned how to snare the health- and diet-conscious with words like lean, fat-free and natural. There was a time when the term "lite" could appear on a bag of potato chips and mean nothing more than light in color. Fortunately, the government has also set guidelines on nutritional claims. Here's a rundown of the most common:

Free: The product contains none or only a "trivial" amount of something such as fat, saturated fat, cholesterol, sodium, sugar or calories. For example, fat-free means the product contains less than half a gram of fat per serving. Acceptable synonyms include: "without," "no" and "zero."

Low: This term can be used on foods that can be eaten frequently without exceeding dietary guidelines. For example, low fat means three grams (or less) per serving; low saturated fat, one gram (or less) per serving; low sodium, 140 mg. (or less) per serving; very low sodium, 35 mg. (or less) per serving; low cholesterol, 20 mg. (or less) per serving; and low calorie, 40 calories (or fewer) per serving. Acceptable synonyms include "little," "few" and "low source of."

Lean and Extra-Lean: These terms are used to describe the fat content of meat, poultry, seafood and game meats. Lean means it contains less than ten grams of fat per 100-gram serving. Extra-lean means less than five grams.

High In ... : The product contains 20 percent or more per serving of a nutrient the government says you need on a daily basis. A "Good Source of ..." product contains 10 to 19 percent.

Reduced: The product contains 25 percent less of a nutrient or calories than the original product had. Not to be confused with "less," which means the product contains 25 percent less of a nutrient or calories than the generic brand.

Light: The product has one-third fewer calories or half the fat of the original. It may also mean that the sodium content of an already low-calorie, low-fat product has been reduced by 50 percent.

More: The product contains at least 10 percent more of a particular nutrient than the generic brand. When such terms as "fortified, "enriched" and "added" are used, the product has been nutritionally altered to contain at least 10 percent more than the original.

Fresh: Can be used only on a food that is raw, has never been heated and contains no preservatives, such as "fresh frozen" or "fresh milk."

Natural: The FDA has no regulation for this term, but "naturally sweetened" usually means the product has been sweetened with fruit or juice rather than sugar. Check the ingredients.

No Preservatives/No Artificial Colors: These terms can be misleading because they imply that a product is healthier when it may not be. They apply only to food additives.

For Further Reading

A good guide to eating healthy and keeping slim is *The California Nutrition Book* by Paul Saltman, Joel Gurin and Ira Mothner (Little, Brown).

Cancer specialists
Kenneth D. Tew, Ph.D., (left)
and Gerald R. Hanks, M.D.

We're Leading The Fight Against Prostate Cancer.

Here at Fox Chase Cancer Center, internationally known cancer experts Kenneth Tew, Ph.D., and Gerald Hanks, M.D., head a team of researchers and physicians working to fight prostate cancer.

Fox Chase dedicates all of its resources to fighting cancer, from research to determine the most effective new drugs, to innovative techniques in radiation therapy that kill cancer but protect surrounding normal tissue. We are also exploring new combinations of chemotherapy for more advanced prostate cancer.

At Fox Chase, science and medicine work together to give you the latest cancer treatment. Fighting cancer is all we do. All day. Every day.

For information, call (215) 728-3688.

FOX CHASE
CANCER CENTER
Discovery & Hope

CHAPTER 5

Storm Warnings

Catching cancer early could save your life

The American Cancer Society estimates that more than 570,000 people in the United States will die of cancer this year. Cancers caused by cigarette smoking and alcohol abuse are the most preventable. Stop smoking and drinking! Equally important to prevention are certain routine screenings—mammographies, mole checks, fecal occult blood tests, etc. Along with self-examinations, they detect cancers at an early stage, when treatment is more likely to be effective.

A wide spectrum of cancer treatments is available at many area hospitals. (See Chapter 12.) For complicated or advanced cases requiring cutting-edge, high-tech care, you may want to contact a National Cancer Institute-designated comprehensive cancer center. These hospitals are heavily engaged in research as well as clinical trials of experimental protocols for which you may be eligible. There are 27 in the United States, two of which are in Philadelphia:

Fox Chase Cancer Center
7701 BURHOLME AVENUE, PHILADELPHIA, PA 19111;
728-6900

University of Pennsylvania Cancer Center
6 PENN TOWER, 3400 SPRUCE STREET, PHILADELPHIA,
PA 19103; 1-800-383-8722 OR 662-6480

Danger Zones

While it takes a physician to diagnose cancer, your own watchfulness is the best early-warning system. See your doctor if you have:

A change in bowel or bladder habits.

A sore that doesn't heal.

Unusual bleeding or discharge.

A thickening or lump in the breast or any other body part.

An obvious change in a wart or mole.

A nagging cough or hoarseness.

Indigestion or difficulty swallowing.

The skinny on skin cancer

If you are a sun worshiper, don't skip this section. In fact, anybody who spends time in the sun—sailing, tennis, working outdoors—has to face the fact that he's exposing himself to potential skin cancer. The reason is quite simple: Skin cancer is caused by exposure to ultraviolet (UV) rays, whether from the sun in your backyard or the tanning bed at your salon. And it looks like we're all overdoing it in one way or another: According to the National Cancer Institute, close to 50 percent of all Americans who live to age 65 will get skin cancer at least once. The only way to reduce your odds, says Dr. Paul Engstrom of Fox Chase Cancer Center, is to reduce the amount of time you spend unprotected from UV rays. "Skin cancer is one of the most preventable forms of cancer there is," he says, "because we know exactly what causes it."

Most at risk are Caucasians with light-color eyes and hair and fair complexions that don't tan easily. Least at risk are those with naturally dark skin, whose rich pigmentation protects them from UV radiation. For all people, though, sun damage is cumulative: It can take 20 years or more for a cancerous lesion to evolve from that bad sunburn you received as a child. While the most commonly occurring forms of skin cancer are rarely fatal, if ignored they can extend below the skin to the bone and cartilage, causing considerable damage and disfigurement.

Three varieties of skin cancer

The most common type, basal cell carcinoma (*carcinoma* is cancer that starts in the tissue of an organ lining) arises from basal cells in the epidermal layer of the skin. It's slow-growing and rarely spreads—unlike squamous cell carcinoma, the second-most-common form of skin cancer, which begins in the squamous cells of the epidermis and can, if untreated, spread to other parts of the body. Together, these cancers are referred to as "nonmelanoma skin cancers" to distinguish them from melanoma, which develops in the skin's melanocytes (the cells that produce the pigment). Melanoma is the most serious form of skin cancer because it can spread to other parts of the body through the lymph systems; left untreated, it is usually fatal.

The warning signs

With basal cell and squamous cell cancers, the first warning sign is a change in the skin, especially a new growth or a sore that won't heal. These types of skin cancers may start as firm red lumps or as small, smooth, shiny, pale or waxy bumps; either type may crust or bleed. They may also begin as flat red spots that are rough, dry or scaly.

The first sign of a melanoma is most often a change in the size, shape or color of a mole, or the appearance of a new mole on the body. A normal mole is a brown, black or tan spot on the skin that can be flat or raised, round or oval. Any change in a mole should be brought to the attention of your doctor immediately, according to the following "ABCD" characteristics outlined by the National Cancer Institute.

Asymmetry: The shape of one half of the mole does not match the shape of the other.

Border: The edges are ragged, notched or blurred.

Color: The color is uneven. For example, shades of black, brown or tan are present, or areas of white, red or blue can be seen.

Diameter: There is a change in size. Other signs of melanoma can include scaling, oozing or bleeding of a mole or a change in the way the mole feels; it may become hard, lumpy, itchy, swollen or tender. In men, melanoma occurs most often on the trunk of the body; in women, on the arms and lower legs.

Diagnosis and treatment

Skin cancers are usually diagnosed via biopsy, the surgical removal of all or part of the growth. The tissue is then examined under a microscope and a diagnosis is made. The stage of the disease is based on the thickness of the tumor, the depth of skin penetration and whether the cancer has spread to nearby lymph nodes or other parts of the body.

More than 95 percent of nonmelanoma skin cancers are completely curable; the choice of treatment depends on the size and type of growth, its location and whether it has the potential to spread. The most common methods of removal include surgery, which may involve skin grafting if the area affected is large; curettage, a common "scooping out" method used to treat very small growths; and cryosurgery, in which liquid nitrogen is sprayed on the growth to freeze and kill abnormal cells. Radiation therapy, chemotherapy and laser treatment are also used, depending on the type of cancer and its stage of advancement. All may result in scarring.

People who have had nonmelanoma skin cancer are at risk for recurrence of the original cancer and development of new ones, so they should be examined regularly by their physicians and also examine their own skin on a monthly basis for new growths or changes.

What's done may be undone

Sun damage is cumulative, and the best you can do is start taking care of your skin today to reduce your lifetime risk of getting the disease. However, for some precancerous conditions (those in which cells show the kind of abnormal growth that is a precursor to skin cancer), there is hope. Retinoic acid (known commercially as Retin-A, the "miracle" antiwrinkle cream) has been shown to reverse some squamous cell cancers. And current research evaluating the effectiveness of massive doses of vitamin A and its precursor, beta-carotene, in patients with rare skin diseases is showing promise as well.

The best way to avoid getting skin cancer is to reduce your exposure to UV rays. Avoid the sun during the hours of the day when it's strongest—those hours when your shadow is shorter than you are. The remainder of the day, wear a sunscreen with a Sun Protection Factor (SPF) of at least 15. Wear a wide-brim hat and cover your arms and legs with clothing whose weave is tight enough to seal out the sun's rays. And remember that snow, ice, sand and concrete reflect from 10 to 50 percent of the sun's damaging rays. It should go without saying, says Fox Chase's Engstrom, that children should never go into the sun without protection. "We've got to reschool society from day one that a suntan is *not* a sign of physical beauty," he says. "Any tan at all is a sign that the skin has marshalled a defense against UV rays." So teach your kids that using a sun block is as routine and necessary as brushing their teeth. In 30 years, they'll thank you for it.

Warning signs of other cancers

Each type of cancer has its own particular configuration of symptoms. Don't panic if you suddenly begin to experience one of them; many cancer signs are also common to benign illnesses. However, do take note of the following warnings, and if they persist, the American Cancer Society recommends checking in with your doctor.

Lung cancer: Persistent cough, sputum streaked with blood, chest pain, recurring pneumonia or bronchitis.

Colon and rectum cancer: Rectal bleeding, blood in the stool, change in bowel habits.

Breast cancer: Persistent breast changes, such as a lump, thickening, swelling, dimpling, skin irritation, distortion, scaliness, pain or tenderness of the nipple.

Prostate cancer: Weak or interrupted urine flow; frequent urination, especially at night; blood in the urine; pain or burning on urination; continuing pain in lower back, pelvis or upper thighs.

Uterus and cervix cancer: Bleeding outside of the normal menstrual period or after menopause or unusual vaginal discharge.

Leukemia: Early signs may include: fatigue, paleness, weight loss, repeated infections, bruising, nose bleeds or other hemorrhages.

Hodgkin's disease: Swollen glands, itching, night sweats, weight loss and fever.

Non-Hodgkin's lymphoma: Swollen glands, anemia, weight loss and fever.

Bladder cancer: Blood in the urine. Usually associated with increased frequency of urination.

Oral cancer: A sore or red or white patch that bleeds easily and/or doesn't heal; a lump or thickening.

FYI: Cancer Information Services

The American Cancer Society's information service phone is 1-800-ACS-2345. Free booklets about cancer and information about services and activities in your area.

The National Cancer Institute maintains a vast information network available to the public, and since your tax dollars pay for it, you ought to take advantage.

Cancer Information Service (CIS)
1-800-4-CANCER

A free service available Monday through Friday, 9 to 5. In the Delaware Valley, the CIS office is managed by the Fox Chase Cancer Center. Callers speak to an NCI-trained and -certified professional, who can provide up-to-date information on cancer prevention, detection and diagnosis; referrals to hospitals and specialists; and free publications.

Physicians Data Query (PDQ)
301-496-7403

This comprehensive database contains a wealth of current information about cancer prognosis, staging and treatment, clinical trials, standard therapy protocols, and physicians and organizations active in cancer research and treatment. The database is accessible 24 hours a day from your personal computer, if you have a modem, through the online MEDLARS system. Prices vary according to distributor and search time. If you don't have a PC, call 1-800-338-7657 for a library in your area that subscribes to the NCI's databases.

CancerFax
301-402-5874

Another method for accessing PDQ. Call from your fax machine telephone for a list of code numbers. The only charge is the cost of a telephone call from your fax machine to the CancerFax computer in Bethesda, Maryland.

The Center for Advancement
in Cancer Education
642-4810

This nonprofit agency operates out of a cluttered office in Wynnewood and disseminates information about what's happening worldwide in alternative cancer therapies. Its director, Susan Silberstein, watched her young husband die of cancer and decided she wasn't going to bury with him all that she'd learned in researching nontraditional ways to treat the disease. "There are lots of ways you can make a tumor disappear, at least temporarily," she says, "but if you don't repair the body chemistry, you aren't cured." Most cancer patients die of malnutrition, toxemia and opportunistic infections, not of a tumor. The center endorses approaches that are host-oriented rather than tumor-oriented. That means they don't deal with the disease per se but with ways to fight it by balancing body chemistry and boosting the immune system. Silberstein can tell you about programs that fit into one of three categories: clinical nutrition, botanical medicine and psychoneuroimmunology. For cancer patients who've exhausted the conventional medical menu of chemo and radiation therapy or who are seeking a holistic treatment that offers a better quality of life, Silberstein has much to offer.

Wellness Community
664-6663

The California-based operation now has a branch in Philadelphia. Gilda Radner was among the 15,000 cancer patients who have found solace in this free program, which offers support groups, seminars on nutritional cooking, new cancer therapies and even classes in guided imagery. No medical services are provided because the sole purpose of the Wellness Community is to help sick people fight their disease through mental strength and freedom from stress.

The Common Thread
1-800-959-5555

Sometimes navigating the crowded waters of cancer services can be nearly as daunting as the disease. The Common Thread, a regional program of the Crozer-Keystone Health System, helps cancer patients and their families reach all aspects of the fragmented cancer marketplace—including rehab therapies, support groups, social services, educational programs, home care, bereavement counseling, pain management—and get the care they need. It has offices in Springfield, Upland and Drexel Hill.

ELM Lifelines
609-654-4044

A Medford, New Jersey-based private, nonprofit outpatient group providing cancer counseling and a support program. They offer weekly two-hour sessions, emotional support, relaxation and visualization, nutrition and exercise, stress management, coping strategies and health, healing and wellness materials.

 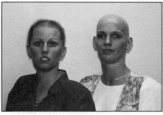

Chances Are,

Your Doctor

Recommended

Our Doctor.

Philadelphia Magazine asked area doctors to recommend the specialists they trust the most. The specialists with the best credentials and proven track records. The specialists they'd see if they got sick. 31 Presbyterian Medical Center doctors were singled out as the best in their specialties. Thirty one "Top Docs"! So the next time you need a specialist, call the doctors' doctors. Call Presbyterian Medical Center. 215-662-9140.

Presbyterian

Presbyterian Medical Center
of Philadelphia

Behind Closed Doors

What every medicine cabinet should have

You've probably got a well-stocked liquor cabinet and a bulging pantry, but is your medicine cabinet ready for an emergency? Or, for that matter, do you have something on hand for the cold you just caught? Every medicine cabinet needs certain staples. But before stocking up, you ought to clean out.

Dispose of all prescription medicines, over-the-counter medicines and birth-control products that have passed their expiration. Get rid of any leftover antibiotics—you really shouldn't have any, because you were supposed to finish the prescription. Throw away eye drops that are not crystal clear or have floating clumps. Get rid of any discolored creams. Trash aspirin that smells of vinegar; this is a sign that moisture in the bottle has caused the pills to decompose. To be safe, don't toss any of this stuff into your garbage can. Instead flush all pills, liquids and creams down the toilet—out of your reach, and your children's.

Store your medicines—the new ones—in a cool, dry, dark place, preferably one that can be locked if small children are in the house. Here's a basic list, with some brand-name examples, of what you should keep on hand:

Aspirin: The world's oldest pain-killer, it's ubiquitous but also dangerous. Aspirin can cause bleeding and stomach distress, so be careful how much you take. Children younger than 15 should never take aspirin because of its link to Reye's syndrome.

Acetaminophen: Tylenol. Its advantage over aspirin is that it does not contain salicylic acid, the ingredient responsible for stomach problems. However, it does not reduce inflammation anywhere near as well as aspirin does. And acetaminophen is not nearly as harmless as believed. Massive overdosage may cause liver poisoning in some patients.

Ibuprofen: Motrin, Advil. These drugs are designed to reduce inflammation from arthritis, muscular aches and sprains, and menstrual cramps. They're less likely to cause upset stomachs than aspirin.

Antibiotic creams: Cortaid. For minor skin rashes and irritation.

Antihistamine: Benadryl, Clortrimeton. For mild allergic symptoms or reactions to bee stings and other insect bites. May cause drowsiness.

Cold medication: Actifed, Drixoral. Most of these combine an antihistamine and a decongestant. Note that if you have a condition like high blood pressure, glaucoma or asthma, you should consult your doctor before taking a decongestant.

Cough medicine: Lots of hospitals use Robitussin.

Antacid: Maalox Plus, Mylanta. For mild cases of upset stomach, indigestion and/or gas.

Antidiarrheal medicine: Pepto Bismol, Kaopectate, Immodium AD. Some doctors recommend leaving diarrhea untreated for a day or so to just let it run its course. Be sure you drink lots of water because dehydration, a common side effect of diarrhea, can be more dangerous than the runs themselves.

Syrup of ipecac: To induce vomiting in cases of accidental poisoning. Vomiting is not recommended for all types of poisoning, so always call the local Poison Control Center (386-2100) before giving ipecac.

Antiseptic: Hydrogen peroxide, for cleaning cuts and scrapes.

Itch remedies: Calamine, the yucky pink lotion you grew up with, is still the best sting remover around for bites and poison ivy.

Sunscreen: Choose one with an SPF of 15 or higher. Then use it!

Ace bandages: Get the three-to-four-inch size. That's best for wrapping a strain or sprain or holding a splint in place on the way to the hospital.

Other supplies: Assorted band-aids and gauze pads; cotton balls or swabs for applying antiseptics.

Eyewash: Bausch and Lomb makes a good one for cleansing the eye to relieve irritation, burning or itching.

Thermometer

BRANDYWINE VALLEY PAIN CONTROL CENTER

Sheng K. Lin, Ph.D, M.D.

Andre O. Williams, M.D.

Satish K. Batta, M.D, D. Sc.

Brent S. Follweiler, M.D.

Craig M. Steiner, M.D.

Board certified physicians trained in the practice of pain management involving:

• Cancer • Back • Neck • Headache • Extremities

For more information, please contact us at

610-383-8489

201 REECEVILLE ROAD, COATESVILLE, PA 19320

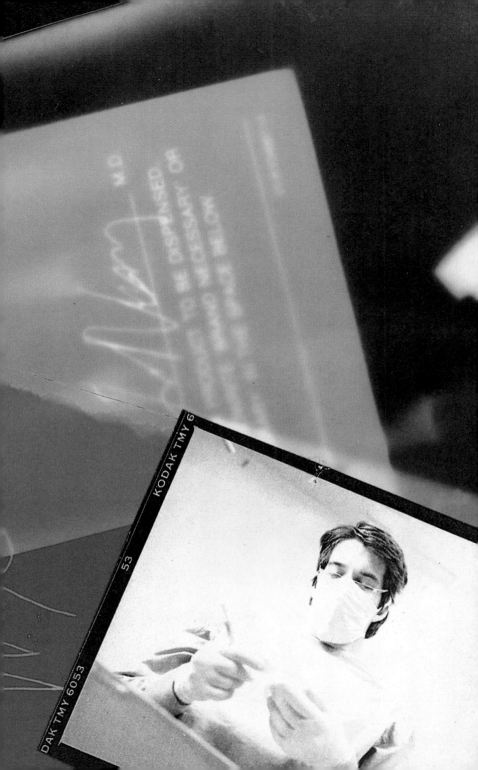

2

Choosing a Doctor

 # OOPER CARES FOR KIDS

At Cooper Hospital/University Medical Center our pediatric specialists provide a wide range of comprehensive services for infants, children and adolescents from throughout Southern New Jersey and the Delaware Valley. We offer many specialized services including:

- Adolescent Medicine
- Cardiology
- Child Development Center
- Critical Care Medicine
- Emergency Medicine
- Endocrine Metabolic Diseases
- Gastroenterology
- General Pediatrics

- Genetics & Birth Defects
- Hematology/Oncology
- HIV & Infectious Diseases
- Neonatology
- Nephrology
- Neurology
- Nutrition
- Pulmonary

Comprehensive pediatric care is available at 3 convenient locations:

Three Cooper Plaza	Main Street	Moorestown Office Center
Camden, NJ	Voorhees, NJ	Moorestown, NJ
609-342-2175	609-342-2175	609-722-9001

Department of Pediatrics

Cooper Hospital/University Medical Center

University of Medicine and Dentistry of New Jersey/Robert Wood Johnson Medical School at Camden

CHAPTER 7

Finding Dr. Right

A shoppers' guide to selecting a personal physician

On the short list of life's important decisions, choosing Dr. Right may well rank up there with choosing a spouse. Like the latter, a doctor can be a confidant, adviser and caretaker. While love is just about the only radar for finding a life partner, you can use a more rational method for your medical needs.

Right now there's a lot of irrational fear that under the new national health-care policies we will lose much of our freedom to choose our doctors. *Managed care*, the centerpiece of whichever health plan Congress approves—either President Clinton's complicated proposal or one of the half-dozen alternatives—does not remove choice; it may, however, limit your options. Managed care is a networking concept that refers to the way doctors and hospitals are paid. Fee-for-service as we know it today will practically vanish, except for those who can afford sky-high premiums. It is being replaced by some kind of set fee paid by insurers to oversee the basic health needs of patients.

As we enter into this new era of health care, your most important doctor will be an updated version of the old-fashioned family doc. Right now if you break your leg and have traditional indemnity health insurance, you can directly call an orthopedist to set it. Under managed care you must first visit a *gatekeeper*, a primary-care physician who guards the entrance to health services. That essentially means that all medical decisions begin with your internist or family practitioner, who's being paid by your insurer to manage all aspects of your health.

If things work as the president envisions, costs should drop and, at the least, basic care should improve because everyone will be likely to develop a long-term relationship with a doctor who knows his or her medical and personal history. Does diabetes run in your family? Are you prone to bouts of depression? What medicines are you taking routinely, and do you have any allergies? The doctor you rush to see only when you're ill has very little context for diagnosis and little time or interest in the all-important area of prevention.

It's increasingly likely that your insurance plan will limit your choices of a primary-care physician to people in its network. Doctors will probably participate in more than one plan, so you should have some freedom to choose within those parameters. I've never understood why so many people put a greater effort into selecting a car or a stereo system than into selecting a doctor. Begin your doctor shopping by considering some of the following:

Office location. Is the office near your home or workplace? Convenient to public transportation? If not, does it have ample parking?

Solo or group practice. If you don't like the busy atmosphere and the chance you will not always see the same doctor, a group practice may not be for you. On the other hand, solo practitioners may not be available weekends or in emergencies.

Hours. Are the office hours compatible with your work schedule? Can you be seen at night?

Hospital privileges. Where does the doctor admit patients and is it a place you'd want to be? If he's in more than one hospital, how does he choose who goes where?

Fees and insurance. What does the doctor charge for initial visits and for follow-ups? Does she accept your insurance plan, and what portion of the fee might you have to absorb? Who does the paperwork and submits the bills?

Once you've narrowed the prospects, schedule a get-acquainted visit. You wouldn't buy a car over the phone, and you shouldn't "buy" a doctor that way either. If the doctor won't agree to meet with you, view it as a warning sign. Once you arrive, check out the office. Are the personnel friendly and the place clean and attractive? How long do patients sit in the waiting room before being seen?

When you meet the doctor, have your questions ready. You'll want to know who covers for him or her on nights and weekends. Would he make an emergency house call? Does she have telephone hours to answer questions? Will you have access to your medical records? State laws regarding release of medical records vary. Pennsylvania law grants hospital patients direct access to their medical records, but private physicians are not required to give you this information, although they may send it to another doctor who requests it. What may not be yours legally certainly belongs to you rightfully, so be sure to establish your physician's policy up front. It will become especially important if you ever fire the doctor and discover your records can't leave with you.

Don't be embarrassed to ask the doctor about his or her qualifications. Where did he go to school? Is she board-certified? This term means that the doctor has received extensive training in a particular area and has passed oral and written examinations administered by the American Board of Medical Specialties. While board certification is not a guarantee of quality medicine, it's certainly a valuable indicator in terms of training and knowledge. Some physicians claim to be board-certified when in fact they're simply affiliated with professional organizations or belong to one of the 100 or so alternative, less-stringent boards. This misrepresentation is particularly rampant in the field of plastic surgery. A study published by the *New England Journal of Medicine* found that 12 percent of the doctors advertising in the Yellow Pages were not certified by the ABMS, and nearly half of the plastic surgeons lacked ABMS certification. (You can check if a doctor is legitimately boarded by calling 1-800-776-CERT.)

If your concern is the doctor's legal track record, you can research his malpractice claims in a book called *10,289 Questionable Doctors*, published by Public Citizen Health Research Group. It's available in the reference section of the business, science and industry department at the Free Library on Logan Square. On the other hand, be warned that doctors can also check up on your litigation record. A new legal service based in Philadelphia researches the number of malpractice suits a patient has filed, thus allowing the doctor to decide if you're worth the risk of treating.

Finally, perhaps the most critical question of all: Do you and the doctor have the right chemistry? Remember, you're beginning what you hope will be a cordial, long-term relationship, so examine the doctor's human qualities. You want a good listener, someone who talks *to you* rather than *at you*—or down to you—someone articulate, considerate, pleasant. Is this the kind of person who might come into the waiting room and apologize for running late? Nowhere is it written that doctors have permission to be immunized against courtesy.

After all this work, you still might find you've made a mistake. In that case, vote with your feet and move on.

Firing a doctor

Patients have an awful time grappling with the idea of changing doctors. They feel embarrassed, they don't quite know what to say, they don't know where else to go. None of these is a sufficient reason to remain with a doctor who isn't meeting your needs or providing the care you're paying for. The doctor is probably much more important to your life than you are to his. I can think of few services people continue to accept with displeasure to the degree they'll keep seeing a doctor they don't like or no longer trust.

If you're uncomfortable confronting the doctor or hurting her feelings, announce your intentions by phone or by letter or to the office manager so that you can request a copy of your medical records. They are full of valuable information your new doctor should have. While you're at it, you'd do the doctor a service by explaining why you're unhappy: The nurses overbook patients and you're sick of waiting an hour every time you schedule a visit. The doctor is never available when you call and in a hurry when you're there. Your appointments seem to last about 30 seconds. She's raised her fees once too often. You aren't getting the care or attention you deserve. While you're flattered being spoken to as if you had a medical degree from Harvard, you can't understand the doctor's explanations. Your son just graduated from medical school and opened an office around the corner. Bye.

Second opinions

Sometimes you can allay doubts about the level of care your doctor is providing by getting a second opinion. And second opinions are absolutely in order when you're considering elective surgery or you've been advised you need major surgery or you're uncertain about a proposed treatment plan. Research by the Rand Corporation, a California think tank, indicates that as many as one in three medical and surgical procedures is inappropriate, suggesting that it's worth the trouble to get another view.

I'd advise against taking a name for a second opinion from the doctor who's given you the first one. (That's where *Philadelphia Magazine*'s list comes in handy.) Too often the referral goes to a pal in the old boys' network. In the worst circumstances, the referring doctor kicks back a piece of the fee, and in the best, there's an unspoken promise to support the original diagnosis—especially when surgery is involved. You wash my back and I'll wash yours.

Also think about taking your bones to someone in a different hospital from the one your specialist is affiliated with. Because philosophies within a given department are frequently similar, you should check out another perspective. And consider reaching beyond your original specialist's discipline. Every specialist has a bias. Internists are more disposed to medical approaches, while surgeons tend to solve problems by cutting them out. Even among surgeons, an orthopedist might take a different tack from a sports medicine specialist.

When a disfiguring or difficult treatment plan is suggested, don't hesitate to consult elsewhere for alternative strategies. Many problems can be treated medically as well as surgically, so explore your options. If you decide the side-effects aren't worth the gains, speak up and say no. A friend of mine was told by a leading cardiologist that he had several clogged arteries and ought to schedule bypass surgery immediately. He took his angiogram results to someone else who recommended trying chelation therapy first. Six months later he swears his cholesterol is down and his arteries are open.

Your second opinion may confirm the first or it may not. Keep looking until a consensus relieves your confusion.

Patient's responsibilities

Certainly the responsibility for delivering quality medicine belongs to doctors, but there's plenty of evidence that people who assertively engage as partners in their treatments have better outcomes. In fact, doctors have told me they actually prefer active to passive patients. Clearly you can improve your chances of having a better doctor by becoming a good patient. That means it's your job to:

_____
Be on time for appointments.

_____
Expedite the efficiency of your visit by preparing your complaints and questions before you get to the office—writing them out, if necessary, to jog your memory.

Take your medication as prescribed, and know the names of the drugs you take. Don't expect doctors to educate you about the medicines they prescribe. It's up to you to ask what the side-effects are, how long before the drug works, whether it interacts with other medications and whether it's best taken on an empty or full stomach. Pharmacists can also be very helpful with drug information.

When talking to the doctor, discuss your symptoms in descending order of concern. A study showed that doctors start to formulate their diagnosis within the first minute of an examination.

Should you require surgery, there are several things you'll want to inquire about. How many of these particular operations has the surgeon done? This is especially important with some of the newer laparoscopic surgeries, where there is a definite learning curve and you don't want to be at the front end. How often does he or she do this procedure? At least two or three times a week is an acceptable base. What's the success rate and rate of complications? Pray he tells the truth.

In general, treat your medical care like any product in the marketplace and exercise the dictum *caveat emptor*. You should question why a particular test has been ordered, what it will reveal and how the results will change your treatment plan. Why put yourself through discomfort simply to satisfy a doctor's curiosity?

And when it's suggested that you try some state-of-the-art procedure, play the skeptic. Not all newfangled techniques—lasers, implants, laparoscopes—are an improvement over the standard ways. They may be more exciting and challenging for the doctor, but of no real advantage to you.

As in everything else, knowledge is power. If you've been diagnosed with a disease or condition, go to the library and read about it. Information on a wide range of medical research can be obtained from CRISP (Computer Retrieval of Information on Scientific Projects), a service of the National Institutes of Health, at 301-594-7267. Some organizations charge a fee and do the research for you: The Health Resource (501-329-5272) or Planetree Health Resource Center (415-923-3680).

Years ago there was a standing joke that many physicians held the highfalutin notion that the initials M.D. stood for *medical deity*. There's a lot less of that attitude around these days, partly because patients have gotten smarter and become health consumers. How fortunate that Philadelphians live in the midst of an outstanding medical center where the shopping opportunities couldn't be better.

1-800-PRO-HEALTH

Call Us for an Introduction...

To the doctor who's right for you

Just make one free phone call to 1-800-PRO-HEALTH to find the right doctor for you—whether that's a family practitioner, pediatrician, obstetrician or specialist in virtually any other field. We can answer your questions about the doctor's location, certifications, office hours and, of course, the insurances they accept. We'll even make your first appointment.

As one of the Delaware Valley's largest health care systems, our extended family of physicians can be found in city and suburban locations convenient to *your* family.

Let us introduce you to the doctor or dentist who's right for you.

MEDICAL COLLEGE HOSPITALS

Main Clinical Campus
Bucks County Campus
Elkins Park Campus

MEDICAL COLLEGE OF PENNSYLVANIA

Medical Practices

 **ST. CHRISTOPHER'S** HOSPITAL FOR CHILDREN

**1-800-PRO-HEALTH
(1-800-776-4325)**

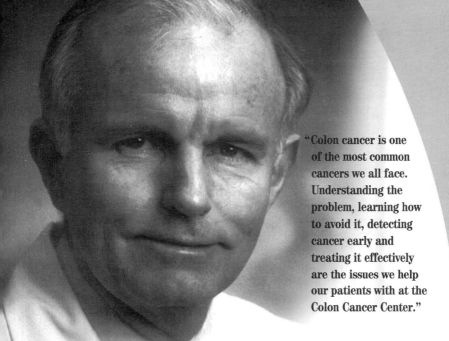

"Colon cancer is one of the most common cancers we all face. Understanding the problem, learning how to avoid it, detecting cancer early and treating it effectively are the issues we help our patients with at the Colon Cancer Center."

Colon Cancer Center.

The Temple University Cancer Center announces the opening of a Colon Cancer Center. Dr. John Macdonald and Dr. Benjamin Kresvsky are Co-Directors of the center which provides a multidisciplinary team approach for the screening, diagnosis and treatment of colon cancer. The Center provides services to include education on the risks of colon cancer, preventative strategies, screenings aimed at early detection of colon diseases and state-of-the-art treatment options. Utilizing standard and research protocols, the Colon Cancer Center is meeting the challenges of patients and their families face in dealing with Large Bowel Cancer .

For more information about the Colon Cancer Center, please contact Dr. John Macdonald or Dr. Benjamin Kresvsky **at 215-707-4000.**

 THE TEMPLE UNIVERSITY CANCER CENTER

215-707-4000

CHAPTER 8

Doctor, Doctor

Why not the best?

Hello," she said. "My name is Mrs. L—, and I'm sorry to bother you but I need some help. I've just learned I need a bypass and I want the best heart surgeon in Philadelphia. Who do you recommend?"

In the ten years we've been publishing our list of the best doctors in Philadelphia, I've gotten calls like this all the time. A woman's gynecologist is retiring and she wants a replacement. Someone's father has colon cancer—where can he find the best treatment? A man new to the area is looking for a first-rate internist. If I were having a hip replacement, where would I go?

At first I thought it awfully strange that people would ask a magazine writer for advice about doctors. Then I learned that many physicians also turn to *Philadelphia Magazine*'s best doctor list when *they* need to make a referral outside of their own specialty. In fact, there are precious few independent and reliable sources that rank medical specialists. Doctor referral lines will give you names, but they don't evaluate performance. Friends will happily bore or scare you with their personal experiences, but those rarely serve as expert opinions. And aren't you sometimes suspicious that the doctor your doctor suggested may be the guy he shares a box with at the Eagles game?

What you really want is the outstanding specialists doctors use for their spouses, their children, their parents and their best friends. And that is exactly what you get from *Philadelphia Magazine*—a painstakingly researched peer review of the doctors' doctors. We begin our assessment by mailing a survey to more than 3,000 doctors and nurses around the Delaware Valley. Our sample includes members of the American College of Physicians, the American College of Surgeons, members of nursing associations and the department chairmen of several dozen hospitals. We ask: "If someone close to you had a problem in one of the following specialties, who would you send them to for the very best care and treatment?"

The names we amass are only the first step. If we merely tallied the results and published the doctors mentioned most often, this would be nothing more than a popularity contest. No fear of that. In an ideal world we might insist on a compassionate bedside manner as a criterion for inclusion. But given the choice between a warm, responsive surgeon with a decent reputation or an SOB with the best hands in the business, is there really a contest? So don't be surprised to find several doctors on this list who are not particularly well-liked but are nevertheless highly regarded professionally. I learn about these little details through an extensive interview process with scores of sources who help me shape and refine the final selections from the thousand or so names that emerge from the survey.

Am I subjected to lobbying efforts? Yes.

Does it help? No.

Are the results subjective? Sure, but that doesn't mean they aren't accurate.

Have we missed anybody? Of course.

There are more than 10,000 physicians within a 100-mile radius of Philadelphia, and while it's easy to weed out the ones who should have studied harder and partied less in medical school, it's impossible to identify every star in this large firmament. While some may have been omitted on purpose, other absences are accidental. We included only doctors who spend a significant amount of their time seeing patients, so you won't find any world-renowned researchers or department heads bogged down by administrative duties. And we no doubt included some people who are so busy you'll be sorry you called them, because their offices operate like assembly lines.

That's one reason we made a special effort to reach out into the suburbs this time around. There is always a preponderance of doctors at teaching hospitals on our list because that's where top docs naturally congregate. It gives them the opportunity to do research, experiment with cutting-edge techniques, hobnob with leaders in their profession and treat the most interesting cases. The downside to teaching hospitals is that these bizarre and exotic medical problems may get more attention than your routine appendectomy. And there's also the chance some or all of the surgery will be done by supervised residents. In many circumstances, you'll do just as well with a great doctor at your community hospital. For that matter, if you're satisfied with the doctor you're seeing, don't change because he or she isn't on this list.

Medical Specialists

Allergy and Immunology

Any allergy, be it hay fever or a penicillin reaction, is an abnormal response by the body's immune system to something ingested or inhaled. The allergist will do skin or sometimes blood tests to identify the cause of the symptoms (hives, rashes or sneezing). If the irritant can't be avoided—like eliminating an offending food—a series of injections is used to develop immunity.

PAUL C. ATKINS, *HUP;* FREDERICK C. COGEN, *CMC/ Holy Redeemer;* ELIOT H. DUNSKY, *Hahn;* GEORGE R. GREEN, *Abington;* ARNOLD I. LEVINSON, *HUP;* JOSEPH E. PAPPANO JR., *Bryn Mawr;* SHERYL F. TALBOT, *Pennsylvania;* BURTON ZWEIMAN, *HUP*

Anesthesiology

A critical part of any surgical procedure is the choice of how to numb the patient. Should he be awake or asleep? Should she have local, regional or general anesthesia? Patients frequently leave these decisions up to the surgeon, but there is no reason why you cannot discuss the options yourself with an anesthesiologist.

JAMES E. DUCKETT, *Presby;* NORIG ELLISON, *HUP (sp: cardiac);* BRETT B. GUTSCHE, *HUP (sp: ob/gyn);* DAVID J. FISH, *Fox Chase;* THOMAS D. MULL, *Bryn Mawr;* STANLEY MURAVCHICK, *HUP (sp: plastic surgery);* J. STEPHEN NAULTY, *Pennsylvania (sp: ob/gyn);* DEBORAH E. RITTER, *Jeff;* HENRY ROSENBERG, *Hahn;* JOSEPH L. SELTZER, *Jeff (sp: cardiovascular);* DAVID S. SMITH, *HUP (sp: neuro);* LINDA SUNDT, *Jeff (sp: cardiovascular)*

Cardiology

Heart problems are classified as congenital (murmurs, valve abnormalities) or acquired (angina, heart failures). The cardiologist treats both kinds. Following diagnosis, this doctor will either recommend surgery to correct the defect or he'll manage the condition with noninvasive measures such as drugs, diet and exercise.

ALFRED A. BOVE, *Temple (sp: heart failure);* SUSAN C. BROZENA, *Hahn (sp: heart failure);* ALFRED BUXTON, *Temple (sp: electrophysiology);* K. CHANDRASEKARAN, *Hahn (sp: echocardiography);* DAVID J. ESKIN, *Abington;* WILLIAM S. FRANKL, *MCP;* IRVING M. HERLING, *HUP;* AMI S. ISKANDRIAN, *Presby (sp: nuclear cardiology);* MARIELL JESSUP, *Presby/ Nazareth (sp: heart failure);* MORRIS N. KOTLER, *Einstein;* PETER R. KOWEY, *Lankenau (sp: electrophysiology);* FRANCIS E. MARCHLINSKI, *Presby (sp: electrophysiology);* BERNARD L. SEGAL, *Presby;* MARTIN ST. JOHN SUTTON, *HUP (sp: echocardiography);* HARVEY L. WAXMAN, *CMC (sp: electrophysiology)*

Cardiac Catheterization

A number of heart problems related to blocked arteries are handled by this specialist, who is an expert at threading an ultrathin tube through the blood vessels to diagnose blockages, open passageways and dissolve clots.

CHARLES E. BEMIS, *Hahn/Holy Redeemer/Einstein;* JAMES A. BURKE, *Temple;* PETER M. DIBATTISTE, *Lankenau/Presby;* SHELDON GOLDBERG, *Jeff;* RONALD S. GOTTLIEB, *Graduate;*

JOHN W. HIRSHFELD JR., *HUP;* HRATCH KASPARIAN, *Graduate;* WARREN LASKEY, *HUP;* J. DAVID OGILBY, *Presby;* MICHAEL P. SAVAGE, *Jeff;* WILLIAM J. UNTEREKER, *CMC*

Dermatology

Any kind of skin irritation—severe dandruff, acne, psoriasis, nail fungus, rashes, moles, eczema, even wrinkles—would be cause to visit a dermatologist. Because of the rise in skin cancer, anyone with a family history of melanoma or suspicious dark spots on the skin should see a dermatologist for an assessment.

EDWARD E. BONDI, *HUP;* ALEXANDER EHRLICH, *HUP/Graduate;* PAUL R. GROSS, *Pennsylvania;* WARREN R. HEYMANN, *CMC (sp: dermopathology);* JAMES J. LEYDEN, *HUP;* MARIE UBERTI-BENZ, *Presby*

Cosmetic Dermatology

Many dermatologists develop specialties that focus on appearance. Their face-saving techniques include dermabrasion, collagen and silicone injections, and chemical peels. Skin-cancer patients may require a special type of surgery called Mohs.

LEONARD DZUBOW, *HUP (sp: Mohs, hair transplantation);* STEVEN S. GREENBAUM, *Jeff (sp: Mohs);* THOMAS D. GRIFFIN, *Graduate;* PAUL R. GROSS, *Pennsylvania;* NATHAN R. HOWE, *Hahn (sp: Mohs);* WAINE C. JOHNSON, *Graduate (sp: hair transplantation);* JAMES J. LEYDEN, *HUP*

Diabetology

Great strides have been made in the management of diabetes, which occurs in one of two forms: The milder type, adult-onset diabetes, can usually be controlled through diet and medication; the more severe juvenile diabetes occurs in adults as well as children and requires daily insulin intake. These specialists treat adult diabetics with either problem.

SETH BRAUNSTEIN, *HUP;* ANTHONY S. JENNINGS, *Presby (sp: thyroid disease);* STEVEN B. NAGELBERG, *MCP/Frankford;* CHARLES R. SHUMAN, *Temple (sp: nutrition/metabolism)*

Endocrinology

Endocrinologists treat a variety of problems stemming from the body's hormone-related systems. These include metabolic malfunctions, thyroid disorders, and adrenal diseases like Addison's disease and Cushing's syndrome.

DAVID M. CAPUZZI, *Lankenau/MCP (sp: lipid disorders);* DOMINIC F. CORRIGAN, *Abington;* SOL EPSTEIN, *Einstein (sp: osteoporosis);* JOSEPH S. FISHER, *Holy Redeemer/Jeff/Nazareth;* ELIHU N. GOREN, *Germantown/Montgomery/Sacred Heart;* JOHN G. HADDAD, *HUP (sp: metabolic bone disease);* ANTHONY S. JENNINGS, *Presby (sp: thyroid);* ALLAN D. MARKS, *Temple;* LESLIE ROSE, *Hahn;* PETER J. SNYDER, *HUP;* FRANK STERLING, *VA;* JOHN L. TURNER, *Graduate (sp: AIDS)*

Emergency Medicine

Unfortunately, too many people use emergency rooms inappropriately for general medicine. That should change with the new Clinton program for universal health coverage, freeing these physicians to handle the real emergencies they've been trained to treat. Warning signs that should send you to an emergency room include: fainting; pain or pressure in the chest or upper abdomen; sudden dizziness, weakness or vision difficulty; breathing problems; repeated and severe vomiting; thoughts of murder or suicide.

STEPHANIE B. ABBUHL, *HUP;* MICHAEL CHANSKY, *CMC;* FREDERIC KAUFFMAN, *Temple;* DAVID K. WAGNER, *MCP/Mercy Catholic;* JOSEPH A. ZECCARDI, *Jeff*

Family Practice/Primary Care

In the good old days before every medical-school graduate opted to became a specialist, GPs were the backbone of medicine. Now family medicine is itself a specialty that involves post-graduate training in preventive medicine, gynecology, pediatrics, orthopedics and minor surgery. With the new emphasis on primary-care physicians, these doctors will be assuming increased importance and responsibility. And some still make house calls.

IRWIN BECKER, *Einstein/Germantown;* BARRY R. COOPER, *Abington;* HARRY FRANKEL, *Graduate;* ROBERT C. MADONNA, *Delco Memorial;* WARREN B. MATTHEWS, *Abington;* EDWARD H. MCGEHEE, *Jeff;* ALEXANDER R. PEDICINO, *Holy Redeemer;* ROBERT L. PERKEL, *Jeff;* JOHN RANDALL, *Jeff;* ANN E. REILLY, *Paoli (adults only);* RICHARD C. WENDER, *Jeff*

Gastroenterology

Digestive disorders—ulcers, cancer, pancreatitis, inflammatory bowel diseases, hiatal hernia, diverticulitis—afflict some 20 million Americans who visit this specialist so they can quit bellyaching.

CRAIG ARONCHICK, *Pennsylvania (sp: therapeutic endoscopy);* WILLIAM M. BATTLE, *Jeanes/Nazareth;* DONALD O. CASTELL, *Graduate (sp: esophagology);* HARRIS R. CLEARFIELD, *Hahn (sp: inflammatory bowel disease);* SIDNEY COHEN, *Temple;* JULIUS J. DEREN, *Graduate (sp: inflammatory bowel disease);* ANTHONY J. DIMARINO JR., *Presby/Underwood;* SUSAN J. GORDON, *Jeff;* MARK JACOBS, *Delco Memorial/Mercy Catholic (sp: therapeutic);* DAVID A. KATZKA, *Graduate (sp: esophageal disease/motility disorders);* WILLIAM H. LIPSHUTZ, *Pennsylvania (sp: inflammatory bowel/esophageal disease);* WILLIAM B. LONG, *HUP (sp: therapeutic);* STEVEN R. PEIKIN, *CMC*

Geriatrics

This relatively new specialty developed from the explosion of longer-living Americans requiring care, so it's specifically targeted to the problems of old age. While most doctors can and do treat older patients, it's often useful to see someone with increased knowledge of the aging body.

BARBARA W. BELL, *Abington;* LESLEY CARSON, *MCP;* THOMAS A. CAVALIERI, *University of Medicine and Dentistry of N.J.;* ALBERT J. FINESTONE, *Temple;* MARY ANN FORCIEA, *HUP;* DAVID E. GALINSKY, *Lankenau/Jeff-Ford;* MARTIN L. LEICHT, *Philadelphia Geriatric Center/Einstein;* JOEL POSNER, *MCP;* BARBARA SCHINDLER, *MCP;* EUGENIA L. SIEGLER, *HUP/VA*

Gynecology/Obstetrics

Once a kindly doctor who delivered babies and talked a woman through menopause, this physician has lately developed into a sophisticated specialist treating the range of female medical conditions that begin with menstruation and continue throughout a woman's life. We divided this group into areas of primary interest.

General Gynecology

Whether it's for a Pap smear, a mammography or a discussion of hormone replacement therapy, every woman should see a gynecologist on a yearly basis.

WILLIAM W. BECK JR., *HUP;* EILEEN ENGLE, *Pennsylvania (sp: menopause);* DAVID M. GOODNER, *Jeff;* MARVIN R. HYETT, *Jeff;* RONALD M. JAFFE, *CMC;* RICHARD K. KRAUSS, *Pennsylvania;* JOEL I. POLIN, *Abington;* MICHAEL R. SPENCE, *Hahn (sp: gynecologic infectious diseases);* BEVERLY M. VAUGHN, *Pennsylvania/Graduate;* ROBERT S. WEINSTEIN, *HUP;* MARTIN WEISBERG, *Jeff*

Gynecologic Oncology

These doctors restrict their practice to treating cancers of the female reproductive system.

MICHAEL J. CAMPION, *Graduate (sp: cancer of the cervix);* JOHN A. CARLSON JR., *Jeff (sp: ovarian cancer);* ENRIQUE HERNANDEZ, *MCP;* W. MICHAEL HOGAN, *Lankenau/Fox Chase (sp: ovarian cancer);* CHARLES E. MANGAN, *Pennsylvania;* JOHN J. MIKUTA, *HUP;* MARK A. MORGAN, *HUP;* JOEL S. NOUMOFF, *Crozer-Chester (sp: endometrial carcinoma);* THOMAS F. ROCERETO, *CMC;* STEPHEN C. RUBIN, *HUP*

Obstetrics

WILLIAM W. BECK JR. *HUP;* DAVID M. GOODNER, *Jeff;* DREW MELLEN, *Pennsylvania;* OWEN C. MONTGOMERY, *Jeff;* JOEL I. POLIN, *Abington;* BEVERLY M. VAUGHN, *Pennsylvania/Graduate;* ROBERT S. WEINSTEIN, *HUP*

Gynecologic Surgery

This covers those procedures related to noncancerous problems of the female reproductive organs, including hysterectomies, sterilization, endometriosis and fibroids. For treatment of fibroids, discuss the possibility of a myomectomy before submitting to a hysterectomy.

STEPHEN L. CORSON, *Pennsylvania/Graduate (sp: laparoscopy, hysteroscopy);* MARVIN H. TERRY GRODY, *Temple (sp: pelvic reconstruction);* FRANCIS L. HUTCHINS JR., *Graduate (sp: endoscopy);* JOSEPH M. MONTELLA, *Jeff (sp: urogynecology);* CRAIG A. WINKEL, *Jeff (sp: laparoscopy/pelviscopy)*

High-Risk Pregnancy

As more and more women delay childbearing, complications related to pregnancy have increased to the point where they are now handled by a select group of obstetricians. Consider this specialist when age, or an existing medical problem like diabetes, threatens either the life of the fetus or the mother's ability to carry to term.

RONALD J. BOLOGNESE, *Pennsylvania;* LINDA K. DUNN, *Abington (sp: genetics);* ANDREW G. GERSON, *Lankenau/Paoli;* MICHAEL T. MENNUTI, *HUP (sp: genetics);* NANCY S. ROBERTS, *Lankenau;* RONALD J. WAPNER, *Jeff (sp: genetics)*

Infertility

Remarkable scientific advances like in-vitro fertilization have made the old temperature chart practically obsolete. Couples should consider seeing a fertility specialist when a year of trying to have a baby has not produced a pregnancy.

LUIS BLASCO, *HUP (sp: male infertility/laparoscopy);* JEROME H. CHECK, *CMC (sp: endocrinology);* STEPHEN L. CORSON, *Pennsylvania (sp: in-vitro);* MARTIN F. FREEDMAN, *Holy Redeemer/Abington (sp: laser surgery);* CELSO-RAMON GARCIA, *HUP/Pennsylvania (sp: gynecological surgery);* LUIGI MASTROIANNI JR., *HUP (sp: fertilization);* JAY F. SCHINFELD, *Abington (sp: laser surgery, lupus);* STEVEN J. SONDHEIMER, *HUP (sp: reproductive endocrinology);* CRAIG A. WINKEL, *Jeff*

Hematology/Oncology

In general, these physicians deal with blood diseases like anemia, hemophilia, leukemia, leukopenia, etc. But a number of them (where noted) concentrate their practice on treating cancer patients.

ISADORE BRODSKY, *Hahn (sp: bone marrow);* JOHN R. DUROCHER, *Pennsylvania;* KEVIN R. FOX, *HUP (sp: breast cancer);* JOHN H. GLICK, *HUP (sp: breast cancer/lymphoma);* DONNA GLOVER, *Presby (sp: breast cancer);* JACK GOLDBERG, *CMC (sp: leukemia/lymphoma);* DUPONT GUERRY, *HUP (sp: melanoma);* DANIEL G. HALLER, *HUP (sp: G.I.);* DAVID H. HENRY, *Graduate (sp: AIDS/AIDS-related cancer);* ROSALINE R. JOSEPH, *MCP;* JOHN S. MACDONALD, *Temple;* KENNETH F. MANGAN, *Temple (sp: bone marrow);* BERNARD A. MASON, *Graduate (sp: lung cancer);* MICHAEL J. MASTRANGELO, *Jeff (sp: melanoma);* SCOTT MURPHY, *Jeff;* ROBERT F. OZOLS, *Fox Chase (sp: ovarian cancer);* SANFORD SHATTIL, *HUP (sp: coagulation);* EDWARD A. STADTMAUER, *HUP (sp: leukemia/bone marrow);* ALAN S. WEINSTEIN, *Burlington County*

Infectious Disease

An infinite number of bacteria and viruses cause infections as they're transmitted person-to-person or from animals to humans, as in the case of Lyme disease. This specialist identifies the source of the infection and selects drugs to help the immune system fight it. In recent years, AIDS has become a major subspecialty of this practitioner.

PATRICK J. BRENNAN, *HUP;* R. MICHAEL BUCKLEY, *Pennsylvania;* KATHLEEN M. GEKOWSKI, *CMC (sp: AIDS);* STEPHEN J. GLUCKMAN, *HUP (sp: HIV/parasitology/tropical diseases);* JOHN J. KELLY, *Abington/Holy Redeemer;* BENNETT LORBER, *Temple;* JEROME SANTORO, *Lankenau (sp: Lyme disease/travel medicine);* PETER G. SPITZER, *Bryn Mawr*

Internal Medicine

Often referred to as the doctor's doctor, the internist is a medical detective trained to identify elusive disorders. Besides being an expert diagnostician, internists also manage patients with complicated medical histories. Their residency includes extra study of the gastrointestinal, endocrine, cardiovascular and respiratory systems as well as in diseases like diabetes and arthritis. With the coming shift to "gatekeeper" medicine, in which referrals to a specialist will come from a general physician, many internists are broadening their scope to include primary care.

BONNIE L. ASHBY, *Bryn Mawr (sp: infectious disease);* MICHAEL J. BAIME, *Graduate;* RICHARD J. BARON, *Chestnut Hill (sp: geriatrics);* DIANE BARTON, *CMC (sp: obesity);* GARY W. CROOKS, *HUP;* ROGER B. DANIELS, *Pennsylvania;* THOMAS DEBERARDINIS, *Lankenau;* BRADLEY W. FENTON, *Presby;* GARY W. DORSHIMER, *Pennsylvania;* HAL S. HOCKFIELD, *Abington;* ISRAEL H. LICHTENSTEIN, *Jeanes;* HOWARD A. MILLER, *Hahn;* WILBUR OAKS, *Hahn;* PAUL M. ROEDIGER, *Abington;* MARIE A. SAVARD, *Pennsylvania;* BRUCE G. SILVER, *Lankenau (sp: geriatrics);* THORNE SPARKMAN JR., *HUP;* ELLEN M. TEDALDI, *Temple;* EDWARD D. VINER, *CMC (sp: hematology/oncology)*

Nephrology

Far more kidney diseases are treated with dialysis than by transplants, so choose this physician carefully. You're likely to have a long-term relationship.

JAMES F. BURKE, *Jeff (sp: transplants);* GARY S. GILGORE, *Lankenau/Montgomery;* MARTIN GOLDBERG, *Temple (sp: hypertension);* ROBERT A. GROSSMAN, *HUP;* BRENDA R. C. KURNIK, *CMC;* MICHAEL R. RUDNICK, *Graduate (sp: renovascular disease);* ROBERT A. SIROTA, *Abington/Holy Redeemer/Jeanes/Nazareth;* BRENDAN P. TEEHAN, *Lankenau*

Neurology

The neurologist uses medication to treat a wide range of disorders involving the nervous system, from headaches to epilepsy to the after-effects of a stroke. You'd also consult one for muscular dystrophy, movement or memory loss, pain, myasthenia gravis or Parkinson's.

ROBERT D. AIKEN, *Jeff;* RODNEY D. BELL, *Jeff (sp: cerebral vascular);* THOMAS M. BOSLEY, *Pennsylvania/Wills (sp: neuro-ophthalmology);* MARK J. BROWN, *HUP (sp: neuromuscular disease);* CHRISTOPHER CLARK, *Graduate (sp: memory disorders/dementia);* DAVID G. COOK, *Pennsylvania;* B. FRANKLIN DIAMOND, *Abington (sp: sleep disorders);* MARC A. DICHTER, *Graduate (sp: epilepsy);* JUNE M. FRY, *MCP (sp: sleep disorders);* STEVEN L. GALETTA, *HUP (sp: neuro-ophthalmology);* STEPHEN M. GOLLOMP, *Lankenau (sp: movement disorders);* JEFFREY I. GREENSTEIN, *Temple (sp: neuro-immunology, MS);* MURRAY GROSSMAN, *HUP (sp: cognitive neurology);* HOWARD I. HURTIG, *Graduate (sp: Parkinson's/movement disorders);* FRED D. LUBLIN, *Jeff (sp: neuro-immunology/MS);* JOAN L. MOLLMAN, *HUP (sp: neuro-oncology);* AMY PRUITT, *HUP (sp: neuro-oncology);* ERIC C. RAPS, *HUP (sp: neuro-intensive care);* DAVID S. ROBY, *Jeanes (sp: Parkinson's);* PAUL L. SCHRAEDER, *CMC (sp: epilepsy);* DONALD H. SILBERBERG, *HUP (sp: MS/neuro-ophthalmology);* STEPHEN D. SILBERSTEIN, *Germantown (sp: headaches);* MATTHEW B. STERN, *Graduate (sp: Parkinson's)*

Ophthalmology

You can have your vision checked by an optometrist or get glasses from an optician, but an ophthalmologist is the only physician trained to operate on the eye and to treat eye problems. This specialty divides into several subspecialties as noted.

General Ophthalmology

Robert S. Bailey Jr., *Wills/Chestnut Hill*; Dion R. Ehrlich, *Jeanes/Abington/Wills*; Marvin H. Greenbaum, *Lankenau/Scheie*; Louis A. Karp, *Pennsylvania/Scheie*; Michael L. Kay, *Wills (sp: cataracts)*; David M. Kozart, *Scheie (sp: cataracts)*; Michael A. Naidoff, *Wills/Jeff (sp: cataracts/corneal transplants)*; Charles W. Nichols, *HUP*; T. Ramsey Thorp, *Chestnut Hill*

Cataracts

As part of the natural aging process, the lens of the eye gradually clouds like a frosty window. The resulting blurred or fuzzy vision is corrected by surgically removing the damaged lens and replacing it with an intra-ocular implant.

Raymond E. Adams, *Wills*; James B. Carty Jr., *Bryn Mawr/Wills*; Stephen B. Lichtenstein, *Wills/Lankenau*; Steven B. Siepser, *Wills/Montgomery*; Myron Yanoff, *Hahn*

Cornea

Anything from a scratch to herpes simplex can damage the transparent membrane covering the eye. Most problems are medically treated; some necessitate corneal transplants.

Elisabeth J. Cohen, *Wills*; Peter R. Laibson, *Wills/Lankenau*; Stephen E. Orlin, *Scheie*; Irving M. Raber, *Lankenau*

Glaucoma

One of the leading causes of blindness is caused by a buildup of pressure within the eye, which can usually be controlled with drugs. Early detection is important, and one reason to get a regular eye checkup after the age of 35.

Marlene R. Moster, *Wills*; George L. Spaeth, *Wills*; Elliot B. Werner, *Hahn*; Richard P. Wilson, *Wills/Lankenau*

Neuro-Ophthalmology

Deals with visual disturbances that stem from medical (and neurological) conditions such as brain tumors, multiple sclerosis, stroke and myasthenia gravis.

Thomas M. Bosley, *Wills/Pennsylvania*; Steven L. Galetta, *HUP*; Mark L. Moster, *Einstein/Temple*; Peter J. Savino, *Wills/Graduate*; Robert C. Sergott, *Wills/Lankenau*

Ocular Oncology

Treats cancers of the eye.

James J. Augsburger, *Wills/Lankenau*; Carol L. Shields, *Wills (sp: retinoblastoma/orbital tumors)*; Jerry A. Shields, *Wills (sp: retinoblastoma/orbital tumors)*

Ophthalmic Plastic Surgery

This specialist corrects drooping eyelids, removes tumors on the lids, fixes defects of the orbit and tear ducts and also performs a popular cosmetic procedure called blepharoplasty.

JOSEPH C. FLANAGAN, *Wills/Lankenau;* JAMES A. KATOWITZ, *Scheie/CHOP (sp: pediatric ophthalmology);* SUSAN M. HUGHES, *Wills/Graduate (sp: eyelid surgery);* DAVID B. SOLL, *CMC/Frankford;* MARY A. STEFANYSZYN, *Wills/Lankenau;* ALLAN E. WULC, *Scheie/Presby/Abington*

Radial Keratotomy

This procedure to correct near-sightedness with surgical cuts that flatten the cornea has become extremely popular, in part because of improved technology. Before selecting a doctor, find out how many of these operations he or she has done; experience is important.

FREDERIC B. KREMER, *Scheie/Wills*

Retina and Vitreous

The retina, like the film that takes the picture in a camera, is the lining on the back of the eye. Any severe blow to the head may cause the retina to detach. The vitreous is the clear gel that fills the center of the eye. It may shrink for a variety of reasons and cause, among other things, a retinal tear. Diabetes often damages these parts of the eye.

WILLIAM E. BENSON, *Wills;* GARY BROWN, *Wills/Chestnut Hill/Jeff;* ALEXANDER J. BRUCKER, *Scheie;* JAY L. FEDERMAN, *Wills/MCP/Lankenau;* STUART FINE, *Scheie;* DAVID H. FISCHER, *Wills/Lankenau (sp: uveitis);* WILLIAM TASMAN, *Wills/CHOP/Chestnut Hill*

Otolaryngology

Back when this specialty was known as ENT (ear, nose and throat), tonsillectomies and earaches were its bread and butter. Today these physicians, many of whom also do surgery, treat a range of problems of the head and neck: hearing loss, cancer of the larynx, taste and smell disorders, tinnitus and vertigo.

JOSEPH ARDITO, *Delco Memorial/Paoli/Bryn Mawr;* JOSEPH ATKINS, *Pennsylvania;* DOUGLAS C. BIGELOW, *HUP (sp: neurotology);* RICHARD E. HAYDEN, *HUP (sp: head and neck cancer);* WILLIAM KEANE, *Pennsylvania/Jeff;* DAVID KENNEDY, *HUP (sp: sinus);* CHARLES L. ROJER, *Abington/Chestnut Hill;* MAX RONIS, *Temple/St. Chris (sp: neurotology);* ROBERT SATALOFF, *Jeff/Graduate (sp: voice problems, neurotology);* HARVEY D. SILBERMAN, *Jeanes/MCP/Einstein*

Pathology

Most patients have little contact with this specialist, who microscopically examines small pieces of tissue (known as biopsies) to determine the cause of an illness, be it cancer or an elusive microbe. When a biopsy is questionable, patients can and should request another expert opinion.

BARBARA F. ATKINSON, *MCP (sp: cytopathology)*; HUGH BONNER, *Chester County/HUP (sp: lymphoma, leukemia)*; EDISON CATALANO, *CMC (sp: hematopathology)*; HARRY S. COOPER, *Hahn (sp: G.I.)*; HORMOZ EHYA, *Hahn (sp: cytopathology)*; DAVID ELDER, *HUP (sp: pigmented lesions)*; PRABODH K. GUPTA, *HUP (sp: cytopathology)*; VIRGINIA LiVOLSI, *HUP (sp: surgical)*; FRANCIS McBREARTY, *Lankenau;* ARTHUR S. PATCHEFSKY, *Hahn;* GIUSEPPE G. PIETRA, *HUP (sp: lung and heart disease)*; MIN SOHN, *Graduate;* JOHN TOMASZEWSKI, *HUP (sp: urogenital and kidney)*; JAMES WHEELER, *HUP (sp: GYN)*

Physical Medicine

Also known as physiatrists, these doctors not only provide rehabilitation to victims of accidents, strokes and sports-related injuries, they also treat persistent neck and back pain with exercise and therapy rather than with surgery or drugs.

ERNEST M. BARAN, *Lafayette Hill Medical Center/Nazareth (sp: electrodiagnostic medicine)*; FRANCIS J. BONNER JR., *Graduate/Sacred Heart;* JOHN F. DITUNNO JR., *Jeff;* GARY GOLDBERG, *Moss (sp: electromiography/stroke)*; GERALD J. HERBISON, *Jeff (sp: electrodiagnosis/spinal cord)*; NATHANIEL H. MAYER, *Moss;* JOHN L. MELVIN, *Moss/Einstein (sp: disability evaluation)*; FRANCIS NASO, *Jeff (sp: rehab)*; JAY SIEGFRIED, *Lankenau (sp: cardiopulmonary rehab)*; CURTIS SLIPMAN, *HUP (sp: neck and back pain)*; WILLIAM E. STAAS JR., *Magee/Jeff (sp: spinal cord)*; THEERASAKDI VACHRANUKUNKIET, *Abington/Moss (sp: gait and motor control)*

Psychiatry

Unlike psychologists, who among other things use a wide variety of talk therapies rather than drugs for coping with emotional problems, psychiatrists are permitted to augment their patients' therapy with drugs. Several nationally known psychiatrists who work in Philadelphia see patients primarily by consultation and referral, and devote most of their energy to teaching, writing and research. Because of their prominence, we've noted them on a special list. The rest spend at least half their time clocking the 50-minute hour.

Emeritus

Mainly consultation and referral.

AARON T. BECK, *HUP (sp: cognitive therapy)*; GARY GOTTLIEB, *HUP (sp: geriatric)*; JOSEPH MENDELS, *Philadelphia Medical Institute (sp: psychopharmacology)*; CHARLES P. O'BRIEN, *HUP/VA (sp: substance abuse)*; KARL RICKELS, *HUP (sp: psychopharmacology)*; ALBERTO C. SERRANO, *Child Guidance/CHOP/HUP (sp: family therapy)*; ALBERT STUNKARD, *HUP (sp: obesity)*; PETER WHYBROW, *HUP*

General

SALMAN AKHTAR, *Jeff, (sp: psychoanalysis)*; PETER B. BLOOM, *Institute (sp: medical hypnosis)*; DAVID D. BURNS, *Presby (sp: cognitive)*; PHILIP J. ESCOLL, *Institute (sp: psychoanalysis)*; PAUL FINK, *Einstein (sp: violent behavior)*; ROBERT GREENSTEIN, *HUP (sp: post-traumatic stress disorder)*; ALAN M. GRUENBERG, *Institute (sp: diagnostic testing)*; LASZLO GYULAI, *HUP (sp: bipolar)*; IRA N. HERMAN, *HUP (sp: cognitive)*; RICHARD KLUFT, *Institute (sp: dissociative dis-*

orders); LAWRENCE A. REAL, *Belmont (sp: severe and persistent mental illness)*; BRADLEY H.
SEVIN, *Pennsylvania (sp: psychoanalysis)*; DERRI SHTASEL, *HUP (sp: schizophrenia)*; JAMES L.
STINNETT, *HUP (sp: medical psychiatry)*; TROY L. THOMPSON II, *Jeff (sp: geriatric/ psycho-
analysis)*; MICHAEL VERGARE, *Einstein/Belmont/Chestnut Hill (sp: geriatric)*; EDWARD A.
VOLKMAN, *Einstein*

Eating Disorders

SUSAN ICE, *Belmont*; RONALD LIEBMAN, *CHOP*; MICHAEL PERTSCHUK, *Graduate*; NEAL R.
SATTEN, *Institute*

Family Therapy

HOWARD DICHTER, *Belmont*; ROBERT GARFIELD, *Hahn (sp: men's issues)*; MARTIN
GOLDBERG, *Institute*; MARIE J. MIGNOGNA, *Temple (sp: geropsychiatry)*; IVAN B. NAGY, *Hahn*

Geriatric

WILLIAM R. DUBIN, *Belmont/Einstein*; BARRY W. ROVNER, *Jeff/Wills (sp: Alzheimer's)*;
GEORGE E. RUFF, *HUP*; BARBARA A. SCHINDLER, *MCP*

Substance Abuse/Addiction

CHRISTOPHER D'AMANDA, *North Philadelphia Health System*; CHARLES V. GIANNASIO,
Belmont/Abington; DONALD J. GILL, *Institute/Pennsylvania*; WILLIAM S. GREENFIELD, *Penn
Recovery Systems/Institute*; JOHN G. MEZOCHOW, *Presby*; JOSEPH R. VOLPICELLI, *HUP*;
GEORGE E. WOODY, *HUP/VA*

Psychopharmacology

KEVIN P. CAPUTO, *Crozer-Chester*; EDWARD SCHWEIZER, *HUP*; GEORGE M. SIMPSON, *MCP*;
STEVEN D. TARGUM, *Crozer-Chester*; HARRY ZALL, *Institute*

Pulmonary

Lung specialists handle diseases like emphysema, bronchitis, pleurisy, pneumonia
and lung cancer. The symptoms that might send you to one of these doctors include
prolonged coughing, shortness of breath, chest pains or blood in the sputum.

MICHAEL P. CASEY, *Pennsylvania*; PAUL E. EPSTEIN, *Graduate (sp: occupational lung therapy)*;
STANLEY FIEL, *MCP (sp: cystic fibrosis)*; WILLIAM G. FIGUEROA, *Lankenau*; JAMES E. FISH, *Jeff
(sp: asthma)*; MICHEAL A. GRIPPI, *HUP*; JOHN HANSEN-FLASCHEN, *HUP*; MARK A. KELLEY,
HUP; EUGENE M. LUGANO, *Pennsylvania*; HAROLD I. PALEVSKY, *HUP (sp: vascular diseases)*;
DONALD D. PETERSON, *Lankenau (sp: sleep disorders)*; MELVIN R. PRATTER, *CMC*; RICHARD
W. SNYDER, *Abington*; MICHAEL UNGER, *Pennsylvania (sp: laser bronchoscopy)*

Radiology

High-tech equipment like CAT scans and MRIs have taken this specialty light years
away from simply reading X-rays. The modern radiologist falls into one of two
major subgroups: diagnosing problems from pictures and treating diseases with
radiation.

Diagnostic Radiology

ABASS ALAVI, *HUP (sp: nuclear medicine);* PETER H. ARGER, *HUP (sp: ultrasound);* LEON
AXEL, *HUP (sp: cardiovascular MRI);* AKBAR BONAKDARPOUR, *Temple (sp: skeletal);* MARC P.
BANNER, *HUP (sp: genito-urinary);* BERNARD A. BIRNBAUM, *HUP (sp: CT scan);* CONSTANTIN
COPE, *HUP (sp: body interventional);* MURRAY K. DALINKA, *HUP (sp: musculo-skeletal);*
STEPHEN A. FEIG, *Jeff (sp: mammography);* MARY STUART FISHER, *Temple (sp: mammogra-
phy/chest);* SETH N. GLICK, *Hahn (sp: G.I.);* BARRY B. GOLDBERG, *Jeff (sp: ultrasound);*
ROBERT I. GROSSMAN, *HUP (sp: neuroradiology);* ROBERT W. HURST, *HUP (sp: neuro-inter-
ventional);* IGOR LAUFER, *HUP (sp: G.I.);* DAVID C. LEVIN, *Jeff (sp: interventional);* WALLACE
T. MILLER, *HUP (sp: chest);* VIJAY M. RAO, *Jeff (sp: ENT);* MITCHELL D. SCHNALL *HUP (sp:
MRI);* RICHARD J. WECHSLER, *Jeff (sp: CT scan/chest)*

Radiation Oncology

LUTHER W. BRADY, *Hahn;* LAWRENCE R. COIA, *Fox Chase (sp: G.I.);* WALTER J. CURRAN JR.,
Fox Chase (sp: lung/brain tumors); BARBARA FOWBLE, *HUP (sp: breast);* JOHN R. GLASSBURN,
Pennsylvania/Northeastern; RACHELLE M. LANCIANO, *Fox Chase (sp: GYN);* GERALD E.
HANKS, *Fox Chase (sp: prostate);* WILLIAM D. POWLIS, *HUP/Presby/VA (sp: lymphoma);*
MELVYN RICHTER, *Abington;* LAWRENCE J. SOLIN, *HUP (sp: breast);* RICHARD WHITTINGTON,
HUP (sp: G.I./prostate)

Rheumatology

A rheumatologist mainly treats patients with arthritis. This inflammatory disease of
the joints manifests itself in various ways, from gout to crippling rheumatoid arthritis. This is also the specialist to see for lupus, a connective-tissue disease.

RAPHAEL J. DEHORATIUS, *Jeff (sp: lupus);* BRUCE FREUNDLICH, *Graduate;* WARREN A. KATZ,
Presby; ANTONIO J. REGINATO, *CMC;* BARRY M. SCHIMMER, *Pennsylvania;* H. RALPH
SCHUMACHER, *HUP/VA (sp: early diagnosis)*

Surgical Specialists

Cardio/Thoracic

Some studies suggest that heart-bypass surgery is performed more frequently than
necessary. If you are a candidate for this procedure, it's wise to get a second opinion
from a cardiologist. A list of the mortality rates for cardiac surgeons can be obtained
by calling the Pennsylvania Cost Containment Council at 717-232-6787. The
results, however, should be considered in a broad context. Most heart surgeons also
operate on the chest, where they may remove tumors from the lung, the esophagus
or the trachea.

ANTHONY J. DELROSSI, *CMC;* VERDI J. DISESA, *MCP;* RICHARD N. EDIE, *Jeff;* TIMOTHY J.
GARDNER, *HUP;* SCOTT M. GOLDMAN, *Lankenau;* W. CLARK HARGROVE,
Presby/Pennsylvania; GERALD M. LEMOLE, *Christiana (Delaware);* LARRY R. KAISER, *HUP (sp:
lungs);* JAMES D. SINK, *Presby (sp: cardiomyoplasty);* MICHAEL D. STRONG III, *Hahn/Crozer-
Chester;* GLENN WHITMAN, *MCP*

Colon and Rectal

The most common reason for visiting this type of surgeon is hemorrhoids. Others include ulcerative colitis, Crohn's disease and colon cancer, which now ranks third among adult cancers in the United States. However, the prognosis is good if it's detected early.

THOMAS L. DENT, *Abington (sp: endoscopy/laparoscopy);* GERALD MARKS, *Jeff;* MARK J. PELLO, *CMC;* ALAN RESNICK, *Jeff/Graduate*

General Surgery

In addition to all kinds of routine operations like hernia repair, appendectomy and gallbladder removal, most skilled general surgeons also devote a large part of their practices to excising cancerous tumors.

HERBERT E. COHN, *Jeff (sp: thoracic);* DANIEL T. DEMPSEY, *Temple (sp: G.I.);* MOREYE NUSBAUM, *Presby/Graduate (sp: inflammatory bowel disease);* DAVID L. PASKIN, *Pennsylvania (sp: abdominal);* ERNEST F. ROSATO, *HUP (sp: G.I.);* FRANCIS E. ROSATO, *Jeff (sp: G.I. malignancy);* DAVID ROSE, *Bryn Mawr (sp: laparoscopy/oncology);* JEROME J. VERNICK, *Jeff (sp: G.I.);* CHARLES C. WOLFERTH JR., *Graduate*

Oncologic Surgery

Practice restricted to cancer.

BURTON L. EISENBERG, *Fox Chase (sp: G.I.);* MICHAEL H. TOROSIAN, *HUP;* JAMES L. WEESE, *Graduate*

Breast Cancer

MARCIA C. BORAAS, *Jeanes/Fox Chase;* ANNE ROSENBERG, *Jeff/Lady of Lourdes;* GORDON F. SCHWARTZ, *Jeff;* ROBERT G. SOMERS, *Einstein*

Neurosurgery

The development of the operating microscope has greatly increased the scope of procedures that these surgeons can successfully perform on the brain and spinal cord. These include operations on aneurysms, brain and pituitary tumors, seizure sites and discs.

LEONARD A. BRUNO, *Germantown;* WILLIAM A. BUCHHEIT, *Temple (sp: acoustic neuroma);* EUGENE S. FLAMM, *HUP (sp: aneurysms/vascular malformations);* THOMAS A. GENNARELLI, *HUP (sp: pituitary tumors/head injury);* H. WARREN GOLDMAN, *MCP/Roxborough/Chestnut Hill;* MICHAEL J. O'CONNOR, *Graduate;* FREDERICK A. SIMEONE, *Pennsylvania (sp: micro-neurosurgery)*

Organ Transplants

The introduction of drugs to fight rejection made it possible to successfully transplant not only kidneys but hearts, livers and pancreases, too. The need for organs continues to outdistance supply, however, and anyone desiring information about organ donation should dial KIDNEY 1.

Heart

Jeffrey B. Alpern, *Hahn;* Valluvan Jeevanandam, *Temple*

Kidney/Liver/Pancreas

Clyde F. Barker, *HUP;* Michael J. Moritz, *Jeff (kidney, liver only);* Michael C. Morris, *Einstein;* Ali Naji, *HUP*

Lungs

Larry R. Kaiser, *HUP*

....

Orthopedics

Broken bones, severed tendons, defective or deteriorated joints and sports injuries are the reasons people seek orthopedists who, as noted below, tend to concentrate on particular body parts.

Foot and Ankle

Some of the surgeons in this category have been trained as podiatrists rather than orthopedists. They correct congenital deformities of the feet such as bunions and other problems that are caused by accidents.

Paul Angotti, *Abington;* Michael S. Downey, *Presby;* Ira M. Fox, *CMC;* Gary M. Gordon, *HUP/Abington/MCP (sp: sports medicine);* Paul J. Hecht, *Jeff/Pennsylvania;* Richard M. Jay, *Graduate;* Kieran T. Mahan, *Presby;* Alan J. Mlodzienski, *Presby;* Paul Quintavalle, *West Jersey (sp: diabetes);* Harold D. Schoenhaus, *Graduate;* Keith Wapner, *Jeff*

General

Christopher T. Born, *CMC (sp: trauma);* Michael Clancy, *Temple (sp: pediatric/ sports medicine);* Malcolm L. Ecker, *Chestnut Hill/CHOP/HUP (sp: scoliosis);* John L. Esterhai, *HUP (sp: bone infections);* Robert P. Good, *Bryn Mawr (sp: sports medicine and joint replacement);* Eric L. Hume, *Jeff/Presby (sp: hip and knee reconstruction);* Mary Ann Keenan, *Einstein (sp: neuro-orthopedics);* Frederick S. Kaplan, *HUP/VA/CHOP (sp: metabolic bone disease);* Richard D. Lackman, *Jeff/Einstein (sp: orthopedic oncology)*

Hands

F. William Bora Jr., *HUP;* James M. Hunter, *Jeff;* Mark Nissenbaum, *Abington/Holy Redeemer;* A. Lee Osterman, *Jeff/CHOP/Delco Memorial;* Lawrence H. Schneider, *Jeff*

Joints

Robert E. Booth, *Pennsylvania/Jeff (sp: knee replacement);* John M. Fenlin, *Jeff (sp: shoulders);* William J. Hozack, *Pennsylvania/Jeff (sp: hip and knee replacement);* Joseph P. Iannotti, *HUP (sp: shoulders);* Norman A. Johanson, *Temple (sp: total joint replacement);* Paul A. Lotke, *HUP/Delco Memorial (sp: knees);* Richard H. Rothman, *Pennsylvania/Jeff (sp: hip and knee replacement);* Marvin E. Steinberg, *HUP (sp: adult hip surgery)*

Spine

RICHARD A. BALDERSTON, *Pennsylvania/Jeff;* RANDALL R. BETZ, *Temple/St. Chris (sp: scoliosis);* JEROME M. COTLER, *Jeff;* HENRY H. SHERK, *MCP*

Sports Medicine

ARTHUR R. BARTOLOZZI, *Pennsylvania/Jeff (sp: knees/shoulders);* FREDERICK BALDUINI, *Graduate (sp: knees/shoulders/Achille's tendon);* NICHOLAS A. DINUBILE, *Delco Memorial (sp: knee arthroscopy);* VINCENT J. DISTEFANO, *Graduate/Paoli;* JOHN R. GREGG, *Graduate/CHOP;* PHILLIP J. MARONE, *Jeff;* LAWRENCE S. MILLER, *Lankenau/Mercy Haverford (sp: shoulders/knees);* RAY A. MOYER, *Temple;* JOSEPH S. TORG, *HUP (sp: knees/cervical spine)*

Plastic Surgery

These surgeons are gifted in repairing disfigurement caused by burns, injuries, mastectomies, birth defects or just about anything else.

Reconstructive

SCOTT P. BARTLETT, *HUP/CHOP (sp: facial with birth deformities);* ARTHUR S. BROWN, *CMC;* JAMES W. FOX IV, *Jeff (sp: breasts);* RALPH HAMILTON, *HUP/Presby/CHOP;* JOSEPH F. KUSIAK, *Fox Chase (sp: head and neck cancer);* DON LAROSSA, *HUP/CHOP (sp: cleft palate/breast);* AMIT MITRA, *Temple/St. Chris;* J. BRIEN MURPHY, *Bryn Mawr/Lankenau;* R. BARRETT NOONE, *Bryn Mawr/Lankenau (sp: breasts);* HARVEY M. ROSEN, *Pennsylvania/HUP (sp: orthanathic);* LINTON A. WHITAKER, *HUP/CHOP (craniofacial)*

Facial/Cosmetic Surgery

Some doctors in this category are board-certified plastic surgeons; some are cosmetic surgeons trained in ear, nose and throat. Their practices include a full range of beauty services—face-lifts, eye-lifts, nose jobs and chemical peels.

RICHARD L. DOLSKY, *Mercy Haverford/Graduate/Presby (sp: noses);* HERBERT KEAN, *Jeff (sp: noses);* PAUL S. KIM, *Paoli Memorial/Brandywine;* JULIUS NEWMAN, *Graduate;* R. BARRETT NOONE, *Bryn Mawr/Lankenau;* CHARLES E. PAPPAS, *Chestnut Hill/Jeff;* C. RICHARD SCIPIONE, *Graduate/Mercy Haverford (sp: noses);* LINTON A. WHITAKER, *HUP*

Liposuction

The fastest-growing cosmetic procedure is quite safe and can produce excellent results in the right hands.

RICHARD L. DOLSKY, *Mercy Haverford/Graduate/Presby;* R. BARRETT NOONE, *Bryn Mawr/Lankenau;* ZAKI S. FTAIHA, *Graduate*

Trauma Surgery

If you've been injured in an accident, try to get to a hospital where one of these people does emergency operations.

ROBERT F. BUCKMAN, *Temple;* WILLIAM G. DELONG JR., *CMC (sp: pelvic and spine fracture);* STEVEN E. ROSS, *CMC (sp: critical care);* WILLIAM SCHWAB, *HUP;* JEROME J. VERNICK, *Jeff*

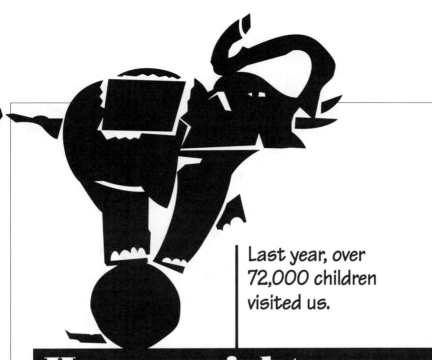

Last year, over 72,000 children visited us.

Heavyweights in pediatric care.

We're known throughout the country as one of the best children's hospitals with over 220 specialists providing advanced medical care for serious diseases and childhood illnesses of all kinds.

The knowledge and expertise we have in the fields of medical care and research benefit each and every child, everyday. Last year alone, over 72,000 children visited us. Because our specialists are leaders in the field of pediatric medicine, we help to train some of the best physicians from one of the nation's top medical schools, Thomas Jefferson University.

We're minutes away from Chester and Delaware counties, with easy access from Routes 202 and 476 in Wilmington, Delaware.

To find out more about our specialists and the services we offer call, ***1-800-829-KIDS.***

Only for children.

A.I. duPont Institute
A CHILDREN'S HOSPITAL
Wilmington, Delaware

Urology

This specialty deals with organs of the urinary tract—kidneys, bladder, ureters—and the problems they manifest, such as cystitis and kidney stones. It's also the male counterpart to gynecology for matters of the prostate and genitals.

DEMETRIUS H. BAGLEY, *Jeff (sp: kidney stones);* P. KENNETH BROWNSTEIN, *Jeff;* RICHARD E. GREENBERG, *Abington/Fox Chase (sp: urologic oncology);* PHILIP M. HANNO, *Temple (sp: interstitial cystitis/sexual dysfunction);* IRVIN H. HIRSCH, *Jeff ; (sp: male fertility/impotence);* A. RICHARD KENDALL, *Temple (sp: oncology);* TERRENCE MALLOY, *Pennsylvania (sp: erectile dysfunction);* JOEL L. MARMAR, *CMC (sp: male fertility);* S. GRANT MULHOLLAND, *Jeff (sp: oncology);* THOMAS C. SANSONE, *Bryn Mawr;* ALAN J. WEIN, *HUP (sp: cancer/voiding dysfunction/ incontinence);* KRISTENE E. WHITMORE, *Graduate (sp: incontinence)*

Vascular Surgery

When a narrowing or blockage of the arteries impedes blood flow, bypass surgery provides an alternate route for the blood to reach the organs. This specialist operates mainly on arteries of the abdomen and the limbs rather than the heart or brain.

HENRY D. BERKOWITZ, *Presby/HUP (sp: aneurysms/triple bypass);* R. ANTHONY CARABASI III, *Jeff;* ANTHONY J. COMEROTA, *Temple;* DOMINIC A. DELAURENTIS, *Pennsylvania;* PETER R. MCCOMBS, *Abington;* ANDREW B. ROBERTS, *MCP;* STANTON N. SMULLENS, *Jeff (sp: carotid artery disease);* MICHAEL S. WEINGARTEN, *Graduate (sp: wound healing)*

The following abbreviations have been used for area hospitals:

Abington—ABINGTON MEMORIAL HOSPITAL; *Belmont*—BELMONT CENTER FOR COMPREHENSIVE TREATMENT; *Bryn Mawr*—THE BRYN MAWR HOSPITAL; *Burlington County*—MEMORIAL HOSPITAL OF BURLINGTON COUNTY; *Chester County*—THE CHESTER COUNTY HOSPITAL; *Child Guidance*—PHILADELPHIA CHILD GUIDANCE CENTER; *CHOP*— THE CHILDREN'S HOSPITAL OF PHILADELPHIA; *CMC*—COOPER HOSPITAL, UNIVERSITY MEDICAL CENTER; *Crozer-Chester*—CROZER-CHESTER MEDICAL CENTER; *Delco Memorial*— DELAWARE COUNTY MEMORIAL HOSPITAL; *Einstein*—ALBERT EINSTEIN MEDICAL CENTER, NORTHERN DIVISION; *Fox Chase*—FOX CHASE CANCER CENTER; *Frankford*—FRANKFORD HOSPITAL; *Germantown*—THE GERMANTOWN HOSPITAL AND MEDICAL CENTER; *Graduate*— THE GRADUATE HOSPITAL; *Hahn*—HAHNEMANN UNIVERSITY HOSPITAL; *Holy Redeemer*— HOLY REDEEMER HOSPITAL AND MEDICAL CENTER; *HUP*—THE HOSPITAL OF THE UNIVERSITY OF PENNSYLVANIA; *Institute*—THE INSTITUTE OF PENNSYLVANIA HOSPITAL; *Jeff*—THOMAS JEFFERSON UNIVERSITY HOSPITAL; *Jeff-Ford*—THOMAS JEFFERSON UNIVERSITY HOSPITAL-FORD ROAD CAMPUS; *Magee*—MAGEE REHABILITATION HOSPITAL; *MCP*— HOSPITAL OF THE MEDICAL COLLEGE OF PENNSYLVANIA; *Mercy Catholic*—MERCY CATHOLIC MEDICAL CENTER; *Montgomery*—MONTGOMERY HOSPITAL; *Nazareth*—NAZARETH HOSPITAL; *Paoli*—PAOLI MEMORIAL HOSPITAL; *Pennsylvania*—PENNSYLVANIA HOSPITAL; *Presby*—PRESBYTERIAN MEDICAL CENTER OF PHILADELPHIA; *Scheie*—SCHEIE EYE INSTITUTE; *St. Chris*—ST. CHRISTOPHER'S HOSPITAL FOR CHILDREN; *Temple*—TEMPLE UNIVERSITY HOSPITAL; *Underwood*—UNDERWOOD-MEMORIAL HOSPITAL; *VA*—VETERANS ADMINISTRATION HOSPITAL; *Wills*—WILLS EYE HOSPITAL

More pediatricians said they'd take their kids to The Children's Hospital of Philadelphia.

In a *Philadelphia Magazine** survey of 1,000 area pediatricians, more said they would take their kids to specialists at Children's Hospital than to any other area hospital.

Maybe it's because they know we're one of the leading pediatric centers in the world.

Maybe it's because we were named as one of the top two children's hospitals in the country by a *U.S. News and World Report*** survey of the nation's leading pediatricians.

And maybe, like you, they simply want the very best care available for their children.

CHAPTER 9

For Children Only

Who are the area's best pediatricians?

The doctors on this list are those most highly recommended by their peers. We compiled it in much the same way we put together our list of adult specialists—by surveying more than 1,000 pediatricians throughout the Delaware Valley and asking "If your child had a medical or surgical problem, to whom would you send her?" Their responses provided a working roster that was then refined by extensive interviews with our sources. Doctors who spend most of their time in research and administration rather than in dealing with patients were eliminated.

We did our best to get a geographical spread, but despite that effort a preponderance of the doctors who made the cut work at Children's Hospital and to a lesser extent at St. Christopher's. We are extremely fortunate to have in Philadelphia two renowned institutions for treating children—one world-class and the other of national stature. Obviously, these places are top-heavy with leading physicians.

Some readers may be disappointed that their wonderful and caring neighborhood pediatrician isn't included. The difficulty in compiling these kinds of lists is that qualified doctors quietly doing very good work outside of hospital settings are very hard to judge. And generally speaking they're perfectly fine for handling routine care. Almost all the pediatricians named here are people you'd turn to for a special problem. We hope you don't need them very often.

The Doctor Is In

My child won't eat anything except peanut-butter sandwiches. Should I be worried?

The rate at which a child grows and gains weight can be one of the most sensitive indicators of general health. When children are poor eaters, it may be difficult to tell simply by observation whether they're eating enough. That's why it's a good idea to have your pediatrician plot a height and weight chart as a guideline. Say, for example, a child at age two is very tiny, and ranks in the fifth percentile of the national average. If he remains in that percentile year after year, he's growing normally. But if at age four he's in the 50th percentile and at age seven he's fallen much lower, that's a sign there's a problem.

Normal children usually manage to get the calories they need to grow without being forced to eat. In fact, I never saw a child who was losing weight because the mother wasn't trying hard enough to get food in him. If your child goes through a phase of eating nothing but hot dogs and macaroni and cheese, let him have as much as he wants and don't worry about it. Your role is to limit his options: no dessert without dinner first, no chips between meals if lunch is left on the plate.

DR. BRUCE TAUBMAN, GENERAL PRACTICE
Cherry Hill

When should I be alarmed about a high fever?

Parents tend to be overly concerned about fevers. They are usually a sign of a common, minor viral infection, but sometimes they do indicate a more serious problem. What causes the worry is wondering which it is, and that depends more on the sick child's behavior than on the thermometer reading. There is little reason to be upset with a 104 fever if the child is playing with his toys and acting normally. On the other hand, a child can be much sicker with a 102 fever if he is extremely lethargic and weak, and not eating.

Another thing to look for is how the fever responds to medication. Within a half hour of a dose of Tylenol, the fever should drop one or two degrees. A study at CHOP showed that two-thirds of the children brought to the emergency room with high fevers had not been given enough medication. The dosage changes with the weight of the child, so read the package insert to be sure you're using the right amount.

You can put a child in a tepid water bath to lower the fever, though usually that's not necessary. Alcohol rubs are definitely not recommended. And there is no need to fear febrile seizures. They occur in only 2 to 5 percent of children between the ages of six months and six years, and are more frightening than dangerous.

DR. STEPHEN LUDWIG, GENERAL PRACTICE
Children's Hospital of Philadelphia

When should I call the doctor in the middle of the night?

If you are really concerned about something, you should always feel free to call your pediatrician. However, some things are more important to check out than others. They include the following: Any temperature above 100 in a child under three months, or a fever above 100 in an older child who is extremely lethargic, hard to rouse or crying uncontrollably; severe, persistent abdominal pain that isn't helped by Tylenol and lasts more than 30 minutes; the sudden onset of a croupy cough that sounds like a barking seal and doesn't respond to steam within 30 minutes; the acute onset of ear pain the doesn't respond to ear drops or an analgesic after 45 minutes; when a child with a bad cold wakes up and can't catch his breath; when a baby cries for over three-quarters of an hour and can't be consoled.

In general, vomiting and diarrhea often look more threatening than they are, and don't require special attention unless they persist for 12 to 18 hours. Since sick children may have trouble taking medication by mouth, it's a good idea to keep acetaminophen suppositories in your medicine cabinet for wee-hour emergencies.

Dr. WILLIAM ZAVOD, GENERAL PRACTICE
Philadelphia

Why do so many children today get ear infections, and how are they best treated?

One explanation for the increase is day care. More children are repeatedly exposed to infections at an early, vulnerable age. In fact, inner-ear infections and fluid in the middle ear are the most common reason children get referred to my office. I think pediatricians are simply more aware of these problems, because of better diagnostic techniques and an understanding of the potential hearing loss they may cause.

The initial treatment for ear infections is antibiotics. When these aren't effective in controlling recurrent problems (six bouts a year or more), we put in ear tubes. This very safe and highly effective surgery became popular in the mid '60s and is today the most common operation performed on children. In response to complaints that it was being performed too often, a study was done, which led to guidelines that most otorhinolaryngologists strictly follow. Since the introduction of ear tubes, complications once caused by ear infections have almost disappeared, and we see far less ear disease in young adults as a result of prompt treatment in childhood.

Dr. GLENN ISAACSON, OTORHINOLARYNGOLOGIST
St. Christopher's Hospital for Children

Should children take vitamins?

Genuine isolated vitamin deficiencies, like scurvy and rickets, are extremely rare in this country, partly because many of our foods are fortified. If children eat an age-appropriate and varied diet, they really don't need vitamins. However, most children eat funny. They get very picky, and often eat only those foods they like. While some narrow ranges are fine, others are not. Because parents worry their children aren't getting the proper nutrition, there is no harm in a one-a-day multiple vitamin. But I'm concerned about giving too much of a supplement, so parents should stick to the recommended dose.

I prefer those vitamins that have iron, and I'd also suggest that if the child has an allergy or intolerance to milk, the parent should consider a calcium supplement.

Dr. VIRGINIA STALLINGS, NUTRITIONIST
Children's Hospital of Philadelphia

My child gets sick a lot and often takes antibiotics. Is there any danger in taking these medicines too often or for too long?

There are definite advantages to antibiotics in treating bacterial infections and preventing the development of possible complication. But as with all good things, there are problems, such as allergic reactions ranging from mild hives to serious rashes, and side effects that show up as diarrhea, nausea and vomiting.

The important consideration is whether the illness is bacterial or viral. There is rarely any reason to put a child on an antibiotic for a viral infection like a cold, the flu, bronchiolitis, mononucleosis or a sore throat that cultures negative for strep. Parents sometimes ask whether taking antibiotics will create resistance to them. It's possible, but it's not common, and when it does occur, there are always alternate choices that can be used. The risk of not treating the bacterial infection is greater than the risk of taking an antibiotic.

DR. ROSEMARY CASEY, GENERAL PRACTICE
Children's Hospital of Philadelphia

With so many stories appearing about complications due to vaccines, should parents be concerned about routine immunizations?

One of the standard components of routine care for healthy children is an immunization schedule. Every vaccine used for infants and toddlers has been developed, licensed and put into circulation because of a bona fide need to prevent a disease that's life-threatening or could alter a child's ability to function at peak level. Virtually every one of these vaccines has some clinical side effects, which in recent years have been severely overblown and sensationalized by the media. Real public-health data and close scrutiny of pediatric practices don't support the fear generated by this hoopla. To the contrary, they show the overwhelming safety and efficacy of routine childhood immunizations compared to the problems caused by the diseases they're targeted to prevent.

DR. ALLAN M. ARBETER, INFECTIOUS DISEASES
Albert Einstein Medical Center

Medical Specialists

Adolescent Medicine

When your child seems too old to visit a doctor's office teeming with crying babies and not old enough for the doctor you use, you may want to schedule an appointment with this specialist, who treats not only the physical ailments of adolescents, but some of the sensitive emotional issues as well— i.e., sexually transmitted diseases and drug and alcohol abuse. While not trained as gynecologists, they do pelvic examinations and discuss things like birth control that would make some pediatricians blush.

PAULA BRAVERMAN, *St. Chris;* DONALD SCHWARZ, *CHOP/HUP;* GAIL SLAP, *CHOP/HUP*

Allergy

Allergies are an abnormal response by the immune system to a substance that's been ingested or inhaled. Allergists attempt to pinpoint the cause for the responses primarily through skin and food-elimination tests. They then create treatment programs combining diet, environmental management, medication and injections. Since asthma, a major childhood disease, is often caused by an allergic reaction, a large portion of this specialty is devoted to treating asthma cases.

JEFFREY GREENE, *CHOP;* LILLIAN KRAVIS, *CHOP;* HERBERT MANSMANN, *Jeff;* STEPHEN J. MCGEADY, *Jeff;* STEPHEN A. RAPHAEL, *St. Chris*

Anesthesia/Intensive Care

While the thrust of this specialty is sedating children for surgery, a large part also involves providing breathing assistance to critically ill children in intensive care. These doctors are experts in treating shock and monitoring life-support systems.

JOHN DOWNES, *CHOP;* ROBERT G. KETTRICK, *du Pont;* DAVID LOWE, *St. Chris;* RUSSELL RAPHAELY, *CHOP*

Cardiology

More and more congenital heart defects are being discovered in childhood by these specialists, who, in addition to evaluating patients for heart surgery, also treat acquired heart problems like rheumatic fever and arrhythmias.

IAIN F.S. BLACK, *St. Chris;* RICHARD DONNER, *St. Chris;* SIDNEY FRIEDMAN, *CHOP;* JIM HUHTA, *Pennsylvania;* VICTORIA L. VETTER, *CHOP;* HENRY WAGNER, *CHOP;* PAUL M. WEINBERG, *CHOP (sp: neonatology)*

Dermatology

It would be natural to assume that the bulk of the pediatric dermatologist's practice consists of acne patients, but in fact this specialist is more likely to see eczema cases and problems like chronic hives and port-wine stains.

PAUL J. HONIG, *CHOP;* PETER KOBLENZER, *St. Chris;* WALTER TUNNESEN JR., *CHOP*

Diabetes

One in 600 children is diabetic. The warning signs are frequent urination, unusual thirst and weight loss. When this disease occurs in childhood, it affects normal development, so besides manipulating insulin doses, this specialist also gets involved in the dietary and psychological management of the patient.

LESTER BAKER, *CHOP;* ROBERT KAYE, *MCP;* IRAJ REZVANI, *St. Chris*

Emergency Medicine

Few children make it to adulthood without at least one visit to the emergency room, for a fracture, a cut requiring stitches, ingestion of a poisonous substance, a severe head injury or any of the other accidents that put gray hair on a parent's head. Today these specialists are trained to pick up signs of child abuse in what look like routine injuries.

FRED HENRETIG, *CHOP (sp: pediatric toxicology);* MARK JOFFE, *St. Chris;* STEVEN SELBST, *CHOP;* DAVID WAGNER, *MCP/St. Chris (sp: pediatric surgery)*

Endocrinology

In youngsters, endocrine disorders other than diabetes tend to show up as problems with growth (the child is unusually short or tall) or sexual development (the changes related to puberty appear too soon or too late). The treatment plan usually involves drugs or hormones.

ANGELO M. DIGEORGE, *St. Chris;* THOMAS MOSHANG, *CHOP;* JUDITH L. ROSS, *Jeff/Bryn Mawr;* CHARLES A. STANLEY, *CHOP*

Gastroenterology

The symptoms that would send a child here include chronic vomiting, internal bleeding, diarrhea, constipation and stomachaches. The problems seen by this specialist include inflammatory bowel disease, ulcers, chronic liver and pancreatic disease, and lactose intolerance.

STEVEN ALTSCHULER, *CHOP;* IAN GIBBONS, *Jeff;* EMANUEL LEVENTHAL, *Hahn;* DAVID PICCOLI, *CHOP;* STEVEN WIDZER, *St. Chris/Einstein/Bryn Mawr*

General Pediatrics

It would go beyond the scope of this list to name every competent neighborhood pediatrician in the Philadelphia area. If you are satisfied with your doctor, stay where you are. We have noted two highly regarded diagnosticians. These are the experts a pediatrician calls when there's a problem figuring out what's wrong with a child or the need for a second opinion. You can use them too. The others are considered by their peers to be outstanding generalists.

Diagnosticians: Patrick Pasquariello Jr., *CHOP;* David Smith, *St. Chris*

Generalists: Stewart Barbera, *Holy Redeemer/St. Chris;* Rosemary Casey, *CHOP;* J. Ronald Halenda, *private practice, Media;* Stephen Ludwig, *CHOP;* Edward Rosof, *private practice, Marlton;* Steven A. Shapiro, *private practice, Norristown;* Bruce Taubman, *private practice, Cherry Hill;* John M. Tedeschi, *private practice, Cherry Hill;* William Zavod, *private practice, Philadelphia*

Genetics

As advanced techniques in gene analysis have made it possible to identify so many inherited disorders from Tay-Sachs to Down syndrome to muscular dystrophy, this specialty has mushroomed. It includes a wide variety of pre- and postnatal diagnostic procedures and family counseling.

Laird G. Jackson, *Jeff;* Adele Schneider, *Einstein;* Kathleen E. Toomey, *St. Chris;* Elaine Zackai, *CHOP/Lankenau*

Hematology

In the old days, a mother would pull down the lower lid of her child's eye and if the rim was pink instead of red, she'd start spooning in cod liver oil. Today anemia is more appropriately treated by a hematologist, who also handles other blood diseases, such as sickle-cell anemia and thalassemia.

Alan Cohen, *CHOP;* Carlton D. Dampier, *St. Chris (sp: sickle-cell anemia);* Gregory Halligan, *St. Chris;* Kwaku Ohene-Frempong, *CHOP (sp: sickle-cell anemia);* Marie J. Stuart, *St. Chris*

Immunology

Some immunologists concentrate on allergic problems; those listed here focus on identifying and treating chronic, severe and frequent infections that do not respond to normal antibiotics.

Steven Douglas, *CHOP;* Harold W. Lischner, *St. Chris*

Infectious Diseases

Any parent with a school-age child will attest to the fact that infections seem to leapfrog from one kid to another. But you wouldn't visit this specialist unless your child had a virus or bacteria that failed to respond to traditional antibiotics and required more aggressive therapy.

Allan Arbeter, *Einstein;* Margaret C. Fisher, *St. Chris;* Sarah Long, *St. Chris/Temple;* Stuart Starr, *CHOP;* Terrence L. Stull, *MCP;* Sidney J. Sussman, *Cooper*

Metabolic Disorders

When the body has difficulty converting food to energy in a way that interferes with normal physical or mental function, the problem may be metabolic. Diseases in this category include fructose intolerance, amino acid disorders, Gaucher's syndrome, Lesch-Nyhan syndrome and carbohydrate abnormalities. To counteract the defect, the doctor will create a combination drug and diet program.

GERARD T. BERRY, *CHOP;* STANTON SEGAL, *CHOP;* MARC YUDKOFF, *CHOP*

Neonatology

When newspapers report the miraculous survival of a one-pound infant, the doctors responsible for saving the baby are neonatologists. Biomedical advances have contributed enormously to the burgeoning of this specialty and its enhanced ability to diagnose and treat sick newborns who years ago would have died shortly after birth.

SORAYA ABBASI, *Pennsylvania;* ROBERTA BALLARD, *CHOP;* VINOD K. BHUTANI, *Pennsylvania;* FRANK W. BOWEN, *Pennsylvania;* MARIA DELIVORIA-PAPADOPOULOS, *HUP;* JOHN G. DEMAIO, *Lankenau/Paoli;* JEFFREY S. GERDES, *Pennsylvania;* HALLAM HURT, *Einstein;* RICHARD POLIN, *CHOP;* S. DAVID RUBENSTEIN, *St. Chris/Temple;* PAMELA B. RUSSELL, *Lankenau/Paoli;* ALAN SPITZER, *Jeff/Methodist (sp: apnea);* ALAN B. ZUBROW, *MCP*

Nephrology

Don't be alarmed if your pediatrician sends you to a nephrologist to have your little girl's urinary-tract infection treated. That's one of the common childhood problems seem by this specialist, who also deals with kidney disorders and hypertension, which in youngsters is often a result of kidney malfunction.

JORGE BALUARTE, *St. Chris;* BONITA FALKNER, *MCP;* BRUCE KAISER, *St. Chris;* BERNARD KAPLAN, *CHOP;* MIKE NORMAN, *Christiana/du Pont;* MARTIN POLINSKY, *St. Chris*

Neurology/Child Development

This covers a wide range of disorders of the nervous system from birth injuries to seizures to chronic headaches to sleep disorders. In addition, when little Johnny is far too slow in walking, talking or even rolling over, the developmental delay may be the first sign of a neurological problem. School-age children are also referred to neurologists for suspected attention deficit disorders and some learning disabilities.

PETER BERMAN, *CHOP;* LAWRENCE BROWN, *CHOP;* THOMAS J. CASEY, *Bryn Mawr;* ROBERT CLANCY, *CHOP (sp: neonatal epilepsy);* LEONARD J. GRAZIANI, *Jeff;* SAM TUCKER, *CHOP*

Nutrition

This specialist works in consultation with others to treat children whose problems require special diets and/or feeding supplements.

VIRGINIA STALLINGS, *CHOP*

Oncology

While oncologists treat all kinds of malignancies, the most commonly occurring cancer in children is leukemia. As the treatment team captain, the oncologist manages chemotherapy, works with the radiotherapist and supports the emotional needs of the family. Because you will have an intense and long-term relationship with this physician, it's especially important that you feel comfortable and develop a good rapport.

MILTON H. DONALDSON, *Cooper;* AUDREY EVANS, *CHOP;* BEVERLY LANGE, *CHOP;* ANNA T. MEADOWS, *CHOP/HUP;* ROBERT S. WIMMER, *Einstein/Temple (sp: hematology)*

Pathology

It's unlikely you would have any personal contact with the person who microscopically examines small pieces of tissue (known as biopsies) to determine the cause of an illness. If you have doubts about a biopsy report, don't hesitate to request a second opinion.

JANE CHATTEN, *CHOP;* J.D. DECHADAREVIAN, *St. Chris;* LUCY B. RORKE, *CHOP (sp: neuropathology)*

Psychiatry

Some of the emotional problems of children and teenagers—depression, anxiety, sexual identity, anorexia—are no different from those of adults. But with the increase of divorce, drugs and sexual abuse has come a new range of issues that require the special training of these physicians, who can prescribe medication as an adjunct to therapy.

MARY ANNE DELANEY, *Hahn;* JOSEPHINE ELIA, *MCP (sp: attention deficit disorder);* DAVID M. ELLIS, *Institute;* GAIL EDELSOHN, *Jeff;* JOAN M. FREIMUTH, *Bryn Mawr;* HAROLD KOLANSKY, *HUP/Einstein (sp: psychoanalysis);* HAROLD KOLANSKY, *Belmont;* HERBERT S. LUSTIG, *Temple/Belmont;* HERBERT E. MANDELL, *Belmont/Einstein (sp: child development);* DEWITT H. MONTGOMERY JR., *Lankenau;* HENRI PARENS, *Belmont (sp: psychoanalysis);* ANTHONY L. ROSTAIN, *Child Guidance/CHOP/HUP (sp: attention deficit disorder);* JOHN SARGENT, *Child Guidance/CHOP/HUP (sp: adolescents);* BARRY JAY SCHWARTZ, *Institute;* JOEL L. SCHWARTZ, *Northwestern (sp: psychoanalysis);* G. PIEROOZ SHOLEVAR, *CMC;* ELLEN H. SHOLEVAR, *Temple;* ANNIE G. STEINBERG, *Seashore House/Child Guidance (sp: sensory disabilities)*

Pulmonary Medicine

The function of this specialist is to help children breathe easier. Many patients come from the one in every 3,000 to 5,000 youngsters suffering from cystic fibrosis. These doctors also treat severe asthma, recurrent lung infections and breathing abnormalities.

MICHAEL M. GRUNSTEIN, *CHOP/HUP;* DOUGLAS S. HOLSCHLAW JR., *Hahn;* HOWARD B. PANITCH, *St. Chris;* THOMAS F. SCANLIN, *CHOP/HUP;* CRAIG M. SCHRAMM, *CHOP/HUP;* DANIEL V. SCHIDLOW, *St. Chris*

Radiology

Once upon a time this was the doctor who just read X-rays. But the modern radiologist works in an imaging center whose tools include ultrasound, nuclear medicine, MRIs, CAT scans, angiography and various intervention techniques to help repair vessel problems without surgery.

ERIC N. FAERBER, *St. Chris (sp: CAT, MRI)*; KENNETH E. FELLOWS, *CHOP/HUP*; SYDNEY HEYMAN, *CHOP*; SOROOSH MAHBOUBI, *CHOP (sp: CAT, MRI)*; HENRIETTA ROSENBERG, *Einstein (sp: ultrasound)*; ELEANOR M. SMERGEL, *St. Chris (sp: angiography)*; BARBARA J. WOLFSON, *St. Chris*; ROBERT A. ZIMMERMAN, *CHOP (sp: neuroradiology)*

Rehabilitation Medicine

This rapidly expanding specialty includes a wide range of diagnostic, evaluation and treatment services. For those with physical or neurologic handicaps such as cerebral palsy and muscular dystrophy, they provide occupational and physical therapy. They also work with children who have speech and hearing impairments, learning or retardation problems, developmental delays and hyperactivity.

MARK L. BATSHAW, *Seashore House/CHOP*; EDWARD B. CHARNEY, *CHOP/Seashore House*; MAUREEN A. FEE, *St. Chris/Paoli Memorial*

Rheumatology

The painful inflammation of the joints known as rheumatoid arthritis strikes children as well as adults. However, a large number of patients referred to this specialist in recent years have turned out to be suffering from Lyme disease, which affects the joints in its more severe stage.

BALU H. ATHREYA, *CHOP/Seashore House*; DONALD P. GOLDSMITH, *St. Chris*

Surgery

Cardio-Thoracic

This surgeon repairs rare and congenital heart defects in infants and children.

WILLIAM I. NORWOOD, *CHOP*; PIERANTONIO RUSSO, *St. Chris*

General Surgery

The bulk of this surgeon's practice involves fairly common procedures such as hernias, obstructions of the bowel and bile duct, malformations of the GI tract and, of course, appendectomies.

JAMES A. O'NEILL JR., *CHOP*; LOUISE SCHNAUFER, *CHOP*; JOHN M. TEMPLETON, *CHOP*; CHARLES P. VINOCUR, *St. Chris*; WILLIAM H. WEINTRAUB, *St. Chris*

Neurosurgery

The delicate work of correcting defects of the central nervous system is the domain of this surgeon. These would include hydrocephalus (swelling of the brain caused by fluid retention), spina bifida, epilepsy that doesn't respond to drug treatment and brain tumors.

PAUL KANEV, *St. Chris/Temple;* LOUIS SCHUT, *CHOP;* LESLIE N. SUTTON, *CHOP/HUP/ Pennsylvania*

Ophthalmology

About 80 percent of the operations performed by this specialist involve correcting defects of the eye muscles, the most common being turned eyes, caused by a deviation that prevents the eyes from working in sync, and amblyopia, the term for decreased vision. Other conditions include congenital cataracts, glaucoma, droopy eyelids and blocked tear ducts. It's important to treat vision problems early, so the child doesn't miss out on the visual stimulation so critical to learning.

JOSEPH H. CALHOUN, *Wills;* LEONARD B. NELSON, *Wills/Lankenau/CHOP;* GRAHAM E. QUINN, *CHOP;* DAVID B. SCHAFFER, *CHOP*

Orthopedics

In addition to dealing with the inevitable fractures and sports injuries that accompany the growth of active children, these surgeons correct congenital deformities of the spine, such as scoliosis, and of the limbs, such as clubfoot.

PHILIP D. ALBURGER, *St. Chris;* RANDALL BETZ, *Temple/Shriner's;* RICHARD BOWEN, *du Pont;* RICHARD S. DAVIDSON, *CHOP/Shriner's (sp: clubfoot);* DENIS S. DRUMMOND, *CHOP;* JOHN R. GREGG, *CHOP;* A.LEE OSTERMAN, *CHOP/Jeff (sp: hands);* PETER D. PIZZUTILLO, *Jeff*

Organ Transplants

With the advent of drugs to fight rejection, no one is considered too young for a transplant these days. The dramatic pleas of parents who turn to the media to solicit organs for their children attests to how greatly the need exceeds the supply.

Bone marrow: NANCY BUNIN, *CHOP*

Heart: MARSHALL L. JACOBS, *CHOP;* PIERANTONIO RUSSO, *St. Chris*

Kidney: STEPHEN P. DUNN, *St. Chris*

Liver: STEPHEN P. DUNN, *St. Chris;* HENRY T. LAU, *CHOP*

Otorhinolaryngology

A few decades ago, the ear, nose and throat specialist was best known for removing tonsils. Today his bread and butter is putting tubes in kids' ears to combat chronic infections. They also operate on tumors of the head and neck.

STEVEN HANDLER, *CHOP;* GLENN ISAACSON, *St. Chris/Holy Redeemer;* WILLIAM P. POTSIC, *CHOP;* RALPH F. WETMORE, *CHOP*

Plastic/Craniofacial

These highly skilled surgeons are able to perform wonders on children who were once doomed to live with disfigurements. Their face-saving techniques repair birth defects such as cleft palate, deformities due to injuries (including burns), tumors and other aesthetic problems.

DON LAROSSA, *CHOP/Presby;* PETER D. QUINN, *CHOP (sp: maxillofacial);* LINTON WHITAKER, *CHOP/HUP*

Urology

Pediatric urology involves repairing complications of the bladder, the kidney and the urinary and genital tracts. In addition, these surgeons do reconstruction of inadequately developed sex organs, which can make it impossible to tell if a baby is a boy or a girl or both.

JOHN W. DUCKETT, *CHOP;* HYMAN H. RABINOVITCH, *St. Chris/Bryn Mawr;* HOWARD McCRUM SNYDER III, *CHOP/HUP*

The following abbreviations have been used for area hospitals:

Belmont—BELMONT CENTER FOR COMPREHENSIVE TREATMENT; *Child Guidance*— PHILADELPHIA CHILD GUIDANCE CENTER; *CHOP*—THE CHILDREN'S HOSPITAL OF PHILADELPHIA; *Christiana*—CHRISTIANA MEDICAL CENTER OF DELAWARE; *Cooper*—COOPER HOSPITAL, UNIVERSITY MEDICAL CENTER, CAMDEN; *du Pont*—ALFRED I. DU PONT INSTITUTE FOR CHILDREN, WILMINGTON; *Einstein*—ALBERT EINSTEIN MEDICAL CENTER; *Hahn*— HAHNEMANN UNIVERSITY HOSPITAL; *Holy Redeemer*—HOLY REDEEMER HOSPITAL AND MEDICAL CENTER; *HUP*—HOSPITAL OF THE UNIVERSITY OF PENNSYLVANIA; *Jeff*—THOMAS JEFFERSON UNIVERSITY HOSPITAL; *MCP*—HOSPITAL OF THE MEDICAL COLLEGE OF PENNSYLVANIA; *Paoli*—PAOLI MEMORIAL HOSPITAL; *Presby*—PRESBYTERIAN MEDICAL CENTER OF PHILADELPHIA; *Roxborough*—ROXBOROUGH MEMORIAL HOSPITAL; *Seashore House*—CHILDREN'S SEASHORE HOUSE; *Shriner's*—SHRINER'S HOSPITAL FOR CRIPPLED CHILDREN; *St. Chris*—ST. CHRISTOPHER'S HOSPITAL FOR CHILDREN; *Temple*—TEMPLE UNIVERSITY HOSPITAL; *Wills*—WILLS EYE HOSPITAL.

The First to Meet the Challenge

We at Children's Seashore House dedicate ourselves to helping children with developmental disabilities, chronic illnesses and other conditions requiring habilitation and rehabilitation, reach their full potential through excellence in patient care, research and training. We strive to learn from each child in order to improve the health of all children.

As the first facility of its kind in the nation, we've been meeting children's physical and developmental challenges since our inception at the Jersey Shore over 120 years ago.

Our inpatient interdisciplinary specialty programs are:
- Respiratory Rehabilitation
- Neurorehabilitation
- Musculoskeletal
- Biobehavioral
- Feeding
- Developmental Disabilities

We also provide outpatient clinics in the areas of attention deficit/hyperactivity disorder, behavioral medicine, cerebral palsy, Down syndrome, child development, feeding, neurorehabilitation and rheumatology. Each clinic has support services from occupational and physical therapy, psychiatry, psychology, audiology and speech/language pathology.

To find out more about our specialized care setting, contact Children's Seashore House, Philadelphia Center for Health Care Sciences, 3405 Civic Center Blvd., Philadelphia, PA 19104-4388. (215) 895-3613. EOE.

Children's Seashore House

A Regional Hospital for Specialized Care and Rehabilitation
Philadelphia • Atlantic City

Circle No. 22 on Reader Service Card

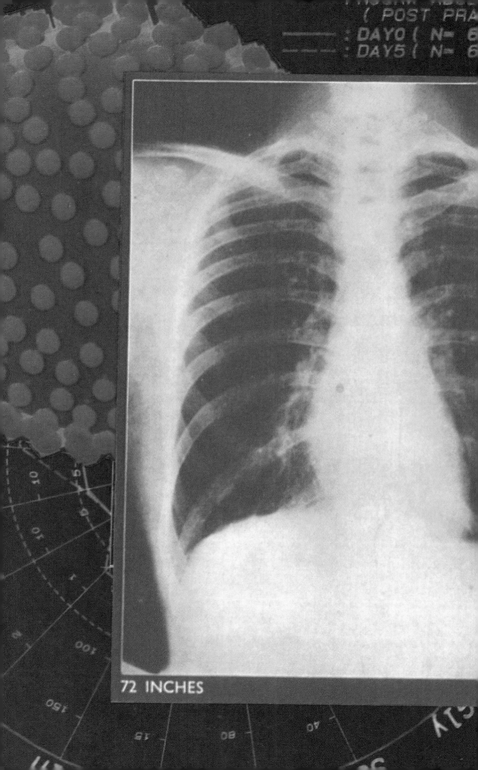

3

DREW   ID: 633848   RC
        HEIGHT: 67 (in) SE
SARCOIDOSIS   RE

PRE BRONCHODILATOR
ACTUAL   %   PREDICTEI
4.46   92   4.83
4.54   94   4.83

Choosing a Hospital

CHAPTER 10

The Wise Patient

How to take care of yourself in the hospital

Everybody has heard or read one of those "you won't believe what happened to me in the hospital" stories. Hospitals are big, hectic places, operating under intense pressure. So it's not surprising that sometimes somebody gets the wrong medication, develops an infection other than the condition he is being treated for, or wets the sheets because it took too long for a nurse to bring a bedpan. While you aren't always able to prevent these kinds of things, there are ways you can control them.

Health care is the nation's major business. It eats up the largest chunk of our GNP—14 percent, compared with 12 percent for defense and education combined. Yet where hospitals are concerned, there's often not enough correlation between cost and customer satisfaction. Charles Inlander, president of People's Medical Society, a nonprofit consumer watchdog group, points out that as consumers we're more likely to consult the Better Business Bureau about a roofer we're thinking of hiring than to check on the record of the hospitals we're entrusting with our lives. While nobody expects a stay at the hospital to be a day at the beach, we do expect that as long as a hospital has accreditation, it's a safe place to be. Yet sometimes hospitals fail state inspections even after having been granted the seal of approval of the Joint Commission of Healthcare Organizations, which has been known to allow slipshod conditions to persist for long periods without revoking accreditation.

Wash your hands

Even when the institution is performing up to standard, the *Los Angeles Times* reported that on a national level "as many as 6 percent of all people admitted to hospitals end up with infections they would not otherwise get." In the trade, these hospital-acquired diseases are called nosocomial infections; before you check into a local hospital, you can call and ask for its rate of nosocomial problems, which range

from urinary tract infections to pneumonia. At least half of these could be prevent-
ed, says Inlander, if staffs used better hygiene. Before anyone in the hospital touches
you, don't be embarrassed to ask: Did you remember to wash your hands?

Actually, you shouldn't be embarrassed to ask anything at all in the hospital.
"Patients need to express their needs, because nurses can't guess what they are, and
physicians don't try," says a former patient representative from Thomas Jefferson
University Hospital. "Yet most people are reticent about asking for service. They're
afraid if they rock the boat, the nurse will take it out on them." In reality, she advises that it's just the opposite: "The more noise you make, the more help you get."

Speak up for yourself

The average patient would just as soon keep silent and assume that Doctor knows
best. In several surveys examining what role patients wanted to play in making decisions about their medical treatment, almost half preferred to leave the choices to
their physicians. The University of Pennsylvania's Claire Fagin, a strong advocate of
consumerism in health care, says, "The hospital system is innocently designed to
make patients powerless. You must intervene and be assertive. Become a participant
in your care. What's the worst thing that can happen to you if you speak up and ask
questions? You'll be called a crank."

Why, why, why?

What should you question? Just about everything. If your doctor orders tests, don't
submit automatically. Studies indicate that far more tests than necessary are performed. You want to know what the doctor is looking for in results, what will happen to you if you don't have the procedure done, what risks are involved in the test,
and whether the potential advantages outweigh the dangers. Don't allow anybody in
a lab coat to come into your room to draw blood or haul you off to X-ray without
asking who ordered the test and reminding yourself that you can refuse it. "They go
nuts in a hospital when a patient says no," Inlander points out. "Suddenly everyone
rushes to explain what's happening."

Pay particular attention to the drugs you're given and when you're given
them. Nationally, the average hospital makes 60 medication errors an hour, admin-
istering the wrong drug or the wrong dosage or the right drug at the wrong time.
Question all medication: What is this? Why am I taking it? If you've been getting
green, red and purple pills and the nurse brings blue and yellow, don't swallow
them until you talk to the doctor. If you are on a 2-6-10 o'clock schedule and the
nurse comes with medicine at 4, make sure you ask to see the written order.

What happened to Florence Nightingale?

Although hospitals seem inflexible, rooms can be changed, and so can nurses.
Should you get stuck with one who is sullen or unacceptably inattentive, request

someone else. In most hospitals, every patient is assigned a particular nurse, and he or she is accountable for your case. That nurse is where the buck stops. Find out who your nurse is, and then have a little chat up front about your specific needs. Let the nurse know as soon as you have a problem.

Regardless of how solicitous the nurses are, you'll probably feel that nursing care isn't what it used to be. You're right. Hardly anybody gives back rubs or sponge baths like they did in the old days. As hospitals have increasingly come to cater to acutely ill people, the priorities of nursing have changed, and the Florence Nightingale philosophy is obsolete. Today's nurse, no matter how well-intentioned, is overworked, overpressured, understaffed and perhaps more focused on efficiency than on compassionate care. Often the nurse's goal isn't taking care of you; it's getting you to take care of yourself. A floor nurse at Pennsylvania Hospital explains, "Nursing now is geared toward making the patient as independent as possible."

Someone to watch over you

The more dependent the patient, the greater the need for the family to take over. When you're worried about a desperately ill relative, ask permission to stay after hospital visiting hours end, and, if necessary, tell the nurse you want to spend the night. Would you leave a frightened, bewildered child alone in the hospital? Then why should you be forced to abandon an adult too sick or confused to fend for himself? While the hospital may not be particularly pleased to have you as an overnight guest, if there is a medical reason for your presence and you aren't interfering with the delivery of care, they can't send you home. In some cases, they'll even order a cot for you.

Don't assume that anything reasonable is impossible until you talk to the patient advocate. The law in Pennsylvania requires hospitals to have some kind of grievance procedure. In the little handbook you're given at admission (which too few people take the time to read), you'll find the name of a patient representative or advocate whose job it is to help you in the hospital. Patient reps can get all kinds of things done for you. When a man at Jefferson Hospital demanded "a goddamn bedboard" and the nurse couldn't find one, patient rep Susan Miller got the carpentry shop to build one. When a woman who was very anxious about a scheduled test voiced her worries to Miller, she arranged for some TLC as well as special cushions to alleviate back pain during the long test. A teenager in the pediatric intensive care unit who couldn't sleep because of the incessant ringing of the phone near his bed was given earplugs until he could be moved. The rule of thumb in the hospital is, if you need something, ask for it.

A decent meal

While patient reps can sometimes move mountains, they can't do much about hospital food. Inlander's solution to the dreaded hospital tray—"Send out for pizza." Unless you're limited to a special diet, that's not a bad idea, and there are no rules against it. Nor are there any laws requiring you to eat the tasteless oatmeal and dry pork chops lovingly prepared by food service. You can make arrangements for your family to supply your meals, and alert the hospital upon admission that you do not want the meal plan and will not pay for it. Some hospitals have actually introduced gourmet menus, complete with wine. Check on their availability.

You don't have to be a VIP to get VIP treatment. Although special services may not be automatically offered to you, they won't be denied if you're willing to pay the extra charges. Most hospitals have plush suites, reserved for board members or doctors' families, that are available to the public when not in use. Jefferson, for instance, has two suites with fancy meals that will add $200 a day to your bill. Requests for these or for private rooms should be made in advance through the patient services office, with the understanding that emergencies may make it impossible for the hospital to deliver what was promised. We heard of a woman who threatened to check herself out of one area hospital because she didn't like her room and quickly found herself in the private quarters she'd originally asked for. Nurses may complain about the complainer, but she's the one who gets the attention.

Helpful hints

Finally, some general dos and don'ts that can make your hospital stay safer and more pleasant. When you're scheduled for an elective procedure, tour the facility in advance. If the rooms look dirty and dreary and the staff seems surly and uncooperative, go somewhere else. Be certain to see the doctor before your sedation starts, or pin a note on your gown reminding him what he's supposed to be doing. A surgeon told me he had a patient who drew a circle on her leg with a marker and wrote, "This is the spot where you're operating." Don't take valuables or money with you. Do take a pad and pencil to jot down questions, as well as some family photos or a poster to decorate your room and a Walkman with your favorite tapes. It's widely believed that the more cheerful your attitude, the more quickly you'll heal.

It's also smart to demand an itemized bill for your stay, and to check it line by line. A study by a national auditing company found that 98 percent of hospital bills in excess of $10,000 had errors, approximately 75 percent of which were in the hospital's favor. Lastly, don't go home without a copy of your medical records. When your car leaves the repair shop, you're entitled to a slip detailing exactly what the mechanic did to it. You deserve at least the same information about your body.

For Your Information

People's Medical Society, 462 Walnut Street, Allentown, PA 18102, 770-1670, is a first-rate resource for help in getting the best care and advice on what to do when you feel you've been wronged. For general information, I highly recommend the society's paperback, *Take This Book to the Hospital With You*, published by Rodale Press and available at local bookstores.

CHAPTER 11

Inside Story

A glossary of the many techniques used to see inside the body

Wilhelm Roentgen, a German physicist, holds the distinction of having been the first man to get under anybody's skin. In 1895, while experimenting with the cathode ray, Roentgen accidentally generated electromagnetic radiation so powerful that it could pass through virtually any substance and make an impression on a plate painted with a photographic emulsion. One of the first "pictures" he took was of the bones in his wife's hand. He called it an X-ray because of its mysterious nature. Within a year, doctors all over the world were taking X-ray pictures.

Before that, the knife was the only tool for seeing inside the human body. Doctors would use their hands and ears to locate internal problems, and when their probing and tapping indicated trouble, they had no alternative to cutting open the patient to see what was wrong. By then, it was often too late. The X-ray provided a window into a previously invisible world, and enabled doctors to diagnose all kinds of problems at the crucial early stages. Amid all the excitement, nobody realized how dangerous X-rays were—until people working with them began to die from overexposure. From that point on, the search was launched to find safer ways to reveal the body's intricacies.

From the crude still photos of bones that were early X-rays, radiology has progressed to the stage today where it's possible to view the heart and brain in action. It's a world Roentgen would hardly recognize. Here are explanations of some of its latest techniques.

CT scans: A slice of life

More than anything else, medical imaging owes its spectacular advancement to computers—and to Godfrey Hounsfield, a British scientist with an ear for music. While working on a project with the Beatles that involved the use of X-rays and electronic music, he began toying with other applications for bytes and rads. His inventiveness was later combined with the research of a mathematician. The result was computerized axial tomography, popularly known as the CT scan—the first practical application of the marriage of computers and X-rays. He and the mathematician won the Nobel Prize in medicine for creating a way to take cross-sectional pictures of the body from head to toe.

What made these pictures so amazing was their unique perspective. Before the CT scan, X-rays could photograph only through the front or side of the body, frequently showing organs superimposed on each other, which made accurate readings difficult. But these new pictures seemed to dissect the body without a knife, depicting body parts in thin, individual cross-sections, each as clearly defined as a drawing in a biology textbook.

For the patient, the procedure is quite painless. You report to the hospital or imaging center as an outpatient, and soon find yourself lying on a table in a brightly lit room, with the part of your body to be examined placed in the hole of what looks like a huge metal doughnut. A physician usually begins the scan by injecting a contrast solution into your bloodstream through a vein at the end of your elbow. This solution affects how much X-ray will be absorbed, and also enhances certain features of the final image. A computer uses the information on the amount of X-ray being transmitted through the tissue, and translates it into numbers, from which it makes a picture. In just seconds, images of your lung or brain or stomach, one slice after the other, appear on a computer screen. Not only is there an outline of the suspicious organ, but a sense of its density as well.

In rare instances someone gets a severe allergic reaction to the contrast solution. More typical symptoms are nausea, hives, a warm flush or an unpleasant metallic taste, though many people experience nothing more annoying than the prick of the injection itself. These can be pretty much eliminated with newer nonionic contrast materials that are safer but more expensive. If you're allergic, you might want to ask about them.

CT scans aid in evaluating tumors and inflammatory diseases by showing their exact size, their location and whether they are solid or filled with fluid. In the case of tumors, these can be important clues to whether a growth is benign or malignant. CT scans are also useful for checking the extent of an injury or infection. Where X-rays would show only a bone fracture, a more exacting CT scan could reveal internal bleeding, or cuts on an organ.

Magnetic resonance imaging: May the force be with you

Although scientists have managed to reduce the dosage of radiation from X-rays, their dream has long been to find a way to see inside the body without using any ionizing radiation at all. Now that's possible, with a procedure that depends entirely on magnetic force.

Magnetic resonance imaging (MRI) first appeared as a laboratory technique for chemical analysis in the '30s, when it became known that parts of every cell had magnetic properties. Forty years later, researchers learned that normal and abnormal tissues respond differently in a magnetic field. In the '80s, technology advanced to the point where it became possible to translate these differences into a picture. The "camera," if you will, is a piece of high-tech machinery that looks like a giant tunnel and exerts a magnetic force as high as 30,000 times the power of the earth's magnetic field. When a patient lies on a bed inside this tunnel, the intense magnetic force causes a portion of the protons in the body to line up in certain patterns. During this process of spinning and aligning, the protons give off energy signals that can be measured by a radio frequency and assembled into photographic images. Pictures can be made from many different planes: side to side, front to back, and head to toe, to name just a few. The images are actually cross-sections, like slices in a loaf of bread, and some machines can take as many as an image per second.

You may have seen advertisements for MRIs where it isn't necessary for the patient to lie inside a tunnel. These open-sided units, which are an alternative for obese or claustrophobic patients, use a lower magnetic field than the original high-field units—.1 to .3 compared to 1.5—and the stronger the field, the better quality the image. Though the cost to the patient is the same, says Dr. Mitchell Schnall, director of MRI at HUP, "you do sacrifice significant scan quality." You'll see a lot of these units around, because they can be bought for $800,000 versus $2 million to purchase a tunnel unit.

Other than the slight discomfort of lying quietly inside a tunnel, MRI patients have reported no ill effects from the procedure. Any alteration to the body's molecules is slight and transient. According to Dr. Stanley Baum, chairman of radiology at the Hospital of the University of Pennsylvania, studies have indicated that there is no known magnetic strength that has shown any biological effect on cells or chromosomes. MRI produces pictures of striking anatomical clarity, and images of things never seen before, such as changes in bone marrow and the stages of a hemorrhage. Tumors show up very clearly, along with ligaments, tendons and cartilage, which makes this an excellent tool for diagnosing sports injuries. Today MRIs are starting to be used to look at heart problems and catch early breast cancers even sooner than a mammography. And a new offshoot combining radio waves and magnetism called MRA—magnetic resonance angiography—can look into the blood vessels and pinpoint small clots or aneurysms without the risk of a more invasive angiogram. This diagnostic information has many applications in vascular disease.

Angiography: Just dyeing to see you

Like any other heavily trafficked highway, the body's blood vessels frequently need repair. Our rich, fatty diets produce plaque that collects in certain spots and creates roadblocks to impede the smooth flow of blood. Moreover, as we age, the elasticity of the roadbed itself diminishes and vessels harden and narrow, and sometimes sections need replacing. With the development of angiography—a kind of X-ray photography of blood vessels—it's possible to do quite sophisticated medical roadwork.

The angiographer's tools include long thin plastic catheters, guide wires that slide inside them and a colorless contrast solution—popularly referred to as dye—that mixes with the blood and blocks enough X-rays to create an image. Using these instruments, doctors can locate a clogged artery in the heart, pinpoint a blockage causing severe leg cramps or check whether the brain is being sufficiently nourished with blood.

The procedure begins with a small puncture (in the groin, arm or neck) to insert the catheter. These pliable tubes come in a variety of lengths and widths, and often have special curves or hooks on the ends designed to pre-fit particular arteries. By twisting and turning the guide wire, an angiographer manipulates the catheter up one blood vessel and into another. He is directed by a fluoroscope, a device that uses a weak X-ray to picture the route the angiographer is following on a TV monitor. (Years ago, some shoe stores had fluoroscopy machines so customers could check the fit by viewing their feet inside their new shoes.) When the angiographer reaches the spot he wants to examine, he withdraws the wire and injects the contrast solution through the catheter. It squirts out of the far end directly into the blood vessel, and a rapid series of X-ray pictures maps the solution's path.

Angiograms are performed without anesthesia, and patients generally experience little discomfort other than a warm flush from the contrast solution. But there are genuine concerns every time a doctor puts a catheter into a blood vessel, especially when these vessels are already weakened by disease. Excessive bleeding is one possible complication. An extreme example was the 83-year-old woman with unusually hard arterial walls that simply wouldn't seal when the catheter was removed. After several hours of continued bleeding, she had to be taken to the operating room, where the vessel was stitched shut. A more common risk is the chance a blood clot will dislodge, shut off the blood supply and cause a stroke.

Interventional radiology: Critical openings and closings

The practitioners of this delicate art refer to what they do as surgery without a scalpel. With techniques related to those used in angiograms, they are able to reach places deep within the body and correct conditions that once would have demanded a trip to the operating room—or in some cases, would have been untreatable. The interventional radiologist uses a variety of visual tools such as fluoroscopy, ultrasound, CT scan and even MRI to guide him as he threads his tubes and wires to the site of the problem.

Generally their work falls into three categories. The first is opening up blood vessels blocked by fatty plaque or bile ducts and ureters blocked by a stone, a tumor or scar tissue. By far the most common procedure in this category is the balloon angioplasty, where a tiny catheter with a balloon on the end is threaded through the artery to the impasse. When inflated, the balloon flattens out the plaque and clears the passage. The problem in the past with balloon angioplasties was something called stenosis—which basically means the roadblocks tended to come back. To fight that reoccurrence, a metal stent is now inserted after the balloon to act as a scaffolding to keep the opening from closing.

The second category does just the opposite by closing leaks in blood vessels that are hemmorhaging from trauma or bleeding ulcers. Tiny balloons or metal coils are delivered to the site of the leak and left in place to plug it. Lately this procedure has been used to obstruct vessels that feed cancerous tissue, in effect cutting off the blood supply so the cancer can't grow. It's generally tried with liver cancer.

The third application is to remove certain kinds of fluids such as the infected gook of an abscess, urine from an obstructed kidney or bile from an obstructed liver. A tube gets inserted through the skin to the spot where the problem lies and drains the area. A CT scan helps guide the tube and keep it from damaging critical organs. In the past, the removal of this material would have required an operation.

The brainy folks at the University of Pennsylvania are doing amazing things inside the head at the Interventional Neuro Center. They can pass micro-size catheters into the brain, not only for diagnostic purposes but also to treat aneurysms and tumors. Their tools enable them to seal off or open up vessels that are inaccessible through surgery.

A new and very exciting development may save some people from the destruction of an acute stroke. In a method similar to what's used in the emergency treatment of some heart attacks, the neuro-intervential radiologists at Penn have the ability to unblock even the tiniest arteries in the brain with a clot-dissolving drug called urokinase. Clots prevent arteries from delivering oxygen, causing death by starvation to the part of the brain they feed. That results in the loss of speech or motor function, typical of stroke victims. If the clot can be disintegrated and the blood supply quickly restored, the brain cells will suffer little or no damage. "This is an incredible advance in the treatment of stroke," says Dr. Robert I. Grossman, chief of neuroradiology at HUP. "You can take a person who has had a major stroke and by reversing the process, restore them to normal function and productive life."

Unfortunately, the window of applicability is very short—roughly six hours. It is critical that someone showing the symptoms of a stroke—difficulty speaking, weakness or paralysis of a limb—be taken to Penn immediately.

Ultrasonography: From submarines to problem pregnancies

Submarines are tracked by sending sound waves through the ocean's depths. In medicine, the same principle allows doctors to monitor everything from a fetus developing in the womb to the degree of damage to a heart valve. Unique sound pictures are produced from harmless high-frequency sound waves passing over certain areas of the body. The returning signal varies with the density of the tissue it hits. A computer measures that variance—how long it takes the sound to bounce back, as well as how much of it returns. The digital information gleaned from the reflected sound gets translated into a shadowy image, somewhat like the pictures of the Earth's surface taken from a spacecraft.

This noninvasive screening device is widely used in perinatology, the care of unborn babies, since X-rays are far too dangerous to be used during pregnancy. Doctors are now able to study the fetus in its own little world. Is it the normal size for its stage of development? Is there any abnormal bleeding? Are all four chambers of the heart present? With the advent of ultrasound, doctors have reduced the number of stillbirths by diagnosing an absence of critical amniotic fluid and delivering a baby early who would otherwise starve to death. If ultrasound should reveal that a fetal bladder isn't emptying properly, doctors can insert a needle to drain the fetal urine and prevent damage to the unborn's kidney. Ultrasound has also cut the risk of amniocentesis, an important test for birth defects that requires drawing fluids from the womb. In the past, doctors occasionally harmed the fetus when they inserted the needle. With the help of the ultrasound, these accidents can be averted.

In adults, ultrasound routinely diagnoses certain heart problems that previously could be confirmed only with the riskier procedure of cardiac catheterization. Using a technique called Doppler echo cardiography, doctors can watch heart valves opening and closing, see the direction and speed of blood flowing from chamber to chamber, and determine whether there are any leaks or structural defects.

The test is painless. The patient lies on a table while an operator passes what looks like a small flashlight over the heart. The sound waves it emits produce an electrical signal that is translated by computer into moving images on a TV screen. A whooshing sound that accompanies the picture tells an experienced listener how much a valve has actually narrowed. Echo cardiography is particularly successful in diagnosing heart-valve problems, the cause of one out of seven open-heart surgeries in America. Many surgeons use it in the operating room to make certain their valve repairs have completely plugged the leak.

Doppler ultrasound is now available in color, which has opened new avenues for examining other parts of the body. It can give information about the kidneys, detect early ectopic pregnancies and illuminate the body's vascular roadways. Through different colors and different gradations of a single color, it shows both the structure of blood vessels and the speed of blood flow. Color Doppler ultrasound in the vagina is a good screening device to identify before surgery whether ovarian growths are malignant or benign.

Nuclear medicine: The magic bullet approach

Despite the ominous implications of its name, nuclear medicine is a relatively safe and inexpensive way to detect certain abnormalities that don't stand out on traditional X-ray pictures. Actually, it's just the reverse of standard X-ray technique. Instead of using machines outside the body to fire radiation through it, nuclear medicine works from the inside out, by sending off very low-level radiation generated by a solution injected into the body.

The field came to prominence after World War II, when research on atomic weapons yielded information about radioactivity that had applications beyond the military. From the men who made bombs, medicine learned how to combine chemicals with radioactive isotopes and study the effect these chemicals have on living tissue. In adapting radioactivity to mapping organs in action, the science of nuclear medicine was born.

First, a solution laced with radioactive isotopes is injected into the bloodstream. Then a special camera, equipped with a crystal that picks up these signals, translates them into an image. With this technique, doctors can see if a transplanted kidney is functioning properly, or whether a thyroid gland is behaving normally. The presence or absence of the tracer indicates whether there's a problem, and also determines the extent of any damage.

Currently, more than 30 kinds of nuclear scans are done routinely in most area hospitals, to diagnose problems such as blood clots in the lung or cirrhosis of the liver. A scan of the spine will tell if cancer has spread, since bones are a common secondary site for the disease. When doctors want to know how fast a stomach empties in a patient with gastric problems, they might feed that patient scrambled eggs seasoned with a tracer, and take a series of images to see how quickly the isotope disappears. A gallium scan, normally used to detect inflammation or infection, has been helpful in diagnosing AIDS through a characteristic lung infection. Another type of isotope that concentrates in dead heart tissue can identify where a heart attack took place, as well as the amount of tissue affected. Even blood flow can be measured radioactively.

Nuclear scans are commonly used in stress tests. The patient walks on a treadmill to build up his heart rate. Toward the end of the exercise period, he's injected with a radioactive isotope that immediately travels to the heart muscle and reveals whether a normal amount of blood is coursing through.

Except for the prick of the needle to inject the isotope solution, nuclear scans are no more painful than X-rays. Allergic reactions are rare; the isotopes are nontoxic, and the most commonly used isotopes have an average half-life of only six hours—which means they are gone from the body faster than the average meal.

PET scans: Windows on the body at work

Most of the machines that peer into the body take what might be called architectural pictures, the kind that show the basic structure of human parts. The advent of positron emission tomography—the PET scan—made it possible to leap from anatomy to function, and see living organs in action. Want to know what happens in the brain when we smell a flower or read a book, when we get upset or have a seizure? Or what happens when our heart doesn't get enough oxygen? PET scans can supply answers like these without invading the body.

Traditionally, researchers who studied the living brain relied on tests done with electrodes, or on whatever was revealed before their eyes when they cut open the body's think tank. Now they can get a wealth of information by injecting nontoxic chemicals laced with radioactive tracers into the bloodstream, then measuring how and where these chemicals are absorbed. By pairing glucose (a chemical that acts in the brain like gas in a car) with a tracer that emits measurable gamma rays, doctors can map the way the brain metabolizes its various fuels. PET studies have shown with precision what parts of the brain process high and low sounds, what regions react to feelings of anxiety and how memory loss due to a stroke differs from that resulting from Alzheimer's disease.

Fewer than 20 hospitals across the country are doing PET research, because the radioactive isotopes usually need to be manufactured in costly cyclotrons right on the hospital grounds. (Penn has one of them.) Some of the isotopes have a half-life of just 30 seconds, and can't be transported. PET scans pose relatively little danger to patients. Depending on the test, the chemical compounds are either injected or inhaled, and the pictures are taken by machinery that looks similar to that used in CT scans.

PET scans are opening up all kinds of hidden secrets. For instance, we can now identify certain areas of damaged brain cells in stroke victims, because they do not absorb glucose or oxygen. By following whether these areas resume activity, doctors can chart the course of recovery. Such monitoring could eventually lead to an understanding of why some people recover from strokes, and perhaps make it possible to initiate recovery where it doesn't occur spontaneously. With patients suffering from seizures, PET scans can pinpoint the exact area in the brain responsible for triggering the attacks—a flaw not always revealed on standard brain-wave tests. Once identified, the abnormal tissue can sometimes be removed, and the seizures will disappear. PET studies of schizophrenics have shown a pattern of glucose metabolism markedly different from that in normal brains. These findings support the biochemical theory of mental illness, and could be instrumental in identifying its causes.

Another fruitful arena for the PET scan is in the diagnosis and treatment of cancer. It provides information useful in evaluating the disease, determining prognosis and differentiating scar tissue from diseased tissue following chemotherapy. For example, because active tumors gobble up glucose, doctors can measure glucose intake with a PET scan and use that information to evaluate how effective chemotherapy is, and whether to step it up or stop it.

PET scans are also gaining a place in cardiac care, because they are able to show blood flow into the heart muscle with greater accuracy than traditional thallium scanning. This information is valuable is deciding whether to proceed with heart surgery.

For researchers in particular, PET scans provide a priceless opportunity to bypass animal models and study a variety of human conditions as they occur in their natural settings. Their potential is virtually unlimited, because the number of available radioactive tracers has increased in a decade from a few to a few hundred. Compared to still photography, the PET scan is like a movie that will provide medicine with endless living studies of the way our marvelous engine works.

You Might Be At Risk For A Heart Attack.

If you have chest pains, palpitations and a family history of heart disease, you need to do something about it. Call Episcopal Hospital's Heart Institute. Their skilled team of specialists provide the highest level of personal care, attracting patients from across the country and around the world.

Episcopal's Heart Institute offers a full range of services to diagnose and treat any type of heart problem. And, as a teaching hospital, Episcopal has the most innovative, state-of-the-art cardiovascular techniques available.

Don't wait until it's too late. Call Episcopal's Heart Institute at 427-6200. Their quality care and caring staff will make you feel right at home.

Episcopal Heart Institute
100 E. Lehigh Avenue
Philadelphia, PA 19125
427-7000

Need an eye doctor?

Put Wills Eye's Sightline to the test.

Just one call to the Sightline puts you in touch with a Wills Eye doctor. It's a hotline for scheduling routine eye exams at Wills Eye Hospital or with a Wills ophthalmologist in your area.

In addition to basic eye care, you can arrange to see a Wills expert for special needs such as cataract evaluation, children's eye care, retinal problems or glaucoma. A Wills doctor can diagnose what's wrong – and recommend the best treatment.

It's what you'd expect from America's oldest and largest eye hospital.

Of course, you can have your eyes checked where you buy your glasses. But at Wills, you're examined by an ophthalmologist – a doctor with advanced training and qualifications.

Call the Sightline today. Find a Wills Eye doctor and see what you've been missing.

215-928-EYES
215-928-3937

))) Wills Eye Hospital
900 Walnut Street, Philadelphia, PA 19107

CHAPTER 12

Check It Out Before You Check In

Mini-profiles of area hospitals

I t's hard to turn on the television or pick up a magazine these days without being confronted with an advertisement for a hospital. In the competitive field of health care, hospital marketing has burgeoned into big business. Americans spend over $200 billion for hospital care—more than $1,000 for every man, woman and child in the country. No wonder hospitals are selling their services the way stores sell clothes and appliances. Since hospitals have entered the consumer marketplace, you, the buyer, need information to be a wise comparison shopper. That's why we compiled the following hospital profiles. We did not rate or evaluate individual hospitals. Rather we let them present themselves as they'd like to be seen. Some hospitals choose not to answer everything we asked, particularly in regard to costs. If you want to know more, ask them directly.

Be aware that the more expensive hospitals do not necessarily provide better care. At times, the costliest hospitals are likely to be teaching institutions, because of the added expense of maintaining academic programs. In general, use the hospital charges listed in these profiles as benchmark figures, because what you see is not usually what you pay, Like the sticker price on an automobile, hospital costs wind up being discounted and negotiated, especially by insurers. Hospitals are frequently reimbursed at reduced rates by insurance companies, HMOs, Medicare and Medicaid. And some people pay nothing at all. In 1992, area hospitals provided $147.7 million in free care.

Pennsylvanians are fortunate in that the state's Health Care Cost Containment Council gathers, analyzes and gives away, free of charge, an immense amount of information about area hospitals, ranging from mortality rates to costs to how many back operations a particular place has done. You can get copies of the Council's Hospital Effectiveness Report by calling 717-232-6787 or by writing to the Council at 225 Market Street, Suite 400, Harrisburg, Pa 17101.

Not surprisingly these reports have been criticized by both doctors and hospitals. They complain the statistics don't reflect the difficulty of the cases they admit or the severity of the patient's illness. Doctors caution that publishing mortality rates for individual surgeons may make some of them stop operating on really sick patients, to improve their performance records. The Council says its studies are adjusted to compensate for these differences. Bear in mind when you're interpreting these kinds of data that the success of any surgery depends on a variety of factors, including the patient's health, the surgeon and the anesthesiologists's skill, the cleanliness of the hospital, the attention of the nursing care and the overall quality of the support staff. Studies suggest that you're more likely to live and less likely to have complications when you undergo a given procedure at a hospital where that procedure is done with a frequency approaching 200 cases a year.

For more information, call the Delaware Valley Hospital Council at 735-9695.

Codes

🛏 overnight facilities for families

🖉 pastoral care

🏨 hospice care

💈 barber

⚖ patient advocate

🚭 smoke-free environment

🏥 teaching hospital

E emergency room

✉ prepayment for deductible
required

Abington Memorial Hospital

🛏 🖉 🏨 💈 ⚖ 🚭 🏥 E ✉

1200 OLD YORK ROAD, ABINGTON; 576-2000. 576-MEDI (*physician referral*), 881-5750 (*ElderHelp*) DOCTORS ON ACTIVE STAFF: 453 (*88% board-certified*). NUMBER OF BEDS: 508. 1.54 RNs PER BED. SEMIPRIVATE ROOM COST: $1,075. PRIVATE ROOM COST: $1,102. GOURMET FOOD SERVICE: $15 PER MEAL. ACCREDITATION: JCAHO, PTSF, ACGME, AMA, AABB, CAP, ACR.

Sample charges for surgical services: back and neck procedures without complication, $5,344; vaginal delivery, $1,805; prostate removal, $3,094; hourly operating-room charge, $1,443.

Special surgical units: neurosurgery, gynecology, plastic and reconstructive, vascular, fetal, ophthalmologic, dental, ambulatory surgery, mini-surgery, Surgical Trauma Unit, Abington Surgical Center.

Base cost for an ER visit: $86.

Additional ER services: Level II Regional Trauma Center, Chest Pain Center.

Ob/gyn programs: family-centered maternity care, Level III NICU, high-risk pregnancy and obstetrics, gynecologic oncology, genetic counseling, infertility services including in-vitro fertilization, Mother/Infant Unit, prenatal testing, amniocentesis, Maternal Observation and Monitoring (MOM) unit, PUBS, maternity education, sibling orientation, postpartum depression support group. **Specialized treatment programs:** cardiac radio-frequency ablation therapy, cardiac cath, cardiac rehab, CHAMPS (Children's Hospital/Abington Memorial Pediatric Service), Heart Center and vascular lab, pediatric ICU, hemodialysis, geropsychiatry, Fitness Institute, pain management, occupational medicine, high-dose chemotherapy with peripheral stem cell transplantation for cancer, geriatric assessment, home health care, MRI Center.

Physical rehab services: 26-bed inpatient unit, Falls Prevention Clinic, geriatric rehab assessment, neuromuscular retraining, speech pathology and dysphagia, occupational, physical, and recreation therapy, stroke program, prosthetic/orthotic clinic, outpatient center.

Outpatient health and wellness programs: childbirth/parenting classes, *Look Good, Feel Better* (for women with cancer), *Reach to Recovery* (for breast cancer), CPR and first aid training, diabetes education, smoking cessation, nutrition counseling, *Eat Heart-y*, Time Out for Men/Women, Abington Fitness Institute, *ElderMed*, van service for outpatient transportation.

Albert Einstein Medical Center

5501 OLD YORK RD., 456-7890, 1-800-EINSTEIN (*physician referral/health information*). DOCTORS ON ACTIVE STAFF: 660 (*82% board-certified*); NUMBER OF BEDS: 600; 1.16 RNs PER BED; SEMIPRIVATE ROOM COST: $880; PRIVATE ROOM COST; $1,060; ACCREDITATION: JCAHO, ACS, PTSF, ACR.

Sample charges for surgical services including ancillary and supplies: coronary bypass without cardiac cath, $84,134; back and neck procedures without complication, $16,567; vaginal delivery, $6,320; prostate removal, $12,373; standard local anesthesia, $225; hourly operating-room charge, $2,351 (first hour); preadmission testing, $773 (average).

Special surgical units: heart surgery, surgical intensive care, organ transplants. Special intensive care units: surgical, medical, pediatric, neonatal.

Base cost for emergency room visit: $110.

Also available in ER: trauma, *Fast Track*, psychiatric emergency services.

Ob/gyn programs: *Healthy Beginnings Plus, A Better Start*, high-risk obstetrics, Menopause Program.

Specialized treatment programs: Heart Center, Women's Heart, Cancer Center, High-Risk Breast Program, Center for Orthopedic Sciences, Center for Organ Transplantation, Psychiatry (with Belmont Center for Comprehensive Treatment), Geriatric Medicine (affiliated with Philadelphia Geriatric Center).

Physical rehab services: physical, occupational and speech therapy (MossRehab shares the campus with AEMC and also provides intensive medical rehab services). Outpatient centers: Einstein Center One in Northeast Philadelphia for primary and specialty care, radiology, and cancer treatment; Einstein Plaza Jenkintown for primary and specialty care; The Imaging Center of Elkins Park for comprehensive radiology services; *Prime Health* for geriatrics in Northeast Philadelphia.

Brandywine Hospital

201 Reeceville Rd., Coatesville, 383-8000. Doctors on active staff: 135 (*87% board-certified*); number of beds: 218; 1.3 RNs per bed; semiprivate room cost: $681; private room cost: $741; accreditation: JCAHO, AABB, CAP, PDH, ACR.

Surgical charges: not furnished.

Special surgical units: Ambulatory Surgery Center, Short Procedure Unit.

Base cost for ER visit: $150.

Additional ER services: Chest pain emergency unit, Sky FlightCare (a pre- and interhospital aeromedical helicopter based at the hospital).

Ob/gyn programs: Maternity Care Center, pre- and post-natal exercise classes, *Resolve Through Sharing*.

Specialized treatment programs: dialysis, mental health unit, physical and hand rehab, occupational health, Fitness and Wellness Center, Breast Care Center, Pain Control Center, sports medicine, industrial rehab, work hardening.

Bryn Mawr Hospital

130 South Bryn Mawr Ave., Bryn Mawr. Doctors on active staff: 383 (*83% board-certified*); 393 beds; Room costs not furnished. accreditation: PDH, JCAHO, ACGME, ACR.

Surgical charges: not furnished.

Special surgical units: open heart, surgical "greenhouses" (for total hip replacement), minimal access surgery, same-day surgery, SurgiCenter.

Base cost for ER visit: not furnished.

Ob/gyn programs: maternal/fetal medicine, labor/delivery/recovery unit, postpartum unit, newborn nursery, neonatal ICU, maternal and newborn transport, childbirth preparation classes, gynecologic surgery, infertility services.

Specialized treatment programs: inpatient and outpatient dialysis, inpatient psychiatry unit, Dental Clinic, Eye Clinic, pediatrics inpatient unit, ICU, coronary care unit, cardiac catheterization labs, electrophysiology.

Physical rehab services: physical, occupational and speech therapy.

Outpatient health and wellness programs: monthly blood pressure screenings, StressSmart, adult/infant/child CPR, baby-sitting course, nutrition counseling, adult health fair, Life Without Diets, travelers' advisory service, diabetes screening and counseling, childbirth preparation, cancer and cholesterol screenings, children's health fair.

The Chester County Hospital

🛏 🦿 ⊞ 🔋 ⚖ 🚫 🦽 E

701 EAST MARSHALL ST., WEST CHESTER, 431-5000. DOCTORS ON STAFF: 250; NUMBER OF BEDS: 250; 1.76 RNs PER BED; ROOM COSTS NOT FURNISHED. ACCREDITATION: JCAHO, NLN, CAP, AABB.

Surgical charges: not furnished.
Special surgical units: endoscopy suite for diagnostic and surgical procedures, Ambulatory Care Center, cardiac cath lab.
Base rate for ER visit: not furnished.
Ob/gyn programs: 27-bed obstetrics unit with specially designed LDR rooms, Level II nursery, prenatal clinic, childbirth and sibling classes, genetic counseling, antenatal testing unit, sibling classes, *Stork Alert*, Childbirth Connection information line.
Specialized treatment programs: Occupational Health Center, critical care, Emergency Department, Cancer Program (with University of Pennsylvania Cancer Center).
Physical rehab services: Center for Health and Fitness, Center for Physical Therapy and Sports Medicine, Center for Cardiopulmonary Rehabilitation, wide range of outpatient wellness programs.

Chestnut Hill Hospital

🦿 ⊞ 🔋 ⚖ 🚫 🦽 E

8835 GERMANTOWN AVE., PHILADELPHIA, 248-8200, 248-8069 (*physician referral*). DOCTORS ON ACTIVE STAFF: 221 (*88% board-certified*); NUMBER OF BEDS: 200; 1.03 RNs PER BED; GOURMET FOOD SERVICE: FROM $6.50 TO $10; ROOM COSTS NOT FURNISHED. ACCREDITATION: JCAHO WITH COMMENDATION, ACGME, CAP, PDH, ACR, AABB.

Surgical charges: not furnished.
Special surgical units: Outpatient Surgical Center.
Base cost for ER visit: $79.
Ob/gyn programs: family-centered maternity care, antenatal testing, perinatology, labor/delivery/recovery rooms, childbirth education.
Specialized treatment programs: family practice unit, dialysis, endoscopy, ICCU, CICU, ICU, cardiac rehab, pain management, breast disease, vascular disease, Hospital HomeCare, Jefferson-Chestnut Hill Radiation Oncology Center, cancer care. Member, Jefferson Cancer Network.
Physical rehab services: physical, occupational, speech therapy.
Outpatient health and wellness programs: *Parents' Place*, childbirth education, sibling preparation, maternity exercise, *Our First*, cardiac rehab, diabetes, smoking cessation, Speakers Bureau, CPR, Senior CHEC, blood pressure and various cancer screenings and support groups.

The Children's Hospital of Philadelphia

🛏 🧑‍⚕️ 🏥 📋 ⚕ 🚫 🎧 E

34TH ST. AND CIVIC CENTER BLVD., 590-1000, 800-TRY-CHOP (*for referrals*). DOCTORS ON ACTIVE STAFF: 260 (*99% board-certified*); NUMBER OF BEDS: 294; 2.4 RNs PER BED; SEMIPRIVATE ROOM COST: $775; PRIVATE ROOM COST: $825; ACCREDITATION: JCAHO, ABP.

Surgical charges: not applicable.

Special surgical units: transplants (heart/liver/kidney and bone marrow), cardiothoracic, craniofacial, craniofacial reconstruction, neurosurgery, urology, orthopedics.

Base cost for an ER visit: $110.

ER services: Level I trauma service, six isolation rooms for patients with infectious diseases, trauma resuscitation room, modern radiology suite, decontamination room.

Specialized programs: Growth Center, pain management, sleep disorders, Diagnostic Center, attention deficit/hyperactivity disorders, hemangioma, lipid heart, obesity clinic, cystic fibrosis, scoliosis, sports medicine, orthopedics, dyslexia testing, neurofibromatosis, sickle-cell, hemophilia, neuro-oncology, Pediatric Regional Epilepsy Program, electroencephalography, neuromuscular program, psychiatric unit, spina bifida, trauma program, neonatal and pediatric follow-up, bone marrow transplantation.

Special treatment units: oncology, surgical (trauma/liver and short-stay), medical (diabetes and asthma, cardiology), cardiovascular surgery and neurosurgery, pediatric ICU (acute, intermediate and isolation), Infant Transitional Unit, infant ICU. Provides physical rehab services through the Children's Seashore House.

Cooper Hospital/University Medical Center

🛏 🧑‍⚕️ 🏥 📋 ⚕ 🚫 🎧 E ✉

ONE COOPER PLAZA, CAMDEN, NEW JERSEY, 609-342-2000. DOCTORS ON ACTIVE STAFF: 456 (*91% board-certified*); NUMBER OF BEDS: 552; 1.45 RNs PER BED; SEMIPRIVATE ROOM COST: $902; PRIVATE ROOM COST: $1,018; ACCREDITATION: AABB, ACS, AHA, CAP, JCAHO, MSNJ.

Sample charges for surgical services: coronary bypass without cardiac cath, $16,234; back and neck procedures without complication, $4,762; vaginal delivery, $2,142; prostate removal, $3,277.

Special surgical units: endoscopic and laser surgery, cardiothoracic, bone marrow transplantation, pediatrics surgery, neurosurgery, gynecologic oncology, colorectal, orthopedics, otolaryngology, plastic and reconstructive, cleft palate program, urology, ophthalmology, traumatology and emergency. Cooper is a Level I Regional Trauma Center.

ER charges: not furnished.

Ob/gyn programs: antenatal testing, comprehensive breast care center, maternal/fetal medicine, perinatal center, gynecologic oncology, reproductive endocrinology, in-vitro fertilization, genetic counseling, maternal advanced care. **Specialized treatment programs:** Comprehensive Cancer Center, Cardiovascular Center, Sleep Disorders Laboratory, Geriatric Assessment Program, Diabetes Care Center, epilepsy program, radiation therapy, high-risk pregnancy program, Colo-rectal Care Center, Perinatal Center, Special Care Nursery, Children's Epilepsy Center, Young Adult Care Center, maternal advanced and intermediate care, Comprehensive Breast Care Center, Institute for Systemic Radiation Therapy.

Specialized pediatric programs: Child Development Center, birth defects and genetic disorders, pediatric hematology/oncology, pediatric and neonatal intensive care, Regional Arthritis Center, sickle-cell anemia, speech pathology, spina bifida, SIDS and infant apnea evaluation, young adult care, play therapy program.

Physical rehab services: physical and occupational therapy, psychiatric evaluations, prosthetics and orthotics, speech pathology, comprehensive oncology rehab, swallowing evaluations, electromyography and nerve conduction studies, audiology, chronic pain, comprehensive lymphedema treatment, balance disorders, gait dysfunction, movement disorder therapy.

Health and wellness programs: Understanding Menopause, breast surgery, pregnancy after 35, heart disease, stress management, diabetes management, childhood nutrition, cancer prevention through nutrition, breast cancer screening.

Crozer-Chester Medical Center

ONE MEDICAL CENTER BLVD., UPLAND, 447-2000, 447-6678 (*physician referral*). DOCTORS ON ACTIVE STAFF: 419 (*74% board-certified*); NUMBER OF BEDS: 480; GOURMET FOOD SERVICE: BETWEEN $15 AND $20; ACCREDITATION: ROOM COSTS NOT FURNISHED. ACS, PTSF, JCAHO, ACR.

Surgical charges: not furnished.
Special surgical units: open-heart surgery, angioplasty, Nathan Speare Regional Burn Treatment Center, the John E. du Pont Trauma Center.
Base cost for an ER visit: $95.
Ob/gyn programs: Antenatal testing unit, Maternity center (9 birthing rooms and 14-bed intensive care nursery), reproductive endocrinology and fertility center. Free outpatient care for the uninsured, special supplemental food program for women, infants, and children, and prenatal care programs through *A Better Start, Health Partners*, family planning service and *Healthy Beginnings*.
Specialized treatment programs: The Silberman Center, medical and social services for seniors in Delaware County, inpatient psychiatry, dialysis, The Cholesterol Center, Center for Diabetes, Sleep Disorders Center, Cancer Center, specialized clinics for low income clients.
Physical rehab services: occupational and physical therapy, speech-language pathology, audiology and dysphagia services, Feeding and Swallowing Center,

Sports Medicine Center, Hand Center, Work Rehabilitation, 30-bed inpatient rehab.
Health and wellness programs: Nutrition Information Center, childbirth education classes, sibling preparation classes, free screenings for cancer, cholesterol, and diabetes.

Delaware County Memorial Hospital

🛏 🧴 🎞 ♿ ⚖ 🚫 ✈ E ⊠

501 NORTH LANSDOWNE AVE., DREXEL HILL, 284-8100. DOCTORS ON ACTIVE STAFF: 276 (*83% board-certified*); NUMBER OF BEDS: 313; .71 RNS PER BED; ROOM COST: $897; GOURMET FOOD SERVICE: $10 PER MEAL; ACCREDITATION: JCAHO, PDH, CAP, ACS.

Sample charges for surgical services: vaginal delivery, $5,200 for a two-day stay; standard local anesthesia, $798; hourly operating-room charge between $756 and $1,264; preadmission testing, $158.

Special surgical units: outpatient surgery, endoscopy, laparoscopic, obstetrics, a complete range of genito-urinary services.

Base cost for ER visit: $71. Additional emergency room services include a paramedic unit.

Ob/gyn programs: prenatal, pregnancy, newborn, breast feeding, birthing, parenting, exercise, GYN oncology, Reproductive Endocrinology, child-care emergency classes, parents' bereavement program.

Specialized treatment programs: alcohol and addiction treatment, dialysis, Sports Medicine Institute, respiratory therapy/pulmonary rehab, cardiac cath, physical medicine and rehab, Delaware County Regional Cancer Center (affiliated with Fox Chase Cancer Network), Hearing and Speech Center, Women's Diagnostic Center, intensive care nursery, perinatal testing.

Physical rehab services: the Stroke Club, amputee, activities of daily living, orthotics, prosthesis, occupational, physical and speech therapy, social work, hearing, specialized nursing.

Outpatient programs: smoking cessation, stress management, CPR, babysitting courses, weight-loss program, nutrition, health and beauty seminar, *ElderMed*, screening programs.

Delaware Valley Medical Center

🛏 🧴 ♿ ⚖ 🚫 ✈ E

200 OXFORD VALLEY RD., LANGHORNE, 949-5000, 946-5116 (*physician referral and general information*). DOCTORS ON ACTIVE STAFF: 282 (*80% board-certified*); NUMBER OF BEDS: 223; 1.2 RNS PER BED; ROOM COSTS NOT FURNISHED; ACCREDITATION: AABB, AOA, CAP, CPDH.

Surgical charges: not furnished.
Special surgical units: Cardiac Cath Lab, ambulatory surgery, laser, orthopedic, endoscopy, podiatry, neuro, gynecology, oral-maxillofacial.
Base rate for ER visit: not furnished.

Additional ER services: helipad, poison control.

Ob/gyn programs: gynecological surgery.

Specialized treatment programs: cardiac and pulmonary rehab, occupational health, pain management, sleep disorders, cardiac telemetry, hemodialysis, "Rediscovery" mental health/substance abuse, home health care, family practice/primary care.

Physical rehab services: audiology, speech pathology, nerve conduction studies, physical and occupational therapy, EMG.

Outpatient health and wellness: CPR, first aid, diabetes and Lyme disease education, weight loss, nutritional counseling, senior citizen and youth programs, cholesterol, blood pressure, smoking cessation, health screenings.

Doylestown Hospital

🛏 🎽 🏢 🏥 ⚖ Ⓢ E

ROUTES 202 AND 611, DOYLESTOWN, 345-2200. DOCTORS ON ACTIVE/ASSOCIATE STAFF: 167 (*82% board-certified*); NUMBER OF BEDS: 213; SEMIPRIVATE ROOM COST: $887; PRIVATE ROOM COST: $942; ACCREDITATION: JCAHO, CARF, PDH.

Sample charges for surgical services: back and neck procedures without complication, $17,764; vaginal delivery, $4,120; prostate removal, $13,034; standard local anesthesia, $269 per unit; operating-room charge first half hour, $1,633 plus $312 each additional half hour; preadmission testing, $468.

Base cost for most prevalent ER visit: $99.

Additional ER services: crisis intervention for mental health, 10 monitored beds for cardiac emergencies, ALS and PALS certified staff.

Ob/gyn programs: Prenatal testing center (amniocentesis and CVS), educational programs, *Baby Bracelets* visiting nurse program after delivery, 10 new LDRP (labor, delivery, recovery, post-partum) rooms opening July 1994.

Specialized treatment units: mental health, telemetry, critical care, cardiac cath lab, endoscopy, oncology nursing, rehab. Comprehensive cancer care available through a cooperative agreement with UPCC.

Physical rehab services: physical, occupational, recreational and speech therapy, psychological services, hand therapy, brain injury program.

Outpatient health and wellness programs: CPR, diabetes education, first aid, cancer education, *Dialogue with a Doctor* physician lecture series, parenting and babysitting education, smoking cessation, stress reduction, blood pressure, cholesterol, diabetes and cancer screenings, senior wellness (exercise).

Alfred I. duPont Institute

🛏 🎽 🏢 Ⓢ 🦷 E

1600 ROCKLAND ROAD, WILMINGTON, DE, (302) 651-4000. DOCTORS ON ACTIVE STAFF: 213 (*95% board-certified*); NUMBER OF BEDS: 128; 2.2 RNs PER BED; PRIVATE, SEMIPRIVATE AND SUITE COST: $535; ACCREDITATION: JCAHO, CARF.

Surgical charges: not furnished.

Special surgical units: neurosurgery, urology, ophthalmology, orthopedic, oto-laryngology, plastic surgery, kidney transplantation.

Base cost for ER visit: $36.

Additional ER services: 24-hour staffing and on-call surgical capabilities, pediatric transport team.

Specialized treatment programs: Traumatic brain and spinal cord injury and comprehensive outpatient rehab, end-stage renal disease program, critical care, NICU, child and adolescent psychiatry and psychology, gastroenterology, neurology, orthopedics, sports medicine, genetics, rheumatology, infectious diseases, endocrinology, growth disorders.

Physical rehab services: 40-bed inpatient rehab unit, physical, occupational and speech therapy, audiology services, cognitive remediation and academic therapy.

Episcopal Hospital

🛏 ⚖ 🔱 E ✉

100 E. LEHIGH AVE., 427-7000. DOCTORS ON ACTIVE STAFF: 191 (*54% board-certified*), NUMBER OF BEDS: 275; 1 RN FOR EACH 1.4 BEDS; SEMIPRIVATE ROOM COST: $795; PRIVATE ROOM COST: $830; ACCREDITATION: JCAHO, AABB, ACS, CAP.

Surgical charges: not furnished.

Special surgical units: laparoscopic cholecystectomy, neurosurgery, cardiothoracic, colo-rectal, laser.

Base cost for an ER visit: $78.

Ob/gyn programs: prepared childbirth classes, maternal infant care, Women, Infants and Children, cocaine outreach services.

Specialized treatment programs: substance abuse, dialysis, dental (pediatric), industrial medicine, Beacon House (residential facility for female drug abusers), cardiac rehab, asthma center, ophthalmology, diabetic foot center.

Physical rehab services: physical and occupational therapy, work hardening and Back School, Pain Management Center. Patient Liaison Program for those who need an interpreter.

Outpatient health/wellness programs: prenatal classes, fitness/circuit training.

Fitzgerald Mercy Hospital

🛏 ⚖ 🏥 📖 🔱 🚫 ⛑ E

1500 LANSDOWNE AVE., DARBY, 237-4000, 800-227-2575 (*physician referral*). DOCTORS ON ACTIVE STAFF: 341 (*78% board-certified*); NUMBER OF BEDS: 469; ROOM COSTS NOT FURNISHED. ACCREDITATION: AABB, CAP, JCAHO, PDH, PDW, ACGME.

Surgical charges: not furnished.

Special surgical units: surgical ICU, short procedure unit.

Base cost for ER visit: $68.

Additional ER services: *FastCare* (for non-life-threatening injuries), toxicology.

Ob/gyn programs: midwifery, perinatology, pre- and postpartum education, exercise classes, neonatology, Gamete Intra-Fallopian Transfer (GIFT) procedure for infertility, parent education.

Specialized treatment programs: dialysis, cardiac rehab, psychiatry, psychiatry crisis, lithotripsy, cardiac cath, ultrasound, skilled nursing facility, CT, MRI, nuclear medicine and occupational health, outpatient drug and alcohol.

Physical rehab services: physical and occupational therapy.

Outpatient health/wellness programs: medical imaging (general radiology, mammography), ambulatory care (ob/gyn, pediatrics, surgery), diagnostic cardiology, speech therapy, audiology, lab, Red Cross Autologous Blood Donor Center, nutrition services, cholesterol, blood pressure, diabetes, cancer screenings, infant CPR, mobile van, *Matter of Fat*, diabetes education, speech, hearing, and swallowing tests.

Frankford Hospital

FRANKFORD CAMPUS: FRANKFORD AVE. AND WAKELING ST., 831-2000; TORRESDALE CAMPUS: KNIGHTS AND RED LION RDS., 612-4000, 612-4888 (*physician referral for both campuses*). DOCTORS ON ACTIVE STAFF: 452 (*74% board-certified*); NUMBER OF BEDS: 370; .96 RNS PER BED; SEMIPRIVATE AND PRIVATE ROOM COST: $1,540; ACCREDITATION: JCAHO, AABB.

Sample charges for surgical services: standard local anesthesia, $423; hourly operating-room charge, $1,353.

Special surgical units: endoscopy suite, ambulatory surgery centers, laparoscopy.

Base cost for ER visit: $71.

Additional ER services: Level II Trauma Center, *Fast Track*.

Ob/gyn programs: family centered maternity program, Women's Health Center, gynecologic oncology, perinatology, neonatology, ob home visit program, *Healthy Beginnings Plus*.

Specialized treatment programs: health center clinics for low income families, radiation oncology, inpatient detox, outpatient drug and alcohol counseling and treatment, pain clinic.

Physical rehab services: physical therapy (in- and outpatient), Work Hardening, home care rehab, Work Health (occupational medicine).

Outpatient health and wellness programs: diabetes education, exercise classes, weight management, nutritional counseling, CPR, first aid, cholesterol and blood pressure screening, maternity fitness and breast feeding classes.

Germantown Hospital and Medical Center

ONE PENN BLVD., 951-8000. DOCTORS ON ACTIVE STAFF: 215 (*92% board-certified*); NUMBER OF BEDS: 226; .90 RNS PER BED; ROOM COST (*all private*): $887.50; ACCREDITATION: JCAHO, CAP, AABB, ACR.

Sample charges for surgical services: back and neck procedures without complication, $13,000; vaginal delivery, $4,300; prostate removal, $8,800; hourly operating-room charge, first half-hour, $1,367, each additional half-hour $788; preadmission testing, $400.

Base cost for ER visit: $138.50.

Additional ER services: *Fast Track.*

Ob/gyn programs: *Healthy Beginnings,* childbirth education and free adjusting to parenthood classes, Women's Health Center.

Specialized treatment programs: skilled nursing facility, Ambulatory Infusion Center, autologous blood donation program, Comprehensive Headache Center, Geriatric Assessment Unit, Northwest Medical Practice (for those who are uninsured or underinsured).

Physical rehab services: biodex, occupational, speech and TMJ therapy.

Outpatient health and wellness programs: *Living Well Health* (free and reduced cost services), blood pressure screenings, Easy Breathers Club, Breast Self-Exam Instruction (monthly), screenings for diabetes, glaucoma, cholesterol, prostate cancer, hearing, colo-rectal cancer. *Passport to Health* is a senior membership program with Center in the Park, free speaker's bureau, Care-A-Van (reduced cost transportation).

Graduate Health System City Avenue Hospital

4150 CITY AVE., 871-1000, 800-654-GRAD (*physician referral*). DOCTORS ON ACTIVE STAFF: 422 (*71% board-certified*): NUMBER OF BEDS: 210; 1.2 RNS PER BED; SEMIPRIVATE ROOM COST: $550; PRIVATE ROOM COST: $600; ACCREDITATION: AOA, CAP, AABB.

Surgical charges: not furnished.

Special surgical units: surgical short procedure unit, carbon dioxide and Yag laser, laparoscopic procedures, sinus endoscopy with video capabilities.

Base cost for ER visit: $70. Level II emergency services available for minor traumas and fractures.

Ob/gyn programs: family-centered maternity care with certified midwives and obstetricians, parenting, perinatology, neonatology, infertility, advanced laparoscopic surgery, childbirth education, certified nurse-midwifery.

Specialized treatment programs: inpatient mental health, podiatry, pediatrics, TMJ clinic, medical short procedures unit for outpatient chemotherapy, pain management, autologous blood donations, ICU, CCU, telemetry.

Physical rehab services: in- and outpatient physical therapy, outpatient audiology and speech pathology.

Outpatient programs: parent support, CPR, first aid, diabetes education.

Graduate Health System Parkview Hospital

🎗 🎚 ⚖ 🚫 ✈ E ✉

1331 East Wyoming Ave., 537-7400, 800-654-GRAD (*physician referral*). Doctors on active staff: 316 (*72% board-certified*); number of beds: 214; 1.1 RN per bed; semiprivate room: $600; private room: $680; accreditation: AOA.

Surgical charges: not furnished.

Special surgical units: laparoscopic procedures, sinus endoscopy with video capabilities.

Base cost for ER visit: $90. ER services include fully equipped cast room with orthopedic specialists available 24 hours, cardiac treatment, trauma treatment, thromolytic therapy.

Ob/gyn programs: full-service ob with labor, postpartum and nursery on same floor, optional rooming-in, modified mother-infant care, classes in sibling and grandparent preparation, childbirth education, breast feeding.

Specialized treatment programs: dialysis, skilled nursing, pediatrics, ICCU, pulmonary care unit, telemetry unit, short procedure unit, minor surgery, chemotherapy.

Physical rehab services: in- and outpatient occupational, physical and speech therapy.

Outpatient programs: family and parenting courses, CPR, skin cancer, blood pressure, prostate, diabetes and cholesterol screenings.

The Graduate Hospital

🛏 🎗 🏥 🎚 ⚖ 🚫 ✈ E ✉

18th and Lombard sts., 893-2000, 800-654-GRAD (*physician referral*). Doctors on active staff: 299 (*86% board-certified*); number of beds: 330; 1.4 RNs per bed; semiprivate room cost: $1,096; private room cost: $1,125; suite cost: $1,195; gourmet food service: $16.75 per day; accreditation: JCAHO, ACGME, ACR, PDH, AABB.

Surgical charges: not furnished.

Special surgical units: open-heart, musculoskeletal tumor surgery, neurosurgery for epilepsy, colon and rectal, surgical oncology, gynecologic oncology, same-day surgery, laser, laparoscopic, minimally invasive spine surgery.

Base cost for ER visit: $116.

Gynecological services emphasize organ preservation and include a range of surgical procedures,including total laparoscopic hysterectomies.

Specialized treatment programs: Arthritis Center, Back Program, Cancer Program, Cardiac Care Unit, Cerebral Blood Flow Lab, Comprehensive Epilepsy Center, Disc Treatment Center, kidney dialysis (inpatient and outpatient), Intra-Operative Radiation Therapy (IORT), Medical/Surgical ICU, Memory Disorders Service, Nutritional Support Unit, Musculoskeletal Tumor Service, Neurological ICU, Occupational Therapy, Parkinson's Disease and Movement Disorders Center,

Physical Therapy, Phase I cardiac rehab, radiation therapy, speech therapy, Stem Cell Transplantation Program, TMJ service, Urinary Incontinence Center, Vascular Blood Flow Laboratory, Wound Care Center. Graduate also operates a Human Performance and Sports Medicine Center in Wayne, PA (688-6767).

Grand View Hospital

700 LAWN AVE., SELLERSVILLE, 453-4000, 453-9676 (*physician referral*), 800-752-2070 (*Cancer Answerline*), 800-752-3060 (*Women's Health Information Line*). DOCTORS ON ACTIVE STAFF: 223 (*87% board-certified*); NUMBER OF BEDS: 250; 1 RN PER 2 BEDS; SEMIPRIVATE ROOM COST: $675; PRIVATE ROOM COST: $723; ACCREDITATION: JCAHO, ACR, PDH, CAP, ACS, AABB.

Surgical charges: not furnished.

Special surgical units: ambulatory surgery (laparoscopy, radial keratotomy), surgical step-down unit.

Base cost for an ER visit: $180.

Additional emergency services: Advanced Life Support Program.

Ob/gyn programs: Women's Health Center, childbirth and sibling education, prenatal testing, pre-conception workshops.

Specialized treatment programs: Sports Medicine, Cardiac Rehab, incontinence, Community Cancer Center (member Jefferson Cancer Network), 20-bed skilled nursing facility, psych/detox unit.

Physical rehab services: physical, occupational, speech therapy; inpatient orthopedic and medical rehab units, Orthopedic Brace and Appliance Center, Industrial Medicine, Work Hardening.

Outpatient health and wellness programs: CPR, first aid, choking safety, smoking cessation, cancer and blood pressure screenings, drug and alcohol prevention for schools, childhood asthma workshop, senior membership, medication screenings by pharmacists, support groups, AIDS prevention, speakers bureau, nutrition education, child immunization clinic.

Hahnemann University Hospital

BROAD AND VINE STS., 762-7000. DOCTORS ON ACTIVE STAFF: 415 (*87% board-certified*); NUMBER OF BEDS: 636; 1.2 RNs PER BED; SEMIPRIVATE ROOM COST: $950; PRIVATE ROOM COST: $990; SUITE COST: $990; ACCREDITATION: JCAHO.

Sample charges for surgical services: coronary bypass without cardiac cath, $28,750; back and neck procedures without complication, $16,100 (back), $20,930 (neck); vaginal delivery, $5,865; prostate removal, $27,600; local anesthesia, $52.90 for each 15-minute period; operating-room cost, $2,156.25 per hour; preadmission testing, $287.50.

Special surgical units: Heart Failure/Cardiac Transplant Center, Dedicated Kidney and Pancreas Transplant Care Unit, Surgical Trauma ICU.

Base cost for ER visit: $65.55.

Additional emergency room services: Level I Regional Resource Trauma Center, University MedEvac helicopter, cardiac resuscitation area, self-contained radiology section, 24-hour triage, minor treatment area.

Ob/gyn programs: Women's Care Center, Reproductive Endocrinology and Infertility Clinic, sports gynecology and Women's Lifestyle Center, birthing rooms.

Specialized treatment programs: renal dialysis, Dental Center, Cardiovascular and Coronary Care ICU, Child/Adolescent Psychiatric Inpatient Unit, Psychiatric Medical Care Unit, Bone Marrow Transplant Unit, Adult Psychiatry Unit, Monty Hall-Variety Club Children's Pavilion.

Physical rehab services: interdisciplinary approach to physical, occupational and speech therapy, Cardiac Rehab Center, Prosthetics Clinic, ALS Clinic.

Outpatient health and wellness programs: vision screening, Executive Health and Wellness Center, CPR.

Affiliated with Allegheny Health Education and Research Foundation.

Holy Redeemer Hospital and Medical Center

🛏 🛁 🎞 📱 ⚕ ⊗ E

1648 HUNTINGDON PIKE, MEADOWBROOK, 947-3000. DOCTORS ON ACTIVE STAFF: 330 (*81.4% board-certified*); 283 BEDS; 1 RN PER BED. ROOM COST: $1,065; GOURMET FOOD SERVICE: $15. ACCREDITATION: JCAHO, ACR.

Sample charges for surgical services: back and neck procedures without complication, $12,492; vaginal delivery, $4,100; prostate removal, $7,783; standard local anesthesia, $47 per half hour; hourly operating-room charge, $1,534.

Special surgical units: infertility (reproductive-endocrinology), corneal transplants, total joint replacements, reconstructive knee surgery, full endoscopic urology service.

Base cost for ER visit: $116.

Ob/gyn programs: maternal/fetal medicine, oncology, perinatology, prenatal education, reproductive endocrinology (infertility), lactation consultation, antenatal testing.

Specialized treatment programs: renal dialysis, cardiac cath lab, neonatology, neonatal follow-up clinic, telemetry, labor, delivery and recovery, sports medicine, ambulatory surgery and care, regional pediatric center, critical care, wellness center.

Physical rehab services: physical therapy, occupational therapy, speech pathology, pediatric development clinic and rehab, EMG/NCU, psychological services, sports medicine, aquatic therapy.

Outpatient programs: Diabetes Educator, Speakers Bureau, Nutrition Counseling, *FreshStart* Smoke Cessation, Fitness & Exercise, Education Series for Expectant Families, health screenings, enterostomal therapy, *Kids Health Connection*, pastoral counseling.

Jeanes Hospital

7600 CENTRAL AVE., 728-2000, 728-2033 (*Women's Healthline*), 728-2100 (*Senior's Healthline*). DOCTORS ON ACTIVE STAFF: 170 (*82% board-certified*); NUMBER OF BEDS: 220; .99 RNs PER BED; SEMIPRIVATE ROOM COST: $780; PRIVATE ROOM COST: $824; ACCREDITATION: JCAHO, PDH, CAP.

Sample charges for surgical services: back and neck procedures without complication, $9,054; vaginal delivery, $2,556; prostate removal, $7,870; standard local anesthesia, $38.25; hourly operating-room charge, $1,091; preadmission testing, $147.50.

Special surgical units: orthopedics, cancer care.

Base cost for ER visit: $50.25.

Additional ER services: Level II general emergency department.

Ob/gyn programs: LDR rooms, whirlpools during labor, Level II NICU, perinatology, videophone to show infant to long-distance loved ones, childbirth education, *UNITE*, women's health, sibling, infant care, and breast feeding class, maternity exercise, physical therapy for expectant and new mothers.

Specialized programs: adult day health care center, diagnostic imaging center, home health.

Physical rehab services: occupational, physical and speech therapy, audiology, cardiac and pulmonary rehab.

Outpatient health and wellness programs: blood pressure screenings, support groups, smoking cessation, speakers bureau, diabetes, Parkinson's Exercise Group, nutritional counseling, *Lifestrides* for adults over 50, arthritis aquatics.

Kennedy Memorial Hospitals

THREE DIVISIONS: CHERRY HILL DIVISION, CHAPEL AVE. AND COOPER LANDING RD., CHERRY HILL, NEW JERSEY, 609-488-6500; NUMBER OF BEDS: 225; STRATFORD DIVISION, 18 EAST LAUREL RD., STRATFORD, NEW JERSEY, 609-346-6000; NUMBER OF BEDS: 236; WASHINGTON TOWNSHIP DIVISION, HURTVILLE-CROSS KEYS RD., TURNERSVILLE, NEW JERSEY, 609-582-2500; NUMBER OF BEDS: 146. KENNEDY OPERATES ONE MEDICAL AND NURSING STAFF FOR ALL THREE DIVISIONS. DOCTORS ON ACTIVE STAFF: 409 (*70% board-certified*); 1.06 RNs PER BED; ROOM COSTS NOT FURNISHED. ACCREDITATION: NJDH, AOA, AND ACR (FOR MAMMOGRAPHY).

Surgical charges: not furnished.

Special surgical units: same-day surgery, laser surgery, (carbon dioxide, Yag, ophthalmologic Yag and argon, pulse dye laser), lithotripter.

Base cost for ER visit: $42.

Additional emergency room services: specialized trauma response teams, crisis intervention in affiliation with Steininger Center (at CHERRY HILL DIVISION).

Ob/gyn programs: perinatology, neonatology, family-centered childbirth, pelvoscopy, laser surgery, dads-on-call beepers, childbirth education classes, genetic counseling, sibling classes, breast-feeding classes, Motherwell maternity exercise and fitness program, Healthy Start, Women's Resource Center, infertility treatment.

Specialized treatment programs: in- and outpatient dialysis, child and adolescent psychiatric unit, adult psychiatric unit, detox, alcohol and drug rehab (inpatient and outpatient), cardiac, respiratory and surgical ICUs.

Physical rehab services: comprehensive physical therapy, sports medicine.

Outpatient health and wellness: CPR training, community education programs, *ElderMed* senior membership program, baby-sitter certification classes, Family Health Centers, home health services, osteoporosis diagnosis and treatment, CLASP (Child Life and Safety Program).

The Lankenau Hospital

100 LANCASTER AVE., WYNNEWOOD, 645-2000. DOCTORS ON ACTIVE STAFF: 302 (*89% board-certified*); NUMBER OF BEDS: 475; 1.35 RNs PER BED; ROOM COSTS NOT FURNISHED. ACCREDITATION: JCAHO, AABB, ACR, CAP, SDA.

Surgical charges: not furnished.

Special surgical units: ambulatory surgery, orthopedic, cardiothoracic surgery, intensive care.

Base cost for ER visit: not furnished.

Ob/gyn programs: reproductive endocrinology, perinatology, midwifery, Antepartum unit, Level III Intensive Care Nursery, osteoporosis management, gynecologic oncology, incontinence treatment, family planning clinic, Norplant implantation.

Specialized treatment programs: Breast Diagnostic Center, Sleep Disorders Center, Cancer Treatment Center, Kidney Transplant program, inpatient psychiatric unit.

Physical rehab services: physical and occupational therapy, speech therapy/pathology, hand therapy, sports medicine rehab.

Outpatient health and wellness programs: free health lectures and screenings, Health Education Center (for children), travelers' advisory service, childbirth education classes, dietary/nutrition counseling, fitness, exercise, diet, smoking cessation classes, various support groups.

The Lower Bucks Hospital

501 BATH RD., BRISTOL, 785-9200. DOCTORS ON ACTIVE STAFF: 260 (*80% board-certified*); NUMBER OF BEDS: 320; 1.1 RNs PER BED; SEMIPRIVATE ROOM COST: $665; PRIVATE ROOM COST: $700; ACCREDITATION: JCAHO, AABB, CAP, ACR.

Sample charges for surgical services: back and neck procedures without complication, $2,577; vaginal delivery, $1,608; prostate removal, $1,590; standard local anesthesia, $76 per unit; hourly operating-room charge, $1,027.

Special surgical units: Regional Eye Center, endoscopy, orthopedic.
Base cost for ER visit: $158.
Additional ER services: advanced pediatric life support, Chest Pain Center.
Ob/gyn programs: Level II NICU, University Women's Center for Endocrinology, Infertility and Antenatal Testing, labor whirlpool, private postpartum wing, childbirth, sibling and VBAC classes, Motherwell Fitness.
Specialized treatment programs: cardiac cath, 30-bed adult Mental Health Unit, sports medicine, pain management, member of the Jefferson Cancer Network.
Physical rehab services: speech, occupational, physical and hand therapy, Sports-Orthopedic Center, Athleticare (recently opened an office at Newtown Racquet & Fitness Club in Newtown, Bucks County, complete with an Aqua Ark for water therapy).
Outpatient health and wellness programs: stress, nutrition, cardiac rehab, senior health, smoking cessation, childbirth classes, CPR, first aid, health screenings, women's services. The Wellness Center offers nutritional programs, cholesterol screenings, speakers and conferences on health-related issues (752-4300).

Medical College Hospitals, Bucks County Campus
🛏 🦺 🏥 ⚖ ⚗ 🚫 ✈ E

225 NEWTOWN RD., WARMINSTER, 441-6600. DOCTORS ON ACTIVE STAFF: 168; NUMBER OF BEDS: 188; ROOM COST: $730; GOURMET FOOD SERVICE: $15 PER MEAL; ACCREDITATION: JCAHO, CAP, PDH, ACR.

Sample charges for surgical services: standard local anesthesia, $896; hourly operating-room charge, $1,105; preadmission testing, $158.50.
Base cost for ER visit: $93.40.
Specialized treatment programs: detox, drug and alcohol, psychiatry (adult and adolescent), dialysis, geriatric assessment and medical programs, incontinence.
Physical rehab services: Achievement Center for cardiac rehab, physical therapy and adult fitness, inpatient rehab unit, speech pathology, audiology, occupational therapy.
Outpatient programs: SurgiCenter (ambulatory surgical procedures), Breast Center and breast cancer education, Diagnostic Imaging Center, *Advantage Passport* (senior membership program), aqua aerobics, aquatic exercise and water walking programs, CPR, first aid, childbirth education classes, diabetes education, Slim-a-Weigh with exercise, Slim Kids, and Slim Teens programs.

Medical College Hospitals, Elkins Park Campus
🦺 ⚖ ⚗ 🚫 E ✉

60 E. TOWNSHIP LINE RD., ELKINS PARK, 663-6000, 1-800-776-4325 (*physician referral*). DOCTORS ON ACTIVE STAFF: 278 (*70% board-certified*); NUMBER OF BEDS: 266; SEMIPRIVATE

ROOM COST: $676; PRIVATE ROOM COST: $682; ACCREDITATION: JCAHO, PDH, CAP.

Sample charges for surgical services: vaginal delivery, $4,000; standard local anesthesia, $60; hourly operating-room charge, $672; preadmission testing, $150.

Special surgical units: general surgery, laparoscopic surgical procedures, pain management, ophthalmological procedures, plastic surgery, gynecological and infertility.

Base cost for ER visit: $32.

Ob/gyn programs: high-risk prenatal care, antenatal testing, level III neonatal care nursery.

Physical rehab services: physical, occupational and speech therapy (in- and out-patient through the Achievement Center).

Outpatient programs: *Advantage Passport* (free membership for individuals 55 and older), Motherwell, Pre-Natal Education, Nutritional Education, Blood Pressure Screenings, a variety of support groups, Community Heart Saver Course and annual health screening programs.

Medical College Hospitals, Main Clinical Campus

🖋 🏥 ⚓ ⚖ 🚫 🪑 **E**

3300 HENRY AVE., 842-6000. DOCTORS ON ACTIVE STAFF: 567 (*90% board-certified*); NUMBER OF BEDS: 465; .95 RNs PER BED; ACCREDITATION: JCAHO, CAP, AABB, ACGME, ACR. ALL MEDICAL COLLEGE HOSPITALS BELONG TO THE ALLEGHENY HEALTH, EDUCATION AND RESEARCH FOUNDATION.

Surgical charges: not furnished.

Special surgery units: critical care, coronary care, medical/surgical ICU, neuro-surgery step-down unit.

Additional ER services: Level I Trauma Center, pediatric and psychiatric emergencies, toxicology.

Ob/gyn programs: Classes for childbirth, breast feeding, siblings, and grandparents, genetic counseling, high-risk pregnancy, infertility, Level III NICU, Center for Women's Health, Mother-Baby Couplet Care, pre-natal testing, gynecologic oncology, bone densitometry, incontinence care.

Specialized treatment programs: adult cystic fibrosis, cardiac cath, cardiovascular services, *Caring Together*, Dental Implant Center, dialysis unit, geriatric assessment, outpatient substance abuse, headaches, Hypertension Center, Lipid Disorders Center, Lyme Disease Center, Mid-Atlantic Regional Epilepsy Center, Sleep Disorders Center, Sports Medicine Center, Travel Health Center.

Physical rehab services: cardiovascular, pulmonary, sports medicine, occupational, physical and speech therapy.

Outpatient health and wellness programs: *Advantage Passport* (a program of free benefits for people 55 and older), *Business Medicine* (occupational/employee health), Center for Continuing Health (fitness for people over 50), diabetes education, smoking cessation.

Memorial Hospital of Burlington County

175 Madison Ave., Mount Holly, New Jersey, 609-267-0700. Doctors on active staff: 220 (*more than 90% board-certified*); number of beds: 402; Room costs not furnished; accreditation: JCAHO, ACR, ACS.

Sample charges for surgical services: vaginal delivery, $1,322; prostate removal, $2,695; standard local anesthesia, $101.25; hourly operating-room charge, $1,119.
Base cost for ER visit: $100.
Additional ER services: Chest Pain Clinic, *Fast Track* (quick service for minor problems).
Ob/gyn programs: a full range of neonatal, perinatal and parenting services through Women's Health Network (609-261-7482).
Specialized treatment programs: dialysis, psychiatry, pediatrics, Speech and Hearing Center, same-day surgery center, geriatric assessment, incontinence program.
Physical rehab services: physical and occupational therapy (inpatient and outpatient).
Outpatient health and wellness programs: Senior Health-Link (a wellness program for those over 55; 265-7900).

Mercy Haverford Hospital

2000 Old West Chester Pike, Havertown, 645-3600. Doctors on active staff: 180 (*99% board-certified*); number of beds: 107; Room costs not furnished; accreditation: AABB, JCAHO, PDH, CAP.

Surgical charges: not furnished.
Base cost for ER visit: $62.
Specialized treatment programs: Substance Abuse Center (inpatient detox), Retina and Diabetic Eye Institute.
Physical rehab services: general medical/surgical, orthopedic physical therapy, speech and occupational therapy, clinical lab, diagnostic radiology, respiratory therapy, cardiac and pulmonary rehab programs.
Outpatient health and wellness programs: Mercy Care Van, educational wellness, diabetic education.

Methodist Hospital

2301 South Broad St., 952-9000, B-R-O-A-D S-T (*physician referral*). Doctors on active staff: 254 (*85% board-certified*); number of beds: 289; 1.3 RNs per bed; Room cost not furnished; accreditation: JCAHO, PDH, DVHC.

Special surgical units: Rapid Recovery Surgical Center, Short Procedure Unit, cardiac cath lab, G.I. Procedure Unit. ER services: Chest Pain Emergency Center, *Fast Track.*

Ob/gyn programs: Family Birth Center, neonatal ICU, antenatal testing services, laparoscopic gyn surgery.

Physical rehab services: physical and occupational therapy, speech pathology, cardiac rehab (affiliated with Magee Rehabilitation Hospital) .

Outpatient health/wellness programs: smoking cessation, weight loss, nutrition counseling, free patient transport van, free screenings and wellness lectures.

Misericordia Hospital

5301 CEDAR AVE., 748-9000, 741-2882 (*physician referral*). DOCTORS ON ACTIVE STAFF: 341 (*78% board-certified*); NUMBER OF BEDS: 276; ROOM COSTS NOT FURNISHED; ACCREDITATION: AABB, CAP, JCAHO, PDH, PDW.

Surgical charges: not furnished.

Special surgical units: surgical ICU, surgical short procedure unit.

Base cost for ER visit: $72.

Additional ER services: hyperbaric oxygen therapy, trauma, toxicology.

Ob/gyn programs: Women's Services, midwifery, parent education.

Specialized treatment programs: detox, acute dialysis, psychiatric crisis, vascular lab.

Outpatient health and wellness programs: weight loss, cancer, blood pressure, cholesterol, lung and glaucoma screenings, CPR, mobile health van, Older Adult Club (nutrition support), cardiovascular risk reduction, breast cancer/low-cost mammography, smoking cessation.

Montgomery Hospital

1301 POWELL ST., NORRISTOWN, 270-2000. DOCTORS ON ACTIVE STAFF: 265; NUMBER OF BEDS: 269; .75 RNS PER BED; SEMIPRIVATE ROOM COST: $615; PRIVATE ROOM COST: $715; ACCREDITATION: JCAHO, ACS, CAP.

Surgical charges: not furnished.

Special surgical units: cardiac catheterization.

Base cost for ER visit: $67.25.

Additional ER services: hospital-based ambulance and paramedics, cardiac, trauma room.

Specialized treatment programs: in- and outpatient psychiatry, dialysis, pediatrics, Cancer Center, obstetrics, Women's Imaging Center, Eye Laser Center. Physical rehab services: cardiac, pulmonary, Back School, physical, occupational and speech therapy.

Outpatient health and wellness programs: cancer screenings, weight loss, stress management, nutrition, cholesterol evaluation.

Nazareth Hospital

2601 HOLME AVE., 335-6000. DOCTORS ON ACTIVE STAFF: 250 (*83% board-certified*): NUMBER OF BEDS: 357; SEMIPRIVATE ROOM COST: $650; PRIVATE ROOM COST: $685; GOURMET FOOD SERVICE: $10 (*avg.*); ACCREDITATION: JCAHO, PDH, CAP, AABB, AMA.

Sample charges for surgical services: back and neck procedures without complication, $7,940; vaginal delivery, $3,283; prostate removal, $5,743; standard local anesthesia, $246.68 per procedure; hourly operating-room charge, $897.
Special surgical units: short procedure unit.
Base cost for ER visit: sliding scale.
Ob/gyn programs: Women's Health Center, NICU, rooming-in, childbirth classes, perinatal testing.
Specialized treatment programs: mental health, perinatal testing, heart testing, Mustard Seed detox, high-risk pregnancy clinic, cardiac cath, psychiatric unit.
Physical rehab services: New 19-bed inpatient unit focusing on the needs of stroke and orthopedic patients, Occupational Health Center, physical, respiratory and speech therapy.
Outpatient programs: nutritional counseling, cardiac rehab.

North Penn Hospital

100 MEDICAL CAMPUS, LANSDALE, 368-2100, 361-4848 (*physician referral and health information*). DOCTORS ON ACTIVE STAFF: 200 (*90% board-certified*); NUMBER OF BEDS: 150. ROOM COSTS NOT FURNISHED.

Surgical charges: not furnished.
Special surgical units: short procedure unit.
Base rate for ER visit: not furnished.
Emergency services available: special trauma treatment rooms, on-site helipad.
Ob/gyn programs: Family BirthCenter, neonatal services, perinatology services, prenatal education.
Specialized treatment programs: North Penn Cancer Program (with Fox Chase Cancer Center), occupational health services.
Physical rehab services: physical therapy/sports medicine, occupational/speech therapy, respiratory care/pulmonary rehabilitation, Risk Profile Management (PRM) Program (cardiac fitness).
Outpatient health and wellness programs: community health education, parent and child skill building, screenings for cancer, blood pressure, cholesterol, height and weight, first aid, CPR (including pediatric and renewal), smoking cessa-

tion, mastectomy fitting, basic life support, *Healthy Heart, Seniority counts*, diabetes education, variety of support groups.

North Philadelphia Health System

DOCTORS ON ACTIVE STAFF: 150 (*50% board-certified*); 1 RN PER 5.5 BEDS; SEMIPRIVATE ROOM COST: $700; PRIVATE ROOM COST: $800; ACCREDITATION: JCAHO, AOA.

The 409-bed health system provides psychiatric services and care for the chemically dependent at Girard Medical Center, and medical, surgical and emergency care at St. Joseph's.

Sample charges for surgical services: prostate removal, $12,465; standard local anesthesia, $595; hourly operating-room charge, $600.

Girard Medical Center

GIRARD AVE. AT 8TH ST., 787-2000, 787-CARE (*clinic, physician and general information*).

Specialized treatment programs: acupuncture, HIV clinic, wound care, dual diagnosis psychiatry.
Physical rehab services: physical, occupational and speech therapy (also at St. Joseph's).
Outpatient health and wellness: primary care, immunizations, travel care, nutrition, well baby care, drug and alcohol rehab.

St. Joseph's Hospital

16TH ST. AND GIRARD AVE., 787-9000, 787-CARE (*clinic, physician and general information*).

Special surgical units: short procedure unit.
Base cost for ER services: $140.
Additional emergency services: *Fast Track* (1-9 p.m.).
Outpatient health and wellness: primary care, immunizations.

Northeastern Hospital of Philadelphia

2301 EAST ALLEGHENY AVE., 291-3000, 291-3390 (*physician referral*). DOCTORS ON ACTIVE STAFF: 275; NUMBER OF BEDS: 231; 1.25 RNS PER BED; ROOM COSTS NOT FURNISHED; ACCREDITATION: ACR, AABB, JCAHO.

Surgical charges: not furnished.
Special surgical units: short stay surgical program.
ER charges: not furnished.

Additional emergency services: *Prompt Care* (for minor problems between 5 p.m. and midnight weekdays), Heart Care, Chest Pain Center.

Ob/gyn: Women's Health Care Center offers family planning, comprehensive gynecologic services and care for patients with special financial needs.

Specialized treatment programs: Industrial Healthcare Center.

Outpatient health and wellness programs: extensive community education course selection.

Our Lady of Lourdes Medical Center

1600 HADDON AVE., CAMDEN, NEW JERSEY, 609-757-3500. DOCTORS ON ACTIVE STAFF: 312 (*81% board-certified*); NUMBER OF BEDS: 375; 1.4 RNs PER BED; SEMIPRIVATE ROOM COST: $690; PRIVATE ROOM COST: $840; ACCREDITATION: JCAHO, CARF.

Sample charges for surgical services: coronary bypass without cardiac cath, $28,397; vaginal delivery, $3,298; standard local anesthesia, $52; hourly operating-room charge, $500 (minor surgery), $750 (major surgery).

Special surgical units: kidney transplantation program, open-heart surgery.

Base cost for ER visit: $164.

Additional ER services: psychiatric emergency service.

Ob/gyn programs: Level III Regional Perinatal Center, NICU, maternal and neonatal transport services, Osborn Family Health Center, newborn nursery and transitional nursery, LDR rooms.

Specialized treatment programs: pediatric, mental health, in- and outpatient dialysis units.

Physical rehab services: physical, occupational, speech and recreational therapy, electromyography, hand rehab, prosthetic-orthotic evaluation, videofluoroscopic swallowing studies.

Outpatient health and wellness programs: prenatal classes; infant, child and adult CPR, asthma workshops, massage, weight loss program, stress reduction courses, Christian yoga, meditation, foot reflexology, dance instruction, nutritional counseling.

Paoli Memorial Hospital

255 WEST LANCASTER AVE., PAOLI, 648-1000. DOCTORS ON ACTIVE STAFF: 180 (*90% board-certified*); NUMBER OF BEDS: 208; 1 RN PER 5 BEDS; ROOM COSTS NOT FURNISHED; ACCREDITATION: JCAHO, CAP, PDH.

Surgical charges: not furnished.

Special surgical units: Short Procedure Unit.

ER charges: not furnished.

Additional ER services: Advance Life Support Program (hospital-based paramedics who respond to emergencies), Lifeline services.

Ob/gyn programs: perinatal testing center, genetic counseling, infertility specialists, LDRP (labor, delivery, recovery, post-partum).

Specialized treatment programs: Breast Cancer Evaluation, Center for Addictive Diseases, inpatient psychiatry, occupational medicine, The Cancer Center (with Fox Chase), STOP (intensive outpatient treatment for alcohol/drug abuse), Wound Healing Clinic.

Physical rehab services: cardiac rehab, physical, occupational and speech therapy.

Outpatient health and wellness programs: arthritis, cancer, and diabetes education, blood pressure, cancer, and cholesterol screenings, cardiology series, health fairs, childbirth classes, Travelers Health, variety of support groups.

Pennsylvania Hospital

800 SPRUCE ST., 829-3000, 829-6800 (*physician referral*), 829-KIDS (*pregnancy health line*). DOCTORS ON ACTIVE STAFF: 330 (*88% board-certified*); NUMBER OF BEDS: 495; SEMIPRIVATE ROOM COST: $1,125; PRIVATE ROOM COST: $1,285; SUITES AVAILABLE; ACCREDITATION: JCAHO.

Surgical charges: not furnished.

Special surgical units: Cardiac Surgery Suite, Vascular Surgery Suite, prostate cryosurgery, 14-room suite for surgery such as colo-rectal, gynecologic oncology, neurosurgery, obstetrics and gynecology, ophthalmology, oral, orthopedics, otolaryngology, plastic/reconstructive, urology.

Base rate for ER visit: based on severity of injury: five levels of service ranging from $80 to $380.

Ob/gyn programs: area's largest obstetrics service, delivering 4,000 babies annually; antenatal testing unit, Birthing Suite (nurse-midwifery), childbirth education classes, genetic counseling, high-risk obstetrics, infertility treatment, perinatal cardiology, postpartum disorders project, Joan A. Karnell Women's Cancer Center.

Specialized treatment programs: Special Care Unit, intensive care nursery, CCU, neurointensive unit, ICU, Sleep Disorders Laboratory, Neurosciences Center, Franklin Dialysis Center, Hall-Mercer Community Mental Health/Mental Retardation Center, Counseling Program (outpatient services for mental health and chemical dependency problems of contracted companies). Its psychiatric facility is the Institute of Pennsylvania Hospital, 111 North 49th Street. The Rothman Institute, one of the country's busiest orthopedic centers, has performed more than 10,000 joint replacements.

Physical rehab services: physical therapy and rehab, occupational therapy, Back School (back care and injury prevention), cardiac rehab, Skilled Care Center (addresses needs of patients during transitional period between stay in acute care hospital and return to daily living at home).

Outpatient health and wellness programs: *Tel-Med*, diabetes education, Travel Medical Service, Society Hill Diet (food and nutrition services), nutrition counseling, free monthly seminars, Speakers Bureau, Child and Parent Center, childbirth education classes, *Health Ways* (a free program to address the needs of people 55 and older), Adult Day Health Center, the first hospital-based adult day care in Philadelphia, provides medically supervised care along with comprehensive rehab and recreational services for older adults.

Phoenixville Hospital

140 NUTT RD., PHOENIXVILLE, 983-1000. DOCTORS ON ACTIVE STAFF: 123 (*93% board-certified*); NUMBER OF BEDS: 143; 1.83 RNs PER BED; SEMIPRIVATE ROOM COST: $565; PRIVATE ROOM COST: $675; ACCREDITATION: JCAHO.

Sample charges for surgical services: back and neck procedures without complication, $7,849; vaginal delivery, $445 (two day stay); prostate removal, $5,907; hourly operating-room charge, $700.
Base cost for ER visit: $102.
Additional ER services: ALS-Medic 95 (physicians and staff certified in emergency care).
Ob/gyn programs: expectant parent course, early pregnancy, preconception care.
Specialized treatment programs: dialysis, pediatrics, oncology, Cancer Center, Maternity Pavilion.
Physical rehab services: physical therapy, cardiac rehab.
Outpatient health and wellness programs: community health education classes, Nutritional Resource Center, healthy birthing/healthy baby.

Pottstown Memorial Medical Center

1600 EAST HIGH ST., POTTSTOWN. DOCTORS ON ACTIVE STAFF: 100 (*100% board-certified*); NUMBER OF BEDS: 295; 1 RN PER 5 BEDS; ROOM COSTS NOT FURNISHED; ACCREDITATION: JCAHO, ACR, CAP.

Surgical charges: not furnished.
Special surgical units: lithotripsy, endoscopy, interventional radiology suite, preadmission surgical testing program.
ER charges: not furnished.
Ob/gyn programs: Maternity and Women's Health Center, women's health care seminars, Baby and Toddler Health Fair, single-room maternity health care.
Specialized treatment programs: Renal Care Center, Center for Behavioral Medicine (psychiatry), ICU/CCU, Cardiac Health Center, chest pain and stroke.
Physical rehab services: Occupational Health Program-Work Recovery, ERGOS Work Simulator.
Outpatient health and wellness programs: senior aerobics, TRIM classes (weight control), *Fresh Start* (smoking cessation), *How to Read Food Labels*, CPR

first aid, Lamaze and grandparenting classes, blood pressure and cholesterol screenings, stress management classes.

Presbyterian Medical Center

39TH AND MARKET STS., 662-1939. DOCTORS ON ACTIVE STAFF: 335 (*84% board-certified*); NUMBER OF BEDS: 344; 1 RN PER 2 BEDS; ROOM COST: $825; SUITE: $870 TO $910; ACCREDITATION: JCAHO, CAP.

Sample charges for surgical services: coronary bypass without cardiac cath, $44,034; back and neck procedures without complication, $14,767; prostate removal, $10,911; standard local anesthesia, $550 for the first hour; hourly operating-room charge, $1,344.

Special surgical units: cardiothoracic, vascular.

Base cost for ER visit: $75.

Specialized treatment programs: In Cardiology: The Philadelphia Heart Institute provides heart failure treatment and research, cardiac risk reduction center, heart disease reversal program, laser heart surgery, cardiac rehab (inpatient and outpatient). In Psychiatry: inpatient psychiatric unit, addictions treatment, cognitive therapy, residential treatment for chronic mental illnesses, geropsychiatric hospital program. Other programs: in-hospital and free-standing skilled nursing homes, vascular diagnosis and treatment center, cancer treatment and clinical research, arthritis program for mature adults, institute for gastroenterology.

Outpatient programs: cardiac evaluation and fitness, weight management, nutrition classes and consultation, stress management, healthy heart forum seminars, cholesterol screenings, vascular screening and management, community outreach programs on breast and prostate cancer prevention.

Quakertown Community Hospital

1021 PARK AVE., QUAKERTOWN, 538-4500. DOCTORS ON ACTIVE STAFF: 175 (*95% board-certified*); NUMBER OF BEDS: 89; SEMIPRIVATE ROOM COST: $750; PRIVATE ROOM COST: $770; ACCREDITATION: JCAHO, CAP.

Surgical charges: No set fees; done based on time in the O.R.

Ob/gyn programs: *Healthy Beginnings*, Women's Center, Prenatal program.

Specialized treatment programs: psychiatry (including behavior disorders program for traumatic brain injury victims), drug and alcohol rehab (adolescents and young adults), dialysis, skilled nursing facility, sub-acute care.

Physical rehab services: outpatient facility including pool therapy.

Outpatient health and wellness programs: smoking cessation, diabetes education, cancer program, mammography and prostate screenings, monthly blood pressure and cholesterol screenings, community support groups.

Rancocas Hospital

218-A SUNSET RD., WILLINGBORO, NJ, 609-835-2900, 800-654-GRAD (*physician referral*).
DOCTORS ON ACTIVE STAFF: 269 (*88% board-certified*); NUMBER OF BEDS: 318; 1.4 RNs PER
BED; SEMIPRIVATE ROOM COST: $775; PRIVATE ROOM COST: $850; ACCREDITATION: JCAHO,
ACR, AABB, CAP, LICENSED BY NJDH. PART OF THE GRADUATE HEALTH SYSTEM.

Surgical charges: not furnished.
Special surgical units: general operating suites, eye surgery center, same day
surgery.
Base cost for ER visit: $55.25.
Ob/gyn programs: Women's Center, mammography and ultrasound testing,
complete childbirth services, neonatology, antenatal testing, genetic counseling, six
LDRs (labor and delivery suites).
Specialized treatment programs: Sleep Laboratory, comprehensive cancer pro-
gram, mental health, Eye Surgery Center.
Physical rehab services: speech, physical, occupational therapy.
Outpatient health and wellness programs: *55 Plus* for older adults when they're
well and when they're sick, State-certified diabetes education, continuous lectures
and screenings throughout the year.

Riddle Memorial Hospital

1068 WEST BALTIMORE PIKE, MEDIA, 566-9400. DOCTORS ON ACTIVE STAFF: 267 (*70.2%
board-certified*); NUMBER OF BEDS: 251; 1.02 RNs PER BED; SEMIPRIVATE ROOM COST: $795; PRI-
VATE ROOM COST: $880; ACCREDITATION: JCAHO, PDH.

Surgical charges: not furnished.
ER charges: not furnished.
Additional ER services: a team of specially trained physicians, nurses, para-
medics and EMTs and *Fast Track*, a program to treat minor ER patients without
losing quality.
Ob/gyn programs: Birthplace (labor, delivery, recovery, postpartum in one
room), Level II NICU, Women's Imaging Center.
Specialized treatment programs: orthopedics, Skilled Nursing Facility on cam-
pus.
Physical rehab services: Back Rehab, Work Hardening Center, Riddle Hand
Rehab Center, inpatient rehab services.
Outpatient health and wellness programs: support groups, nutrition and
weight management, specialty screenings, cancer screenings, health seminars.

Roxborough Memorial Hospital

🛏 🧹 🏥 📋 ⚖ 🚫 ✈ E

5800 Ridge Ave., 483-9900. Doctors on active staff: 144 (*76% board-certified*); number of beds: 186; ratio of RNs to beds varies from 1:1 for intensive care to 1:10 for medical/surgery; semiprivate room cost: $682; private room cost: $737; guest meal service: $6; accreditation: JCAHO, CAP, PDH, AABB, DPW.

Sample charges for surgical services: back and neck procedures without complication, $4,484; vaginal delivery, $3,608; prostate removal, $6,270; standard local anesthesia, $408; hourly operating-room charge, $857; preadmission testing, $406 (average).

Base cost for ER visit: $58. Air Medevac to Hahnemann available.

Ob/gyn services: family planning, fertility procedures, prenatal and sibling classes.

Specialized treatment programs: Breast Prostheses, enterostomal therapy, skilled nursing facility.

Physical rehab services: occupational medicine provided by the Industrial Health Network, Work Hardening.

Outpatient programs: cardiac rehab, diabetes education, screenings for breast, colo-rectal and prostate cancer, community health education, CPR, smoking cessation classes.

Sacred Heart Hospital and Rehabilitation Center

🧹 🏥 📋 🚫 ✈ E

1430 DeKalb St., Norristown, 278-8200. Doctors on active staff: 259; number of beds: 234; 1.7 RNs per bed; Room costs not furnished; accreditation: JCAHO, CARF, CAP, AABB, PDH.

Surgical charges: not furnished.

ER charges: not furnished.

Ob/gyn programs: expectant parent classes, Lamaze instruction, OB Clinic.

Specialized treatment programs: pediatrics, rehab center, diabetes unit, orthopedics unit, oncology, pulmonary progressive care, cardiac progressive care.

Physical rehab services: physical and occupational therapy, speech/language pathology, psychological counseling, social services, pastoral care, pediatric rehab.

Outpatient health and wellness programs: cardiac rehab.

Southern Chester County Medical Center

🛏 🧹 🏥 ⚖ 🚫 E

1015 W. Baltimore Pike, West Grove, 869-1000, 869-1008 (*MEDI-MATE personal emergency response system*). Doctors on active staff: 64 (*80% board-certified*); number of beds: 77; .35 RNs per bed; semiprivate room cost: $585; private room cost: $665; accreditation: JCAHO, PDH, CAP, AABB.

Surgical charges: back and neck procedures without complication, $11,993; prostate removal, $10,269; hourly operating-room charge, $522; average preadmission testing, $178.

Base cost for an ER visit: $87.

Additional emergency services: Mobile Medic 94 Advanced Life Support Unit.

Ob/gyn programs: physicians available

Specialized treatment programs: cardiac rehab, nutrition counseling, sleep disorders center, Addiction Recovery Center.

Physical rehab services: physical and occupational therapy, speech pathology.

Outpatient health and wellness programs: *Culinary Hearts*, CPR, first aid, basic aid training, babysitting, choking safety, diabetes education, occupational health.

St. Agnes Medical Center

1900 SOUTH BROAD ST., 339-4100. DOCTORS ON ACTIVE STAFF: 217 (*66% board-certified*); NUMBER OF BEDS: 259; 1 RN PER BED; ROOM COSTS NOT FURNISHED; ACCREDITATION: JCAHO, AOA, CAP.

Surgical charges: not furnished.

Specialized treatment programs: Burn Treatment Center, comprehensive inpatient rehab, cardiac telemetry unit, renal dialysis center, adult daycare center, cardiac care, ICU.

Special outpatient services: *Work Care, IndustriCare*, home care, rehab, Parish Nurse Program, physical capacity evaluations, pulmonary diagnostics, speech and hearing, cardiac rehab, electrodiagnostic lab, Women's Health Center

Outpatient health and wellness programs: medically supervised/monitored exercise, adult fitness, aerobics, muscular conditioning, weight management, yoga, stress reduction, nutritional counseling, smoke cessation, free van service.

St. Christopher's Hospital for Children

ERIE AVE. AT FRONT ST., 427-5000. DOCTORS ON ACTIVE STAFF: 305 (*80% board-certified*); NUMBER OF BEDS: 183; 2 RNs PER BED; SEMIPRIVATE ROOM COST: $880; PRIVATE ROOM COST: $1,008; SUITE COST: $2,088; ACCREDITATION: JCAHO, ACGME, CAP. A MEMBER OF THE ALLEGHENY HEALTH, EDUCATION AND RESEARCH FOUNDATION.

Surgical charges: not furnished.

Special surgical units: kidney, liver, heart and heart/lung transplantation, cardiothoracic, burns, dental/oral, craniofacial and reconstructive surgery, short procedure.

Base cost for ER visit: $75.

Additional ER services: isolation rooms for patients with infectious diseases, trauma resuscitation room, radiology suite, decontamination room, dedicated suture and orthopedic casting room, trauma capabilities, helipad.

Specialized treatment programs: Burn Center, Pediatric Heart Institute, Marian Anderson Sickle Cell Center, Cystic Fibrosis Center, epilepsy center, Dialysis and Kidney Transplant Center, NICU, family-centered AIDS program, Apnea Center, allergy and rheumatology, child psychiatry, diagnosis and treatment of behavior and attention deficit disorders, cleft lip/cleft palate, spina bifida, PKU, cerebral palsy, leukemia, hematology, genetic diseases, diabetes, Center for Genetic and Acquired Deafness, Diagnostic Referral Service.

Physical rehab services: physical, occupational and speech therapy, audiology, scoliosis and spinal surgery, sports medicine.

St. Mary Hospital

LANGHORNE-NEWTOWN ROAD, LANGHORNE, 750-2000, 750-5888 (*physician referral*). DOCTORS ON ACTIVE STAFF: 284 (*84% board-certified*); NUMBER OF BEDS: 287; 2 RNS PER BED; ROOM COSTS NOT FURNISHED; ACCREDITATION: JCAHO, ACR, CARF, CAP, ACS, PTSF, AABB.

Surgical charges: not furnished.

Special surgical units: cosmetic/plastic, laser, orthopedic, oral-maxillofacial; Eye Institute (cornea transplant); Cardiac Cath Lab; Ambulatory Surgery Unit.

ER charges: not furnished.

Special services: Regional Level II Trauma Center, ER services (urgent care/minor ER care); Regional Dialysis Center; Saint Mary Regional Cancer Center; Outpatient Diagnostic Center; X-Ray services (CAT scan, Ultrasound).

Ob/gyn programs: LDR/birthing suites, Level II NICU (six-bed), midwifery, expectant parent classes (sibling classes), car-seat loaner program, Mother Bachman Maternity Center (for disadvantaged women), Saint Mary Children's Health Center (care to area children in need from birth to 18 regardless of family ability to pay). Physical rehab services: Inpatient and outpatient facility for occupational, physical, recreational, respiratory and speech therapy, clinical psychology, social services, pediatric rehab, Work Hardening, Back School.

Outpatient health and wellness programs: Wellness Workshop, *Industricare* (work-site health promotion), CPR, monthly senior seminar, cardiac and pulmonary rehab, home health services.

Suburban General Hospital

2701 DEKALB PIKE, NORRISTOWN, 278-2000, 270-8370 (*physician referral*), 279-9256 (*ElderMed*). DOCTORS ON ACTIVE STAFF: 214 (*75% board-certified*); NUMBER OF BEDS: 118; 1.15 RNS PER BED; SEMI-PRIVATE ROOM COST: $600; PRIVATE ROOM COST: $635; ACCREDITATION: AOA, CARF, AABB, ACR.

Surgical charges: not furnished.

Ob/gyn programs: modern maternity suite with special birthing rooms.

Specialized treatment programs: pain management, cardiac rehab, Family Practice Clinic, Norristown Regional Cancer Center support groups.

Physical rehab services: The Rehab Station.

Outpatient health and wellness: *ElderMed*, blood pressure, prostate and arthritis screenings, health fairs, support groups.

Taylor Hospital

175 E. Chester Pike, Ridley Park, 595-6000. Doctors on active staff: 180 (*64% board-certified*); number of beds: 213; .86 registered nurses per bed; private room cost: $825; accreditation: JCAHO, CAP.

Surgical charges: not furnished.

Specialized treatment programs: oncology unit, cardiac cath, ambulatory care center, sports medicine.

Physical rehab services: physical, occupational and recreational therapy, TCU (skilled nursing unit), speech pathology and audiology.

Outpatient health and wellness programs: The Women's Source/The Breast Care Center, Hospice, Home Health Agency, Private Duty Nursing.

Temple University Hospital

Broad and Ontario sts., 707-2000, 800-TEMPLE-MD (*physician referral*). Doctors on active staff: 294 (*100% board-certified*); number of beds: 514; 1 RN per bed; semiprivate room cost: $1,120; private room cost: $1,170; gourmet food service: $23 per dinner; accreditation: JCAHO, CAP, PDH, PTCF, HCFA.

Sample charges for surgical services: coronary bypass without cardiac cath, $31,000; back and neck procedures without complication, $10,500; vaginal delivery, $4,100; prostate removal, $7,000; standard local anesthesia, $301; hourly operating-room charge, $1,770; preadmission testing, $584.

Special surgical units: heart, lung, bone marrow, kidney transplants, stereotactic radiosurgery, neurosurgical ICU, oncologic cryosurgery.

Base cost for ER visit: $165. Temple is a Level I Trauma Center and has a Psychiatric Emergency Center.

Ob/gyn programs: maternal-fetal medicine, gynecologic oncology, reproductive endocrinology, nurse midwifery, Center for Women's Health, fetal testing, genetic counseling, perinatal cardiology, diabetes in pregnancy.

Specialized treatment programs: Center for sports medicine, multiple sclerosis, epilepsy, dialysis and oral surgery, Cancer Center, Comprehensive Breast Center, Ventilator Rehab Center. Temple also has a physical medicine and rehab unit.

Outpatient programs: the Nutrition Center, weight loss, stress management, pulmonary rehab.

Thomas Jefferson University Hospital

🛏 ⚗ 🏢 🚫 ☂ E

111 SOUTH 11TH ST., 955-6000, 800-JEFF-NOW (*hotline*). DOCTORS ON ACTIVE STAFF: 678; NUMBER OF BEDS: 717; ROOM COSTS NOT FURNISHED; ACCREDITATION: JCAHO.

Surgical charges: not furnished.

Special surgical units: cardiothoracic, colo-rectal, Jefferson Surgical Center, short procedure unit, kidney and liver transplantation, hand surgery and urology suite.

ER services: Level I Regional Resource Trauma Center, Spinal Cord Injury Center, Neuroimplant Program, access through helicopter and JeffSTAT ambulance retrieval teams, on-site trauma operating room, X-ray room, three trauma bays, patient testing lab, separate acute and intermediate care areas.

ER charges: not furnished.

Ob/gyn programs: in-vitro fertilization, gynecologic oncology, abnormal pap smears and cervical disease, high-risk pregnancy, reproductive endocrinology/fertility, ultrasound, *Teenagers in Touch*.

Physical rehab services: Regional Spinal Cord Injury Center, physical, occupational and speech therapy, Jefferson Comprehensive Rehabilitation Center, Work Fitness Program.

Outpatient health and wellness programs: Alzheimer's disease, Amputee Program, Antenatal Evaluation Center, arts medicine, asthma, Back Center, biofeedback, Bodine Center for Cancer Treatment, Cardeza Foundation (hemophilia and sickle-cell centers), Children's Center for Cerebral Palsy and Neuromuscular Disorders, *Weigh to Go, Smokestoppers*, aerobics, cancer test, *Dining With Heart*, free screening programs, seizure disorders, Comprehensive Rectal Cancer Center, corporate health, dementia evaluation, dietetics, drug and alcohol, dialysis, extracorporeal membrane oxygenation (for newborns), Enuresis Program, Familial Polyposis Registry, cardiac cath, stress testing, echocardiography, foot and ankle surgery, geriatric assessment, hand rehab, infant apnea, Jefferson Center for International Dermatology, medical genetics, Monell-Jefferson Taste and Smell, Multiple Sclerosis Comprehensive Clinical Center, NeuroMuscular Disease Clinic, Occupational and Environmental Medicine Clinic, Pain Center, perinatal addiction services, pigmented lesion, pregnancy loss, psychiatric clinic, psychosomatic treatment, Rape Center, scleroderma, sexual function, sleep disorders, sperm bank, SIDS, Tay-Sachs prevention, urodynamic testing.

Underwood Memorial Hospital

🛏 ⚗ ⚖ 🚫 ☂ E

509 N. BROAD ST., WOODBURY, NJ, (609) 845-0100, (609) 384-8884 (*physician referral*). DOCTORS ON ACTIVE STAFF: 200 (*75% board-certified*); NUMBER OF BEDS: 339; 1 RN TO 4 BEDS; SEMIPRIVATE ROOM COST: $505; PRIVATE ROOM COST: $561; SUITE COST: $617; ACCREDITATION: JCAHO, CAP.

Sample charges for surgical services: coronary bypass without cardiac cath, $17,101; back and neck procedures without complication, $4,4448; vaginal delivery, $1,321; prostate removal, $2,463; hourly operating-room charge, $336.50 (per half hour).

Special surgical units: cryosurgery for prostate cancer.

Base cost for an ER visit: $41.

Ob/gyn programs: Ob clinic, prenatal education, infant CPR classes, prenatal refresher course, fetal loss support group, grandparents, breast feeding and sibling classes.

Physical rehab services: inpatient and outpatient physical medicine, occupational and speech therapy.

The University of Pennsylvania Medical Center

🛏️ 🍴🏥 🍷 ⚖️ 🚫 📞 E

3400 SPRUCE ST., 662-4000, 662-PENN (*Penn Physician Referral*), 800-777-8176 (*Penn Cancer Care*). DOCTORS ON ACTIVE STAFF: 850 (*97% board-certified*); 725 BEDS; 1.18 RNs PER BED; DOUBLE-BED ROOM COST: $850; SINGLE-BED ROOM COST: $960; ACCREDITATION: JCAHO, AABB. ACR, CAP, PDH.

Surgical charges: not furnished.

Special surgical units: Center for Minimally Invasive Surgery (specializing in laparoscopic, endoscopic and thoroscopic techniques); multi-organ transplant center.

ER charges: not furnished.

Additional ER services: Level I Trauma Center, Head Trauma Center, Radiation Emergency Center, Work Injury Evaluation Center.

Ob/gyn programs: infertility and in-vitro fertilization (one of six programs nationwide designated by NIH for research and state-of-the-art treatment); high-risk pregnancy; reproductive genetics; reproductive surgery including laparoscopic procedures; Premenstrual Syndrome Program; Penn Center for Women's Health, a gynecologic clinic specializing in menopause, located in King of Prussia.

Specialized treatment programs: HUP has over 200 specialty programs, clinics and laboratories. Among them are: University of Pennsylvania Cancer Center, one of 28 nationwide designated by the National Cancer Institute, and including 200 cancer specialists; Joint Reconstruction Center; Sports Medicine Center; shoulder service; bone tumor service; Bone and Tissue Bank; Interventional Neuro-Center; neurogenetics; Addictions Research/Treatment Center; Center for Cognitive Therapy; Center for Human Appearance; affective disorders program (manic depression), facial pain/headache/TMJ program; Mood and Memory Disorders Clinic; Cutaneous Ulcer Center; hypertension and clinical pharmacology program; male sexual dysfunction program; male fertility program.

Physical rehab services: Amputee Clinic, Back and Spine Center, stroke rehab, physical, hand and occupational therapy, trauma and transplant rehab, TMJ physical therapy.

Outpatient programs: Penn Physician Referral provides information about medical services and physicians; Penn Cancer Care-nurses and referral counselors on hand weekdays from 8:30 to 5:30; Ralston Penn Center-comprehensive outpatient health evaluation for adults.

West Jersey Health System

CORPORATE OFFICES: 1000 ATLANTIC AVE, CAMDEN, NJ, 609-342-4488. HOSPITALS LOCATED IN CAMDEN (609-342-4000), BERLIN (609-768-6000), VOORHEES (609-772-5000) AND MARLTON (609-596-3500). TOTAL DOCTORS ON ACTIVE STAFF: 889 (*over 85% board-certified*); TOTAL NUMBER OF BEDS: 763; ROOM COSTS NOT FURNISHED. ACCREDITATION: JCAHO, CAP, AABB, AHA, ABP.

Surgical charges: not furnished.
ER costs: not furnished.
Emergency services: regional services including on-ground teams and South Star helicopter rescue team.
Ob/gyn programs: Women and Children's Center (5,000 babies born every year, highest among all southern New Jersey hospitals), NICU.
Specialized treatment programs: Children's Sleep and Breathing Center, after hours Children's Urgent Care, Diabetes Center, Alcove drug and alcohol treatment center, Good Life Center for older adults, Cancer Center, Arthritis Center, hip replacement and orthopedic surgery, cardiac rehab and education, geriatric units.
Physical rehab services: comprehensive regional occupational health services.
Outpatient health and wellness: Tatum Brown Family Practice Center, Ambulatory Care Center, Women's Health lecture series, health education and prevention programs.

Wills Eye Hospital

900 WALNUT ST., 928-3000 (*ophthalmology*), 928-3021 (*geriatric psychiatry*), 928-3400 (*Joslin Center for Diabetes at Wills and Jefferson*). DOCTORS ON ACTIVE STAFF: 434 (*91% board-certified*); NUMBER OF BEDS: 115; .7 RNs PER BED (*ophthalmology and geriatric psychiatry*); SEMIPRIVATE ROOM COST: $750; PRIVATE ROOM COST: $855; ACCREDITATION: JCAHO, PDH, ACGME, AMA, CAP.

Sample charges for surgical services: standard local anesthesia, $173; hourly operating-room charge: $826.
Base cost for ER visit: $126.
Specialized ophthalmic treatment programs: services for contact lens, cornea, cataract and primary eye-care, glaucoma, neuro-ophthalmology, oculoplastics and cosmetic surgery unit, oncology, pediatric ophthalmology, retina, low vision; Foerdere Center for the Study of Eye Movement Disorders in Children, refractive surgery unit, Center for Sports Vision, social service, Ocular Trauma Center.

Non-ophthalmic treatment programs: The Wills Geriatric Psychiatry Program is a 30-bed inpatient unit dedicated exclusively to treating the psychiatric and neurological disorders of the elderly. Joslin Center for Diabetes at Wills and Jefferson is a comprehensive program of self-management, physician care, and education for persons with diabetes.

Outpatient health and wellness programs: free public eye screenings for tristate residents to detect various eye problems.

Zurbrugg Hospital

ONE HOSPITAL PLAZA, RIVERSIDE, NJ, 609-461-6700, 800-654-GRAD (*physician referral*). DOCTORS ON ACTIVE STAFF: 235 (*75% board-certified*); NUMBER OF BEDS: 154; 1.4 RNS PER BED; SEMIPRIVATE ROOM COST: $775; PRIVATE ROOM COST: $850; ACCREDITATION: JCAHO, ACR, AABB, CAP, LICENSED BY NJDH. PART OF GRADUATE HEALTH SYSTEM.

Surgical charges: not furnished.

Special surgical units: same day surgery, eye surgery, general surgery.

Base cost for ER visit: $55.25.

Gyn program: Mammography Center

Specialized treatment programs: Center for Arthritis, MICA Unit (Mentally Ill Chemical Abusers), adult medical daycare center, occupational health, Partial Hospitalization Psychiatric Program, comprehensive cancer program.

Physical rehab services: physical therapy, sports medicine, industrial rehab.

Outpatient health and wellness programs: *55 Plus* to help older adults when they're well and when they're sick, state-certified diabetes education, continuous lectures and screenings throughout the year.

Specialty Hospitals

Children's Seashore House

3405 CIVIC CENTER BLVD., 895-3600, 800-678-3773. DOCTORS ON ACTIVE STAFF: 13 (*100% board-certified*); NUMBER OF BEDS: 77; 1 RN PER BED; SEMIPRIVATE ROOM COST: $995; ACCREDITATION: JCAHO.

Surgical charges: not furnished.

Special treatment units: Respiratory Rehab Unit, Neurorehab Unit, Biobehavioral Unit, Developmental Disabilities Unit, Feeding Program, Musculoskeletal Rehab Unit.

Specialized programs: Attention Deficit/Hyperactivity Disorder, Behavioral Pediatrics Clinic, Cerebral Palsy Clinic, Child Development Center, Cochlear Implant Program (in affiliation with Children's Hospital of Philadelphia), Down

Syndrome, Feeding Clinic, Head Trauma Clinic, Pediatric Rheumatology Center. **Special services:** Communication disorders (audiology and speech/language pathology), child life therapy, nutrition, occupational therapy, physical therapy, prosthetics and orthotics, psychology, psychiatry, rehab nursing, social work.

Deborah Heart and Lung Center

200 TRENTON RD., BROWNS MILLS, NJ, 609-893-6611, 800-214-3452 (*physician referrals*). DOCTORS ON FULL-TIME STAFF: 64 (*more than 90% board-certified*); NUMBER OF BEDS: 161; NURSE TO PATIENT RATIO 1 TO 5 (*telemetry*), 1 TO 1 (*SICU*), 1 TO 1 OR 2 (*MICU*); ROOM COSTS NOT FURNISHED; ACCREDITATION: JCAHO, CAP, AABB, NJDH.

Surgical charges: not furnished.
Specialized programs: adult and pediatric cardiac medicine and adult pulmonary medicine. Phase III clinical trial site for cardiomyoplasty, outpatient cardiac cath, cardiac imaging, home-based pulmonary rehab, sleep apnea clinic, interventional catheterization program includes angioplasty, coronary artery stenting, atherectomy, valvuloplasty; video-assisted thoracoscopy and bronchoscopy.
Outpatient health and wellness programs: full range of cardiac and pulmonary diagnostic testing, cardiac cath and bronchoscopy.

Fox Chase Cancer Center

7701 BURHOLME AVE., 728-6900. DOCTORS ON ACTIVE STAFF: 66 (*94% board-certified*); NUMBER OF BEDS: 100; 2.9 RNs PER BED; SEMIPRIVATE ROOM COST: $795; PRIVATE ROOM COST: $900; SUITE COST: $1,495; ACCREDITATION: PDH, JCAHO, ACS, ACR, AHA, CAP, ACCME.

One of 27 institutions nationwide designated as a Comprehensive Cancer Center by the National Cancer Institute.

Surgical costs: not applicable. Hourly operating-room charge: $1,320.
Special surgical units: Intraoperative Radiation Therapy, Pain Management Endoscopy.
Ob/gyn programs: gynecologic oncology.
Physical rehab services: physical, occupational and speech therapy.
Outpatient health and wellness programs: multidisciplinary evaluation and treatment programs for breast, ovarian, colo-rectal and head and neck cancers, genetic screening and family risk assessment, smoking cessation, mobile mammography, home health, hospice, community education programs.

Pennsylvania College of Optometry

1200 WEST GODFREY AVE., 276-6210. OUTPATIENT ONLY. DOCTORS ON ACTIVE STAFF: 37; ROOM COSTS NOT APPLICABLE; ACCREDITATION: AOA.

Surgical charges: not applicable.

ER charges: not furnished. ER services include immediate eye care, 24-hour on-call ocular emergency service.

Specialized treatment programs: low vision, sports vision, corneal and specialty contact lens, neuro eye. Physical rehab services: low-vision rehab.

Scheie Eye Institute

DEPARTMENT OF OPHTHALMOLOGY/ UNIVERSITY OF PENNSYLVANIA SCHOOL OF MEDICINE AND PRESBYTERIAN MEDICAL CENTER, MYRIN CIRCLE, 51 NORTH 39TH ST., PHILADELPHIA, 662-8119. SHARES SERVICES WITH PRESBYTERIAN MEDICAL CENTER AND HOSPITAL OF THE UNIVERSITY OF PENNSYLVANIA. DOCTORS ON ACTIVE STAFF: 19 (*100% board-certified*); ROOM AND GOURMET FOOD COSTS: REFER TO PRESBYTERIAN MEDICAL CENTER AND HUP; ACCREDITATION: JCAHO.

Sample surgical charges: hourly operating-room charge, $1,820 for the first hour; preadmission testing: lab work, $270; chest X-ray, $132; EKG, $142.

Special surgical units: cornea transplants, trauma, retina/vitreous, cataract and lens implants, glaucoma, oculoplastics, strabismus, radial keratotomy.

Base cost for ER visit: $40-$85. ER services run through Presbyterian Medical Center and HUP.

Specialized treatment programs: primary and tertiary ophthalmological services, genetics, glaucoma, laser treatments for diabetic retinopathy and macular degeneration, oculoplastics, neuro-ophthalmology, pediatrics.

Outpatient health and wellness programs: contacts service; low-vision service provides social service and rehab referrals for low-vision and legally blind patients.

Burn Centers

Crozer-Chester Medical Center
St. Agnes Medical Center
St. Christopher's Hospital for Children

Skilled Nursing Facilities

A SNF is a transitional stop for physician-directed care and rehabilitation. It falls somewhere between a hospital and a nursing home. It's for patients who no longer need the high-tech, acute, expensive care of a hospital, but are not yet ready for the next step. The cost of one night at Pennsylvania Hospital's Skilled Care Center is

There are some things you can always count on in life. The sun coming up. The stars shining. And Holy Redeemer Health System providing the best possible care for you and your family.

We are known for excellent and compassionate care throughout our System. For the newborns we deliver at Holy Redeemer Hospital and Medical Center. For the clients we assist through our Holy Redeemer visiting nurse agencies. For the elderly who reside in our nursing home and life care facilities. All of the people in our community can rely on the full support of our technology, services, facilities and staff to be totally dedicated to their care. For more information about any of our services, call 215-938-3226.

HOLY
REDEEMER
HEALTH
SYSTEM INC.

*Ministry of the
Sisters of the Holy Redeemer*

Holy Redeemer Hospital and Medical Center • Holy Redeemer Managed Care • St. Joseph's Manor • Lafayette-Redeemer • Redeemer Village • Holy Redeemer and Nazareth Home Health Services • Holy Redeemer Visiting Nurse Agency of NJ • Redeemer-Nazareth Medical Supply Co. • Drueding Center-Project Rainbow

$505 as opposed to $1,125 for the same amount of time in a hospital room. The difference lies in the intensity of the services provided. Many hospitals have SNFs on their premises and simply transfer patients there until they are either recuperated sufficiently to return home or able to move into the longer-term care of a nursing home. SNFs provide services such as wound care, tube feedings, colostomy care, insulin injection and I.V. therapy. The following institutions have skilled nursing facilities:

Albert Einstein Medical Center
Doylestown Hospital
Episcopal Hospital
Fitzgerald Mercy Hospital
Germantown Hospital and Medical Center
Grand View Hospital
Holy Redeemer Hospital and Medical Center
Linwood Convalescent Center
Presbyterian Medical Center
Quakertown Community Hospital
Riddle Memorial Hospital
Roxborough Memorial Hospital
Taylor Hospital

Trauma Centers

Trauma Centers offer a more complete range of crisis services than ordinary emergency rooms. They are designated by the Pennsylvania Trauma Systems Foundation as either Level I or Level II. A Level I facility must be equipped to handle situations such as cardiac bypass, pediatric trauma, renal dialysis and re-attachment of limbs. It must also have a general surgical residency, education programs, as well as ongoing research. A Level II facility may have many of the same capabilities but it does not conduct research.

Level I Trauma: Albert Einstein Medical Center, The Children's Hospital of Philadelphia, Cooper Hospital/University Medical Center, Hahnemann University Hospital, Hospital of the University of Pennsylvania, Medical College Hospitals, Main Clinical Campus, Temple University Hospital, Thomas Jefferson University Hospital

Level II Trauma: Abington Memorial Hospital, Crozer-Chester Medical Center, Frankford Hospital, Torresdale Campus, Kennedy Memorial Hospital, St. Mary Hospital

CHAPTER 13

Home Sweet Home

Help that makes house calls

When you're sick in a hospital, help is as close as the nurse call button. But once you get home, there is a whole range of services you may need that are not always easy to find. This chapter is a sampling of resources for the homebound patient. In general, when people talk about *home health care* they're referring to skilled nursing care provided by licensed professionals such as registered nurses and various kinds of therapists. When people use the terms *home care, homemaker care* or *personal care*, they're describing those who help with dressing, feeding, bathing, housekeeping, meal preparation and errands—the kinds of services performed by nonprofessional but trained home health aides or homemakers. You'll find both of these kinds of services at a home care agency. On a full-time, part-time or live-in basis, they provide nurses, aides and companions not only for the elderly, but for anyone physically disabled, ill or injured who needs assistance with personal needs, treatments and therapies.

Home-Care Agencies

Bayada Nurses
546-5000

A private home-care agency founded in 1975, with 21 area offices serving Philadelphia, lower Montgomery and Delaware counties, parts of Bucks County and southern New Jersey. A staff of RNs, LPNs, aides, homemakers and live-in companions provide services 24 hours a day, at fixed hourly or daily rates.

Central Health Services
664-7711

Offers complete in-home care, including nurses, homemakers and companions; child care; I.V. therapy; rehabilitation; and elder care. Insurance accepted.

Community Health Affiliates
642-7696

A member of the Main Line Health System, which includes Bryn Mawr Hospital, Lankenau Hospital, Paoli Memorial Hospital and Bryn Mawr Rehabilitation. Provides visiting nurses, home support services and hospice care. Medicare, Medicaid and private insurance accepted.

Comprehensive Home Health Care
885-0360

Provides nurses and aides; social workers; and physical, speech and occupational therapists. Medicare, Medicaid and private insurance accepted.

Episcopal Community Services
351-1400

Provides free RN-supervised home-care services, including Meals on Wheels, to SSI recipients and lower-income individuals in Philadelphia. Some health-aide services are available on a sliding-fee scale for those ineligible for the free services.

Family Care Associates
431-3141

Provides full-service pediatric home health care, including neonatal health care, therapies for medically fragile children, photo therapy, support services, continuous care for babies and help with developmentally delayed children and adults. Both nurses and home health aides available. Serves Philadelphia, surrounding counties and South Jersey.

Fox Chase Cancer Center Home Health Services
728-3011

Provides nursing support; physical, speech and occupational therapy; medical social services, home health aides, laboratory services and intravenous therapies. They also offer palliative care: For patients in the terminal stages of disease, they provide nursing support, medical social services, pastoral counseling, home health aides, medical equipment and supplies. Accepts many insurance plans.

Help-U-Care
673-5965

For anyone requiring non-medical help with personal needs, including newborn/child care and the disabled. Homemakers, companions and home health aides work under the supervision of visiting nurses. Hourly or live-in fees.

Home Health Care for Jewish Family and Children's Services of Philadelphia
545-3290

Nursing and social-work services for the elderly and homebound.

BAYADA® NURSES
Home Care Specialists

BAYADA NURSES specialize solely in caring for people in their homes. The BAYADA NURSES staff of RNs, LPNs, Home Health Aides, and Live-ins have years of experience in Home Care.

BAYADA NURSES service is available in your own home 24 hours a day, 7 days a week.

Call BAYADA NURSES for help at home.

Philadelphia, PA	(215) 546-5000
Media, PA	(610) 891-9400
King of Prussia, PA	(610) 992-9200
Willow Grove, PA	(215) 657-7711
Cherry Hill, NJ	(609) 354-1000
Burlington, NJ	(609) 386-9300
Lawrenceville, NJ	(609) 695-9500
Atlantic City, NJ	(609) 926-4600
No. Brunswick, NJ	(908) 418-2273
Wilmington, DE	(302) 529-3000

BAYADA NURSES has 12 other offices located in NJ, PA, NC, FL and CO.

BAYADA NURSES HEADQUARTERS
290 Chester Avenue, Moorestown, NJ 08057
(609) 231-1000

© BAYADA NURSES 1994

Home Health Corporation of America
272-1717

Provides nurses, aides and companions; respiratory, I.V., physical, occupational and speech therapies; medical equipment; and pediatric services. Medicare, Medicaid and private insurance accepted.

Homemaker Service of the Metropolitan Area
592-0002

A United Way member agency providing RNs, LPNs and home health aides; physical, speech and respiratory therapists; and medical social workers. Medicare, Medicaid and private insurance accepted.

Homestaff of Delaware Valley
696-4191

Provides nurses and aides; physical, speech and occupational therapists; and medical social workers. Adult and pediatric services. Medicare, Medicaid, Blue Cross and private insurance accepted.

Hospital Homecare
923-0411

Affiliated with Chestnut Hill Hospital, Pennsylvania Hospital and Episcopal Hospital. Provides private nurses (in the hospital or at home); aides, therapists and nannies; and medical equipment. Insurance accepted.

Interim Health Care
664-6720

Provides nurses, aides, live-ins, therapists and homemakers. Medicare certified.

Jewish Family and Children's Service of New Jersey
609-662-8611

Provides trained aides and homemakers through the Carl Auerbach Friends of JFS on a short-term basis (up to 12 weeks).

JEVS (Jewish Employment and Vocational Service) Attendant Care Program
728-4411

Clients must be residents of Northeast Philadelphia or Bucks or Montgomery counties, between 18 and 59, disabled and need assistance with personal care. Services are free to those on medical assistance or Supplemental Security Income, and offered on a sliding scale to others.

Liberty Health System
1-800-676-1161
690-2500 OR 1-800-676-1161

JCAHO-accredited full-spectrum care including medical treatment, nurses and household aides. Medical equipment, respiratory and infusion therapy also offered by calling 1-800-345-8611. Insurance accepted. A special new mother/new baby program matches a new mother with a Liberty professional who assists the mom and teaches her to care for her baby. Also available for working parents, trained personnel to care for a child who's sick or when school unexpectedly closes (690-2532).

Neighborhood Home Health
755-6464

Provides RNs, aides, therapists and medical social workers for homebound patients who are referred by their physicians.

Nursefinders
667-2901 OR 638-2044

Provides home health care and private-duty hospital and nursing home staff. RNs, LPNs, aides and live-ins. Medicare, Medicaid and private insurance accepted.

Olsten Kimberly QualityCare
563-8100

Provides nurses and aides specializing in pediatrics, neonatal care and infusion therapy. Medicare and Medicaid certified.

Premier Medical Services/SRT Med Staff
676-9090

Provides RNs, LPNs and home health aides. Insurance accepted.

Protocall
664-8700

Provides nurses, aides and live-ins and speech, physical and I.V. therapists. Special asthma control and diabetes programs. May be covered by insurance.

Vintage Health Care Service
684-8024

Provides RNs; aides; and physical, occupational and speech therapists. Medicare and Medicaid certified.

The Visiting Nurses Association of Greater Philadelphia
473-7600

One of the oldest nonprofit home health-care agencies in the nation provides health professionals and homemaker services in Philadelphia and lower Bucks and eastern Montgomery counties. Medicare certified, and services for uninsured and underinsured patients.

Post-Hospitalization Home Care

Many hospitals provide short-term (two to eight weeks) home care services for patients covered by insurance—Medicare, Medicaid, Blue Cross and others. Services usually include nursing care; home health aides; hospice care; maternal/child health care; physical, speech and occupational therapists; medical social workers; and medical equipment. (See hospital listings, Chapter 12.)

Equipment/ Home Services

Beckett Apothecary
726-9964

Delivery and repair of home medical equipment. Basic Medicare and Medicaid.

Bright Medical Technology
533-8500 OR 1-800-345-4268

Free delivery and home setup of all equipment. Pharmacy. Medicare, Medicaid and most private insurance accepted.

Caremark Connection
985-4020

Specimen collections, chemotherapy administration, blood transfusions, inhalation therapy, mid-line insertions and counseling for homebound patients. Insurance accepted.

Total Care Home Health Systems
1-800-445-6090

Infusion and respiratory services. Medicare and Medicaid and some private insurance accepted.

Eye Care

Dr. E. David Pollock, O.D.
379-4990

Offers complete vision care at home, including glaucoma testing, vision examination, all optical services, lenses and frames, and low-vision aids. Medicare accepted.

Dental Care

Dentistry-To-You
784-9984

Comprehensive dental care for homebound patients or those in nursing homes. With portable equipment, Kenneth B. Siegel, D.M.D., can do everything from extractions to root canals to crowns.

Mobile Dental Services
732-7053

Dentures and repairs in private homes. Limited to Northeast Philadelphia, Montgomery County and Bristol. Reasonable fees; cash or checks only.

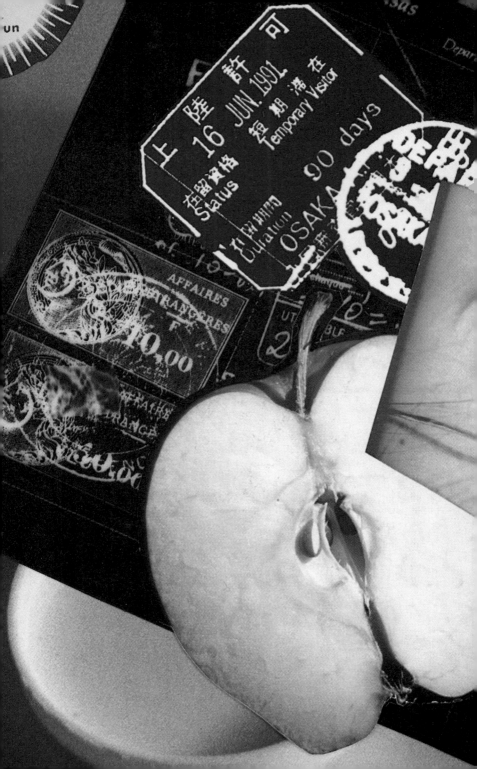

4

Prescriptions for Wellness

CHAPTER 14

Nothing to Sneeze At

A look at some new ways of treating allergies

Clearly, Shakespeare did not have allergies. If he were battling the sneezing and wheezing of a hay-fever attack, he would not have been inspired to pen a sonnet about the perfect days of June, a month that for roughly one in five heralds the miserable arrival of the allergy season. Doctors don't understand why some people experience only a runny nose while others suffer coughing and itching, but they do know you can't catch allergies. And you can't cure them, either, though you can outgrow them, and alter their natural course with allergy shots. Allergies are inherited, and activated by something in the environment. That means a child born in Los Angeles with an allergy to ragweed will never experience symptoms as long as he remains within the state border—because there's no ragweed in California. But let that child come East to visit relatives one August, and chances are he'll still be sneezing a week after the plane lands in Philadelphia.

There are many kinds of allergic disease, ranging from asthma to eczema, but the most common is allergic rhinitis, often characterized by an onslaught of sneezing that seems to raise by tenfold the normal two quarts of mucus produced by the body each day. Mistakenly called hay fever or rose fever, allergic rhinitis isn't aggravated by sniffing hay or roses. The chief offenders are far more ubiquitous, and if you're allergy-sensitive to those that are indoors—dust and animal dander—you'll probably suffer year-round. The outdoor inhalants—pollens and molds—usually cause warm-weather problems that can stretch from April to the first frost of October.

You can do a bit of self-diagnosis by matching your symptoms to the seasons. Trees pollinate in March and April, and there are about eight varieties on the Delaware Valley allergy menu. According to Paul Atkins, a University of Pennsylvania allergist and immunologist, one can be allergic to any number of trees. That's not true of grasses, which pollinate in May and June. It's likely that a problem with one grass leads to a problem with *all*. The weeds come on in July, with ragweed predominating in August and September. If your nose runs from spring until fall, you may be allergic to all of the above as well as mold spores, which start spreading when the weather gets warm and peak when plants begin to decay in the fall.

If you've noticed that you often feel worse as the allergy season progresses, it's because exposure increases effect—it takes a lot more grass pollen to make a grass-allergic person sneeze in January than it does in mid-summer. And to further complicate the problem, allergic people seem primed to react to more than one allergen. A sensitivity to dogs is likely to increase the chances of sensitivity to dust, and so on.

What causes allergies

Allergic disease is essentially caused by a malfunction of the immune system, the body's defense against unwanted foreign invaders. Ordinarily the immune system responds to the threats of viruses and bacteria by forming antibodies against them. But in allergic people, it also reacts to benign substances like house dust and pollen; the initial reaction triggers the production of specialized allergy chemicals known as IgE antibodies. Once they're stimulated, you may be stuck with this unnecessary strike force forever after.

It's akin to having a trained, armed guard lying in wait. The IgE antibodies cluster like millions of detonators around the mast cells lining the skin and the respiratory and digestive tracts. If you inhale the allergen, your nose and eyes react. If you ingest it, the result might be hives or a stomachache. What typically happens on that beautiful June day when you're working in the garden and the air's redolent with grass pollen is that every breath you take brings trouble. The pollen enters your airways and attaches to the mast cells already loaded with the allergy antibody marines. The troops explode into action, releasing a plethora of fire, including histamines and leukotrienes, which trigger other reactions—like swelling and inflammation—that combine to produce the sneezy, wheezy, itchy symptoms of an allergy attack.

Until the '60s, it was believed that histamines were the major culprit released by the allergy arsenal. That led to the development of antihistamine drugs geared toward neutralizing their effect. (ChlorTrimeton and Benadryl are two of the most popular.) For mild symptoms like a runny nose and itchy eyes, antihistamines work fairly well, but they encourage sleepiness. One alternative is a decongestant like Sudafed. Decongestants not only shrink swollen nasal tissues, but may act as a stimulant, which is why drug companies combine them with antihistamines to counteract drowsiness. (Some popular blends are Actifed, Dimetapp, Drixoral and Trinalin.) Unfortunately, decongestants have a variety of unwelcome side effects, including nervousness, palpitations, high blood pressure and even impotence.

Left with the alternatives of feeling jumpy or sleepy, many allergy sufferers turn to nasal sprays like Afrin and Neo-Synephrine II, effective for occasional discomfort but dangerously habit-forming. If used for several days in a row, these sprays create a rebound effect—that is, renewed congestion when the dose wears off. Soon the user is hooked on the spray every few hours to get relief from a problem caused by what was supposedly the solution.

The new nasal sprays

Fortunately, a dramatic increase in understanding the mechanism of an allergic reaction, coupled with better medications to treat the average summer sufferer, has brightened the picture. Doctors now know that an important component of an allergy attack is inflammation, which may occur hours after exposure to an antigen and persist for days.

The latest allergy medications for hay fever are sprayed rather than swallowed. The first, cromolyn sodium, was initially used for asthmatics and found to have a unique effect on allergy tissues by preventing mast cells from releasing histamine. Taken four times daily throughout allergy season, along with antihistamines on an as-needed basis, cromolyn appears to ward off problems before they occur. For casual hay-fever victims, it's been highly effective. Sold as Nasalcrom, the spray costs abut $15 for a 20-day supply. In the view of John Cohn, a Thomas Jefferson pulmonologist, "Its probably the safest drug I give out."

The second, corticosteroids, work best after exposure by reducing the inflammation that aggravates an attack. Any drug with the word *steroid* ought to arouse concern, but in this case there seems to be little to worry about if it is used as the doctor orders. Studies show that very little of the newer topical nasal steroids (trade names Vancanase, Beconase, Nasacort and Nasalide) are absorbed into the bloodstream. Finally, there are now prescription antihistamines available that *don't* usually cause drowsiness, because they don't penetrate the central nervous system. Among the most widely used nonsedating antihistamines are Seldane and Hisminal, but other potent drugs that won't make you sleepy are in the pipeline, so check with your doctor for availability.

Allergy shots

The new medications—in conjunction with the standard precautions for allergy victims (pull up the carpet where dust settles, keep windows closed, change air-conditioning and heating filters often or get an electrostatic air cleaner, and buy tropical fish instead of a dog or cat)—provide the primary defense in allergy treatment. Most responsible allergists will try them before recommending immunotherapy—those dreaded regular shots. Dr. Eliot Dunsky, clinical associate professor at Hahnemann University, reports that none of his patients get shots before first trying medication.

When a patient isn't adequately helped by medication or has significant side effects from the drugs taken to control allergic symptoms, shots can play an important role in treatment by attacking the cause of the allergy rather than the symptom. But if you don't see significant improvement after a year, you're probably wasting your time and money. If you do get relief, after five years you should take a break. With pollen and dust allergies, shots appear to be effective about 85 percent of the time when given in strong enough doses. Lately the success rate has improved as the serums have become more standardized and the concentrations of antigen increased. Still, there is no doubt that shots are often overused because they are a quick and easy income-producer for doctors.

The unwarranted popularity of allergy shots in recent years is also due partly to an overindulged screening tool, the RAST assay. Traditionally, allergists diagnosed allergies by pricking a patient's skin and injecting small amounts of the suspected allergen, then examining the reddened, swollen reaction. The RAST assay was supposed to do the same thing more accurately in the laboratory using a vial of the patient's blood. In fact, RAST is at least three times more expensive than skin testing and much *less* sensitive—mild allergies may not show up at all. Its great appeal is to general practitioners, who can mail off a blood sample to a lab and get back an allergy report with the serum and program plan, all in a neat little package. Dr. Fred Cogen, past president of the Pennsylvania Allergy Association, found in a survey of members that only 4 percent were using RAST routinely. "It seems," he says, "to be the favored test of non-board-certified allergists."

Finding an allergist

The question of who's a qualified allergist is a hot issue among doctors these days as RAST tests make it simple for any physician to treat allergic symptoms. Those who've done related fellowships and gained approval by the American Board of Allergy and Immunology are particularly resentful of the incursion of ear, nose and throat specialists, who've been accused of using allergy shots to fill the void left by the recent decrease in tonsillectomies. The otorlaryngologists argue that they have their own elite Academy of Allergists, founded back in 1941. In their opinion, *they* are trained to treat diseases of the nose and throat, and the allergists are invading their turf.

For Your Information

Many of the newest allergy medications mentioned above are available only by prescription, which means you must see a doctor first. For anything beyond an uncomplicated seasonal rhinitis, the National Institute of Allergy and Infectious Diseases recommends you visit a board-certified allergist, preferably one based in a university practice. Expect to spend as much as $150 for an evaluation (history and medical checkup), excluding skin testing, which is not mandatory and will be covered by most health insurance plans. You can get the name of a board-certified allergist from the American Board of Allergy and Immunology here in Philadelphia at 349-9466. For additional information, including fee printed material, call the Asthma and Allergy Foundation of America in Washington, D.C., 202-466-7643.

CHAPTER 15

Vacation Fever

Here's how to wage germ warfare overseas

The year was 1986. I remember it well because I wound up with the dubious distinction of having traveler's diarrhea on three continents. Like me, many Americans no longer confine their vacations to civilized spots like Paris and London. We've become far more adventurous in exploring the less-developed nations of the world, and as a result we're picking up the microbial souvenirs that aren't sold in tourist shops. Of the more than 10 million travelers who leave the country annually, at least 1 million are exposed to malaria and develop acute diarrhea from something they ate or drank. Diarrhea ruins more vacations than lost luggage, yet most travelers remain better informed about hotels and restaurants than they do about how to be healthy tourists.

The culprit responsible for most cases of diarrhea on the road is an unfamiliar strain of standard intestinal bacteria that comes from contaminated food or water. Beyond Australia, Canada, Northern Europe, New Zealand and some Caribbean Islands, the risks of diarrhea vary from moderate to severe and are best avoided by following the simple rules: Boil it, cook it, peel it or forget it. In short, don't eat any raw vegetables or raw fruit you can't peel or salads made from greens that may have been washed in water. For that matter, don't drink the water—and that includes ice cubes—and don't brush your teeth with it. Stick to carbonated drinks from the bottle unless glasses have been carefully dried—and carry straws with you since the rims of bottles are often contaminated. Take your coffee black (diary products are always iffy) and your alcohol neat.

I am one of those travelers who, despite being terribly careful, always get sick anyway, so I was delighted to discover that there are drugs—such as Cipro and Bactrum—useful for preventing and treating diarrhea. On separate trips to India, Thailand and Mexico, I dosed myself daily with one of them and never had a bad day. However, by killing some strains of bacteria, these drugs may make you vulnerable to others and, in some cases, they can have side effects, which is one reason they're not routinely recommended. But I think it's worth discussing with your doctor despite the wisdom of the moment, which is that this kind of antimicrobial drug should not be taken until the problem occurs.

Uncramping your style

If you choose not to ward off diarrhea with an antibiotic, there's always Pepto-Bismol. Some studies show two tablets taken four times daily to be 60 percent effective as a preventative. The pills should not be used by people with a sensitivity to aspirin, because they contain salicylate.

Common watery traveler's diarrhea usually lasts one to four days. It's a package deal: Cramps, nausea and malaise are all included. Once you're stricken, you can knock it out quickly with one of the above-mentioned antibiotics that should always be packed in your travel medical kit (along with Band-Aids, aspirin, sun screens, antibacterial ointments, antacids and mosquito repellent). The use of over-the-counter medicines like Immodium will relieve cramping and control the runs so you can sit on the tour bus, but they won't kill the bug that caused the problem, and they certainly won't prevent it.

It's extremely important to replace fluid and electrolytes lost with diarrhea. Dr. Michael Braffman, part of a team at Pennsylvania Hospital's infectious diseases department, recommends drinking alternately from a solution of eight ounces of fruit juice, half a teaspoon of honey and a pinch of salt and a solution of eight ounces of carbonated water and a quarter teaspoon of salt. These can be supplemented with tea, broth, salted crackers, rice and toast. If the diarrhea is marked by blood and/or accompanied by a high fever, get yourself to a doctor immediately.

Above the clouds

Another travel malady that attacks randomly and cannot be predicted is altitude sickness, which usually strikes people at heights above 8,000 feet. The awful weak, dizzy, nauseous sensations are due to a rapid change in air pressure, which swells the brain. The best treatment is to get to a lower altitude as soon as possible. A drug called Diamox, a type of diuretic, won't prevent altitude sickness, but it may be taken 24 to 48 hours in advance to hasten the process of acclimatization. "But," cautions Dr. William Shoff, "you should consider any illness at a high altitude is an altitude illness until proven otherwise." Shoff is director of Travel Medicine and Immunization Services at HUP, a clinic that has been operating for 20 years and sees about 1,500 travelers annually.

Jet set

The most unavoidable problem of long-distance travel seems to be jet lag. Nearly every function in our bodies is timed on a day-night cycle that, if it were regulated by external cues from the sun and moon, would make adjusting to different time zones quite simple. Unfortunately, our body rhythms respond to an internal clock, and there is no drug to reach in and reset the hands. However, there are some tips to minimize the discomfort while the body puts itself on local time.

Begin when you board the plane by drinking lots of water or fruit juice during the flight. The cabin air is exceedingly dry, and your system dehydrates by simply sitting there and breathing it. Because they are diuretics, try to avoid coffee and alcohol, and bring along high-fiber snacks to handle the constipation that accompanies dehydration. You may want to pass on the liquor cart entirely and consider taking a mild sleeping pill instead. Dr. Braffman sees nothing wrong with a low-dose sleeping pill if you know you can get six hours of uninterrupted sleep. You might want to pop another pill the night you arrive at your destination so you don't wake up at 3 a.m because your body thinks it's time for breakfast.

See a specialist

When it comes to travel-related medical questions it's wise to bypass your family doctor and consult one of the specialists in travel medicine listed at the end of this article. They can tailor standard travel health advisories to your individual background and needs. Schedule your appointment four to six weeks before departure and bring with you a detailed itinerary, because the length of your stay and the order of your stops will affect what medications you need and when they are given.

Dr. Donald Kaye, who helped organize the travel-health program at MCP, cautions tourists that it's not enough to be informed on what's safe to eat and what shots are on official lists. It's also important to check out the potential dangers related to pre-existing medical conditions. For example, a pregnant woman considering an exotic trip should call a travel medicine specialist before a travel agent. Dr. Kaye says, "I might tell a pregnant woman calling for information on immunizations for East Africa to stay home until the baby is born. There are all kinds of things people don't think about." He points out that Leningrad, which isn't typically considered a Third World city, happens to be a major source of giardia, a parasite that commonly causes severe stomach upsets. Another little-known travel warning concerns contaminated fresh-water lakes or streams in certain parts of Asia, Africa and South America where swimmers can easily pick up a parasitic worm. And because of the altitude, a stop in Mexico City or Cuzco, Peru could be a serious health hazard for people with heart or lung problems.

Needle marks

It's not a bad idea to ask your travel agent about overseas health insurance, since some policies do not cover sickness abroad, particularly emergency evacuation. However, I wouldn't rely on the advice of a travel agent when it comes to required inoculations. Which shots are a must and which are a maybe depends on what parts of a country you visit, what season you go and how long you stay. Until a decade or so ago anybody leaving the United States for developing countries had to carry proof of a smallpox vaccination in their passport. With the elimination of that disease, no shots are necessary. Most vaccines fall into the category of recommended rather than required, and the recommendations may vary depending on the source.

A good jumping-off point for guidelines is the Center for Disease Control, which maintains up-to-date info on disease outbreak. For example, while the yellow-fever vaccine is required by law for entry into certain countries, the virus happens to be active in many places that don't demand inoculation. You may not need a shot to get past immigration, but you may want it for your own protection. The same goes for cholera, which is being reported in parts of Africa, India, Southeast Asia and Central and South America. The vaccine is rather weak, only 50 percent effective against the old strain of cholera and not at all effective against the new one. However, some countries and some localities within countries still require it. "If you arrive in a country that requires cholera," says HUP's Dr. Shoff, "and for some reason you didn't get the shot, for safety reasons we suggest you refuse their offer and change your itinerary."

There are several other vaccinations that adventurous travelers should consider. Typhoid fever, while rare in Europe, is not uncommon in parts of Asia. Shots (or the newer oral vaccine) should be taken for any prolonged stay in the Third World, particularly if you'll be wandering off the beaten path. Rabies is a significant risk in some parts of the world, and shots are suggested for visits exceeding 30 days in the rural parts of certain countries like India. Not long ago six trekkers in Nepal contracted meningitis, which might have been avoided had they been informed of an outbreak in the Katmandu Valley. Fairly current data on the status of diseases is published by the CDC in a weekly bulletin called "Morbidity and Mortality Weekly Report." Pennsylvania Hospital's Dr. Braffman is one travel specialist who receives the publication—and reads it. As a result, he knew when an unusual number of polio cases had occurred in Israel and was able to advise his patients headed for the Holy Land to get a booster shot.

According to the CDC, polio boosters are part of what should be a standard immunization package for Third World travel. That package should include a tetanus booster (lasts ten years), gamma globulin as protection against Hepatitis A (lasts a few months) and an MMR II (measles, mumps, rubella) booster for people born after 1957. Even if you're not planning a trip, you should have this immunization. And if you're planning an extended trek in the wilds of anywhere, look into the Hepatitis B vaccine.

Killer mosquitoes

Unfortunately, there is no inoculation to protect travelers from malaria, a serious and common disease outside the United States. The standard program for malaria protection is either the drug choloraquine or mefloquine, which must be taken before, during and after exposure. Should you come down with a fever or flu-like symptoms within six months of your return home from a malaria-infested area, tell your doctor where you've been—the buggers can last in your system that long. Also, some strains of malaria have become resistant to the standard medications, so it is critical that you discuss prevention medication with a knowledgeable physician. In parts of Thailand, for example, doxycycline may be preferred.

In addition to drugs, common sense must prevail. Malaria-carrying mosquitoes are night creatures that prey from dusk to dawn. When the sun goes down, don't use perfume, spray your clothing and exposed skin with DEET repellent, wear long-sleeved, light-color garments and sleep under netting. It can be terribly romantic.

For Your Information

General information on required and recommended immunizations is available weekdays 8:30-4:30 from the Philadelphia Department of Public Health (875-5640) or the Center for Disease Control (404-639-2572). To order the industry bible "Health Information for International Travel," call the federal government printing office (202-783-3238); it costs $6.50 and can be charged to a credit card (order number 017-023-001-92-2). The International Association for Medical Assistance to Travelers (716-754-4883) provides the names of English-speaking physicians worldwide, but does not evaluate their performance.

There are specialized clinics or services for travelers at the following hospitals:

Bryn Mawr, 526-3400

Cooper Medical Center, 609-342-2439

Hahnemann, 762-8525

HUP, 662-2427

Lankenau, 896-0210

MCP, 842-6465

North Philadelphia Health System, 787-2164

Paoli Memorial, 648-1430

Pennsylvania, 925-8010

CHAPTER 16

A Carrot a Day

A look at over 50 bits of medical lore revealing that Mom knew best. Sometimes

I t is a well-known but little publicized fact that when women become mothers, they automatically get licenses to practice medicine. This is what transforms them into medical mavens who can henceforth, with great authority, advise their children on everything from rashes to anemia. Of course, their admonitions are not always scientifically sound. There's little evidence to support the old threat to pubescent boys that if they masturbate too much, they'll go blind. (Remember the old joke—"Can I do it till I need glasses?") But quite often the folk wisdom of mother's medicine is grounded in a combination of common sense and medical science. We checked out the most popular prescriptions from Dr. Mom to see which ones are worth following and which aren't. Here's what we found.

You'll catch a cold if you get wet or chilled.

Most of the bromides about what brings on or wards off colds are pure bunk. You won't come down with the sniffles by going outside with a wet head, by getting soaked in the rain or by having wet feet. Nor will bundling up in winter keep you from the sneezes.

And there's no reason not to wash your hair when you have a cold. While being damp and shivery makes you feel awful, it does not make you more susceptible to catching a cold. Colds are caused by some 200 different viruses, transmitted either through the air (by coughing and sneezing) or via contact with a person or thing coated with cold germs. The best way to avoid infection? Wash your hands often, and don't touch your eyes, nose or mouth after you've handled an object touched by someone with a cold.

Feed a cold, starve a fever.

Wrong. The average sick person needs to worry more about hydration than nutrition, says Presbyterian Hospital physician Dr. Steven A. Silber.

Drink lots of liquids when you have a cold. Right, says Dr. Silber. People don't store water, and drinking a lot keeps the metabolic processes working normally. It also thins the mucus in your chest, making it easier to cough up the gook that colds produce. However, there's no point in drinking to excess, because you cannot flush a cold out of your system.

A shot of whiskey before bedtime will knock out a cold.

A drink may knock you out for the night, but it won't make you better—although, says Dr. Silber, it's conceivable that bathing the throat in alcohol might kill some germs.

Chicken soup is good for colds.

In 1978, researchers at Mount Sinai Medical Center in Miami fed hot water, chicken soup and cold water to 15 people, then measured the rate at which their noses ran under the influence of each. The hot liquids temporarily increased the flow of mucus, which is one way of ridding the body of viruses. But when these same people sipped chicken soup or hot water through a straw (which meant they weren't absorbing any steamy vapors), only the chicken soup caused more dripping mucus. If you want to accept this as proof that chicken soup works, go right ahead. Be warned, however, that so-called Jewish penicillin is usually fatty, and not a good idea if the cold is accompanied by an upset stomach.

Inhaling steam from a pot of boiling water opens the sinuses.

This does do the trick for heavy congestion, but a hot cloth across the bridge of the nose works just as well and is less dangerous.

If you want to stay warm, keep your head covered.

Absolutely. "A large percentage of blood goes to the brain," explains Dr. Silber, "and wherever there is lots of blood flow, there is lots of potential for heat loss." When the temperature drops, the best way to preserve heat is to wear a scarf and hat.

Don't swim for at least half an hour after eating.

After you chow down, blood flow to your stomach and gut increases to aid digestion, thus reducing what's available for muscle activity. That's why the likelihood of cramping is higher after a meal, says Children's Hospital's Dr. Gail Slap. So eating a big lunch and swimming vigorously to the center of a lake 20 feet deep is courting trouble. What should determine the timing of a postprandial swim is the degree of exertion. Kids splashing around a pool or playing in shallow water have no reason to observe an after-lunch waiting period.

Put butter on a burn, Vaseline on a scrape.

Dr. Slap says neither of these is a good idea. Burns need to be treated pronto with ice-cold water (not ice cubes, which may stick to the wound), because you literally want to stop the skin from cooking. With scrapes, the operative word is cleanliness. Use soap and warm water and a sponge, if necessary, to gently wash away the grit and grime.

Ice is good for swelling; heat is good for pain.

Ah, the old cold-vs.-hot argument. Well, here's the gospel: Ice reduces swelling, especially when the injury is new. (It should never be applied for more than 30 minutes.) But heat is only good for relieving muscular pain, and shouldn't be applied right after an injury. While a heating pad on the stomach may ease the discomfort of a tummyache or backache, Dr. Slap suggests taking an aspirin instead.

An ice pack on the back of the neck stops a nosebleed.

"I do it with my kids," says Dr. Slap, "but I don't know why it works. Maybe it just cools them down and makes them calmer." The recommended approach is to pinch the nostrils together until the bleeding stops.

Hold your breath to stop hiccups.

True. A hiccup is a spasm of the diaphragm. By holding your breath, you put the diaphragm at rest and give the muscles a chance to return to normal.

Dieting shrinks the stomach.

Not so, says the Berkeley Wellness Letter. The only thing that may decrease with dieting is your appetite. By contrast, eating enormous amounts can force your stomach to expand to accommodate your gluttony—but it will later return to normal size.

Cracking your knuckles will lead to arthritis.

"It's not a good idea," says Pennsylvania Hospital rheumatologist Barry Schimmer, "but I'm not sure why." He thinks that repetitive stress on the joints causes trauma to the cartilage over time, which could lead to arthritic degeneration.

Copper bracelets cure arthritis.

"Now, that's something I know is not true," Schimmer says. "Arthritis is a disease that naturally ebbs and flows, and the only reason you'd feel better wearing a copper bracelet is because you happen to be in a period of remission at the same time." The one metal that successfully treats arthritis is gold, which when injected (not worn) reduces inflammation.

No pain, no gain.

No way. Abundant data show that moderate activity can yield all the protective health benefits—weight control, cardiovascular fitness, lowered cholesterol—of hard, hurtful exercise. So don't punish yourself. "Generally speaking, pain is a warning signal, a gunshot that indicates injury," says Dr. Nicholas DiNubile, special adviser to the President's Council on Physical Fitness and Sports. "It may mean you're doing the exercise wrong or not allowing yourself enough time for recovery. In either case, check it out."

Shoveling snow can cause a heart attack.

True. Bitterly cold weather causes the blood pressure to rise, and also constricts the arteries that feed blood to the heart. At the same time, the strenuous effort of shoveling (or any other intense exercise) forces the heart to work harder. The dangerous combination of decreased supply and increased demand can lead to a heart attack or sudden death. Dr. Bernard Segal of the Philadelphia Heart Institute says shoveling snow is verboten for patients with heart disease, and simply a bad idea for healthy people over 40.

Caffeine is bad for your heart.

Coffee jitters may make you feel uncomfortable, but the mild increase in your heart rate is rarely dangerous, says Dr. Frank Marchlinski, of the Philadelphia Heart Institute. Back in the early '80s, studies suggested a relationship between caffeine intake and heart attacks, but more recent research suggests no association with up to four cups of java a day—except in the small percentage of the population for whom coffee causes an abnormal heart rhythm. "In moderation," says Dr. Marchlinski, "we have no conclusive evidence that caffeine is harmful."

A daily shot of whiskey is good for your heart.

Alcohol increases HDL—the good cholesterol—and its relaxing effect reduces stress. According to Lisa Stewart, director of the Chestnut Hill Nutrition Center, this means that one belt a day does have a health benefit. However, new evidence suggests you're better off getting your dose of alcohol from red wine. A recent study from France found that Frenchmen who drink red wine have a lowered incidence of heart disease despite their rich diets.

Tension causes headaches.

Go ahead and blame your headache on your mother-in-law's visit or the pressure of your job, but the truth is, those kinds of things don't cause headaches; they only trigger them. "We used to think that tension-type headaches meant you had some kind of psychological problem," explains Dr. Stephen Silberstein of the Comprehensive Headache Center at Germantown Hospital. "Now we know that headaches are due to abnormalities in the way the nervous system processes pain, as well as to certain changes in the brain chemistry." Lots of things can set those changes off: not eating, not sleeping, too much booze, monosodium glutamate, menstruation and, of course, stress.

Milk is good for ulcers.

Just the opposite, says Lisa Stewart. Milk is full of protein, which stimulates gastric acid production—and acid irritates ulcers. Today it's understood that food has little to do with causing or treating ulcers.

Reading in poor light will ruin your vision.

My mother used this one when she caught me reading with a flashlight in bed; I didn't get my first pair of glasses until I was past 40. "Using your eyes doesn't hurt them, although eyestrain may give you a temporary headache," says MCP ophthalmologist Dr. Sylvia Beck.

Carrots are good for your eyes.

True, sort of. Carrots are a rich source of vitamin A, which is essential to vision because it is involved in a chemical reaction that allows you to see. The lack of it is a sad but treatable cause of blindness in Third World countries. But as long as you're getting as much vitamin A as the normal American diet provides, chomping on Bugs Bunny's favorite won't improve your eyesight.

Staring at the sun will blind you.

The sun's rays will burn your retina like a laser penetrating butter. That is why you must wear special glasses to look at the sun during an eclipse.

If you cross your eyes, you'll become cross-eyed.

Not as far as I know," says Dr. Beck. Crossed eyes are the result of a neurological malfunction of the mechanism that coordinates the movement of both eyes. You can't cause the problem yourself.

Brushing your hair 100 strokes a day will keep it shiny and healthy.

Shiny, yes; healthy, no, says dermatologist Dr. Alexander Ehrlich. Brushing will coat your hair with the natural sebum produced by your oil glands, resulting in a sheen but no health benefits. Don't be too zealous, or you'll irritate your scalp.

Wearing a hat will make you go bald.

Perhaps because bald men often wear hats, people once thought there was a link between the two. There isn't. "The rubbing and friction of a hat may cause hair to break, but not to fall out," says Dr. Ehrlich. Baldness is hereditary, and not the result of anything you put on your head, despite what you may have been told about how the scalp needs to breathe. "The scalp doesn't breathe per se," Ehrlich explains. "It gets its oxygen through circulation of the blood, not from the air."

Cucumber slices relieve puffy eyes.

Anything cool, moist or astringent will temporarily take away swelling, but why waste a cucumber when a ball of cotton soaked in ice water will do just as well? If you tend to have puffy eyes in the morning, Dr. Ehrlich says, it may be because you're sleeping facedown, and gravity causes fluid to accumulate in the loose skin around the eyes. Try sleeping on your back, and the bags may vanish.

The lemon-juice myths—bleaching freckles, killing odors, etc.

Don't count on lemon juice to fade freckles. You're better off with an over-the-counter preparation containing hydroquinone, a chemical that interferes with the production of melanin—which is what causes the dark pigment. As for sucking on a lemon to whiten your teeth, it will actually destroy tooth enamel and make your teeth yellow.

However, rubbing lemon juice on your hands when you're trying to get rid of certain food smells does work, according to Dr. Charles Wysocki, of the Monell Center. (Remember Susan Sarandon in the movie *Atlantic City?*) That's because the acidity of lemon juice lowers the pH of your skin. Fish, for instance, contain smelly amines, which are immobilized by the action of acids provided by lemon juice (or tomato juice). Essentially, the acid prevents the amines from being released into the air. The same thing happens with garlic, whose sulfur-like compounds are also rendered less volatile by a mild acidic rub.

A warm bath laden with tea bags relieves a bad sunburn.

This myth comes from the old belief that tannic acid was good for all kinds of burns. Dermatologist Dr. Paul Gross says you're better off with a cool bath and two aspirin every four hours. Don't substitute acetaminophen, because aspirin's what has an effect on the chemical process that produces a sunburn.

Biting on a tea bag stops the bleeding from a pulled tooth.

True. Tannic acid and pressure help blood coagulate.

Gelatin pills harden soft nails.

Another waste of time. Once ingested, gelatin gets digested like any other food and delivered to the nails as part of a protein package. "Unless you're suffering from inadequate protein, it makes no difference," says Dr. Virginia Stallings, a nutritionist at Children's Hospital. "If you need it, you'd get more protein from a glass of milk."

Olive oil conditions and protects hair and nails.

Any source of grease, even mineral oil, will coat your hair and make the cells stick together, smoothing away split ends. Your hair will look nicer, but it won't be any healthier, says Dr. Gross. Soaking fingernails in water and then rubbing them in olive oil helps seal in moisture, but petroleum jelly works just as well and doesn't smell.

Plucking hair makes it grow in thinner and softer.

Dr. Gross thinks this falsehood may be connected to an old Indian belief that males who removed their facial hair by plucking rather than by using a razor eventually would no longer need to shave. Sometimes repeated plucking damages the nutrient source of the hair root, and you may lose a hair here or there, but nothing in quantity. And it's not true that shaving makes hair grow back faster. "When the hair grows back, it's stubby and looks thicker and coarser," says Dr. Gross. "But it really isn't."

Chocolate causes pimples.

The good news for candy lovers is that this simply ain't so. People with acne frequently have oily skin, and once upon a time it was mistakenly believed that certain foods, chocolate among them, have an effect on production of this oil. Acne occurs when oil secreted by the skin's sebaceous glands clogs the pores and interacts with bacteria trapped there. Hormone levels play a role in this process, but nothing you eat has any effect.

Cotton soaked in brandy relieves a toothache.

Periodontist Louis E. Rose says this isn't a bad idea for mild pain until you can get to the dentist. Alcohol acts as a topical anesthetic, dulling the pain sensation and numbing the inflamed tissue. That's why it's sometimes used on teething babies as well.

Baking soda is a good tooth powder.

Although baking soda can whiten teeth by removing stains, Dr. Rose says that unless the compound is diluted, it's too abrasive for daily use and will irritate the gums. There are toothpastes on the market that contain some baking soda, and they're okay.

A gargle of salt and peroxide tightens the gums.

Nope. Salt water can draw the pus out of an infected tooth, but it has no health value for normal gum tissue.

Eating parsley masks bad breath.

It may act as a breath mint to freshen your mouth, but that's about all. Bad breath comes from bacteria in plaque and decaying food, explains Dr. Rose. What you want to do is brush your teeth as soon as possible after eating, then floss to get rid of those little particles that cause plaque. Another trick is to swallow a chlorophyll tablet, which you can buy in a health food store, after you've eaten garlic or onion. It helps kill the smell that lingers the next day.

Garlic wards off disease.

Dr. Virginia Stallings quips that the medicinal value in garlic may be nothing more than the fact that its odor keeps people from kissing you; consequently, you're less likely to be exposed to germs. But current scientific investigation suggests otherwise. Garlic is an herb that helps break down food for absorption and also lowers blood pressure. It contains allicin, an antibacterial and antifungal agent. To avoid eating it raw, many people take deodorized garlic capsules daily like vitamin supplements.

An apple a day keeps the doctor away.

Actually, it takes five apples a day to do the trick, according to the latest dietary guidelines issued by the federal government. Five servings of fruits and/or vegetables are now considered essential to daily nutrition. While apples are high in fiber, a carrot a day, or perhaps broccoli, would be a better choice; both contain high levels of beta carotene, which is widely accepted as a cancer preventative.

Blackberry brandy helps relieve menstrual cramps.

Strange but possibly true. The brandy may make you forget you have cramps, but it's the blackberries that actually have medicinal value. They belong to the same family as the raspberry leaf, says Lisa Stewart; both contain a substance believed to relax the muscles of the uterus.

Cranberry juice is good for bladder infections.

Bacteria can't flourish in the acidic environment that cranberry juice helps create in the bladder. However, the juice must be unsweetened.

Yogurt helps kill yeast infections.

Yes, but only yogurt listing acidophilus as an ingredient. These bacteria live in the GI tract and get replaced by a yeast overgrowth, explains Lisa Stewart. Eating eight ounces of acidophilus yogurt a day for two weeks puts back the normal bacteria and restores the balance.

Prunes are a natural laxative.

Yes, and so are figs, which are also high in fiber. Start with two to four prunes daily, and make sure to drink a glass of water with them. Fiber needs water to push it through the bowel.

Beans make you toot.

Anybody who's been to a party where franks and beans are served knows this one is true, but we thought you might want to know why. First of all, beans are high in fiber—nine grams per half cup, compared to one gram in a slice of bread—and fiber starts action in the gut. In addition, the digestion of beans releases a sulfhydryl compound somewhat related to what was given off by those high school chemistry experiments that smelled like rotten eggs. The body has trouble handling this compound, and the digestive difficulty produces gas. The good news is that a new product called Beano makes the problem disappear. Just sprinkle a few drops on your first mouthful of beans, and you'll never have to pretend again that somebody else did it.

CHAPTER 17

Now I Lay Me Down to Sleep

How to get a decent night's rest

If reading this makes you drowsy, don't blame it on my writing style. You may be among the four in ten Americans who aren't getting enough sleep. Insomnia has become one of the most common complaints in the doctor's office, spawning nearly 200 sleep-disorder centers around the country and a spate of scientific research on what keeps people from falling and staying asleep.

Nobody ever *died* from lack of sleep. In fact, a DJ in Los Angeles (probably looking for a citation in the *Guinness Book of World Records*) stayed awake on the air for ten days straight until, no longer able to fight it off, he conked out at the microphone. There is no medical evidence that one night without sleep will affect the next day's performance or that a few restless nights damage the immune system. On the other hand, chronic tossing and turning does rob the body and mind of the critical down time we all need to operate at our best.

For most of us, the magic number for a restorative night is eight hours, but that is by no means universal. A woman came to the Abington Memorial Hospital Sleep Disorders Center complaining that she fell asleep each night at midnight and awoke at 4 a.m. Although she rarely felt tired, she was certain she had a sleeping problem, because she'd always been told that people need eight hours. After careful questioning, Dr. B. Franklin Diamond, the center director, told her to go home and stop worrying. "You should judge your sleep needs by the day, not by the night," he says. "How much sleep you require is determined purely by how you feel and function when you're awake. If you're not tired on four or six hours, that's enough for you. And if you're still tired after eight, you need to sleep longer."

The eight-hour myth

The proper amount of sleep for you is what it takes to keep alert during the day. Sleep changes with aging. The elderly sleep fewer hours than teenyboppers despite the fact they seem to be able to party all night. And it's perfectly normal for sleep to be interrupted as we get older—getting up during the night to go to the bathroom is just one of the reasons why.

Experts say that sleep needs are set in the genes, so it's useless to try to train yourself to get by on less sleep. Also in our genes is a program to get sleepy twice in every 24 hours. The peak time for exhaustion is in the dead of night between 2 and 7, at which time the dawn's early light triggers a rise in the hormones that switch on the body's wake-up signal. Then there is another distinct drop in alertness in the afternoon between 2 and 5. Siestas, it turns out, are a biological response and not the result of oversize sombreros or of eating too much at lunch.

What causes insomnia

While people often characterize themselves as "good" or "poor" sleepers, those terms rattle Dr. Karl Doghramji, a sleep specialist and psychiatrist who heads the Sleep Disorders Center at Thomas Jefferson University. When people have persistent sleep difficulties, he believes there is usually an underlying cause—and chronic insomnia has many of them. In the physiological category are identified sleep disorders like restless leg syndrome, a neurological problem characterized by involuntary kicking or twitching of the leg muscles, and sleep apnea, characterized by god-awful snoring to restore a temporary cessation in breathing. In the psychiatric category are common problems like anxiety—usually linked to difficulty with falling asleep—and depression, typically marked by awakening before dawn. Doghramji estimates that 30 percent of the insomniacs who come to his clinic fall into this mentally troubled group. Most of their sleep complaints can be alleviated by strategies that don't require medication or, in some cases, by drugs other than sleeping pills.

Occasionally a drug that's been prescribed for a medical condition winds up creating a sleeping problem. Diet pills, decongestants and certain stimulants for asthma can all interfere with sleep.

By far, the largest group of insomniacs are those who suffer from some kind of stress or tension. Frequently there is a major precipitating cause that upsets the normal pattern of life—a new job, a loss, an illness, a divorce. Other folks, the worrywarts, unable to shut off their thoughts when their head hits the pillow, are simply predisposed to sleeping problems by their very nature. Regardless of the origin, what begins as a few bad nights all too often escalates into a serious sleep problem sometimes referred to as conditioned wakefulness. As Abington's Diamond describes it, "The bed becomes a battlefield. In addition to being worried about whatever they're worried about, they're also afraid they won't be able to sleep. That fear keeps them awake."

The problem with sleeping pills

The all-too-simple cure for "wakeful" insomnia is a sleeping pill. On an occasional basis, especially to get through a crisis, most doctors agree that pills can be quite helpful. "Occasional use of sleeping pills under the direction of a physician to prevent progression of transient insomnia into chronic insomnia is a valid treatment," says Jefferson's Doghramji. That means a low-dose pill every other night for a few weeks or every night from seven to ten days is relatively harmless. But we are not a society geared to moderation, and most people keep on popping the pills without recognizing that after about six weeks sleep medications do more to *disrupt* sleep than enhance it. Eventually the sleeping pills themselves become the cause of insomnia.

Consistent use of pills alters the basic architecture of sleep and diminishes by as much as 50 percent the amount of deep sleep so critical to feeling rested. Added to the disturbance of sleep cycles are the problems of dependency and withdrawal. A rebound effect is likely to occur after a month or so of daily pill usage: The body becomes so dependent on the drug that if it's stopped abruptly the insomnia will return worse than it was originally, leading the sufferer right back to the sleeping pills. The way to avoid this vicious cycle is to gradually wean yourself off the pills. Cut the dosage in half every three nights until there is nothing left to take.

The morning-after effect

The popularity of sleeping medications exploded in the late '60s with the introduction of the benzodiazepines, a new class of sleeping pills in a branch of the Valium family. Previously, most doctors had prescribed barbiturates like Seconal, Nembutal and Luminal as sedatives. These knockout drugs had a potential for lethal overdose: A few too many and the sleep became permanent. The benzodiazepines were heralded as far less dangerous, because rather than depressing the central nervous system as barbiturates do, they seemed to block the stimuli that interfere with sleep. The first of them to hit the market was Dalmane, followed by Halcion, Restoril and most recently Ambien, which is not a benzodiazepine like the others, but shares some of the same properties and appears in clinical studies to be well-tolerated.

Despite the comparative safety of this class of drugs—fatal overdoses are rare—they are not without side effects. Dalmane (flurazepam) can linger for more than 100 hours in the body before being completely eliminated. Moreover, interaction with other drugs—Tagamet, for one—can exacerbate the pill's hangover effect. This buildup explains why people habitually taking Dalmane may feel tired during the day.

Halcion (triazolam) is a short-acting medication, less likely to accumulate in the blood. For many years it enjoyed a reputation as the perfect sleeping pill, particularly among trans-Atlantic travelers. Halcion was recommended to me about four years ago by a physician as a great way to sleep on a plane and get through the first few nights of waking at odd hours after arriving in a far-off time zone. Although I never take sleeping pills at home, I've been using Halcion on long plane trips and have never had the slightest problem.

Others have not been so fortunate. In early 1989, *20/20* aired a segment of horror stories about Halcion. Among others, it described a stockbroker who, after a year on Halcion, became severely psychotic, and a woman who murdered her mother while taking the drug and had no recollection of the crime. Reports of amnesia caused by Halcion crop up fairly regularly in the press. Diamond says he had a patient who gained a great deal of weight using Halcion because he got up every night and went on an eating binge, with no memory of it the following morning.

Despite the negative publicity, Dr. Daniel Hussar, Remington professor of pharmacy at the Philadelphia College of Pharmacy, believes the flap over Halcion is exaggerated and adverse reactions are usually the result of excessive dosage, inappropriately extended usage or interaction with other medication. (That may explain actor Burt Reynold's claim that Halcion nearly killed him. He was taking up to 50 pills a day and lapsed into an eight-hour coma when he tried to quit cold turkey. His recovery took more than a year.) Dr. Hussar explains, "It's not surprising that occasionally people will suffer temporary memory loss from benzodiazepines, since retrograde amnesia is a well-known characteristic of this family of drugs. In fact they are often used just for that advantage. Its cousins, Valium and Versad, are frequently given prior to surgery or in conjunction with other procedures to calm patients and make them forget their discomfort."

Although warnings about Halcion still circulate, fear should be allayed by the findings of the FDA, which, after examining the literature, decided to list only *potential for temporary amnesia* on the drug label. A committee set up by the American College of Neuropsychopharmacology to review all the published data on the pill was chaired by University of Pennsylvania psychiatrist Charles O'Brien, and he reported that the worst problems are rare. Moreover, a recent article in *DICP, The Annals of Pharmocotherapy* examined a large number of studies on benzodiazepines and concluded, "It's not clear that triazolam [Halcion] predisposes patients to amnestic episodes to any greater extent than the other benzodiazepines." The authors do suggest, however, that elderly people and those with a history of psychiatric problems should not take these drugs. The safest course for Halcion is short-term use at the lowest dosage: .25 mg.

A common but not very effective alternative to prescription sleeping pills are over-the-counter preparations like Nytol, Sominex, Sleep Eze, Exedrin P.M. They usually contain the same component that causes drowsiness in antihistamines. Within a week or so the body develops a tolerance, sedation begins to diminish and dependency starts to develop. You'd probably have better results and fewer side effects with a prescription anti-depressant like Elavil or Sinequen taken in a low dose. These drugs have the appeal of making people tired and are actually less habit-forming than sleeping pills. Chronic insomniacs might want to discuss them with their doctor as a long-term possibility.

What to do instead of pills

All the sleep specialists I interviewed approve of sleeping pills for temporary, short-term use *only*. Chronic sleeping problems should be addressed with treatments that don't come from the medicine chest. The most popular is the Bootzin technique, named for the behavioral therapist who's had great success with the following advice: Go to bed only when sleepy; if you can't sleep after 20 minutes, go into another room and read a boring book or watch a dull TV show until you're very tired. Repeat this step as many times as necessary and don't nap during the day at all. (If you must take a quick daytime snooze, do it at a regular time for not more than 20 minutes.) Finally, set your alarm to get up at the same hour every day regardless of how little you have slept or when you turned out the light; apparently a consistent rising time is critical to establishing the circadian rhythm of sleep.

Sometimes simple lifestyle changes can improve sleep. There are no data to support the hard vs. soft mattress argument; it's merely a matter of personal preference. Not so for the hot-room vs. cold-room debate. It's been documented that 60 to 65 degrees is the best temperature; above 75 definitely disturbs sleep. Nothing, however, supports those who believe that people sleep better in an arctic chill. If you live on a street with lots of traffic or even if you have a loud air conditioner, the noise may be affecting your sleep more than you realize. Try blocking it with earplugs or a sleep machine that produces white noise. And if you find that light wakes you too early in the morning, get a sleep mask.

Just because you don't experience the coffee jitters, it's a mistake to assume you aren't sensitive to caffeine. A Coke or cup of cocoa in the late afternoon can be enough to delay sleep that night. When you can't fall asleep, don't try a glass of wine to relax. While alcohol may help you close your eyes, it will fragment the sleep that follows. So will nicotine. You might try a glass of warm milk before bedtime. Even exercise influences sleep—numerous studies have found that a steady exercise program deepens sleep, but it should be done in the morning or late afternoon. And though diet centers might disagree, try a light snack before bed. Too many people go to bed hungry and are awakened in the middle of the night by nothing more serious than growling stomachs. Finally—and this is no joke—use sex as a sleeping pill. Research shows it's safe, it works and it has only positive side effects.

The Big Snooze
How the popular pills work

....

Brand Name: Dalmane
Chemical Name: flurazepam

How Long Until It Works: About 30 minutes
Common Side Effects: 1. You may be drowsy the next day. Dalmane has a very long length of action, remaining in the body at least 24 hours. 2. Withdrawal syndrome. Symptoms include anxiety, restlessness and sweating. 3. Rebound insomnia.

Brand Name: Restoril
Chemical Name: temazepam
How Long Until It Works: About an hour
Common Side Effects: 1. Drowsiness the next day. 2. Withdrawal syndrome. Symptoms include: anxiety, insomnia, restlessness and sweating.

Brand Name: Halcion
Chemical Name: triazolam
How Long Until It Works: Less than 30 minutes
Common Side Effects: 1. Occasional temporary amnesia. Disorientation. 2. Withdrawal syndrome. Symptoms include: anxiety and restlessness. 3. Rebound insomnia.

Brand Name: Ambien
Chemical Name: zolpidem tartrate
How Long Until It Works: Less than 30 minutes
Common Side Effects: 1. Drowsiness. 2. Some dizziness. 3. Lightheadedness. 4. Difficulty with coordination.

For Your Information

All too frequently sleeping problems are a symptom of something else. If you are a chronic insomniac you should check out your problem with a sleep specialist whose treatments include training in biofeedback and other relaxation techniques.

Many local hospitals have sleep-disorder clinics where people can take their complaints and often stay overnight to be monitored. Some clinics have gone through a lengthy accreditation process by the American Sleep Disorders Association to meet rigid standards, which include a broad range of clinical diagnostic services and a board-certified sleep specialist on staff. ASDA accredited Sleep Disorder Centers are:

Lower Bucks Hospital, 785-9751

Crozer-Chester Medical Center, 447-2689

The Lankenau Hospital, 645-3400

MCP (Medical College of Pennsylvania), 842-4250

Thomas Jefferson University Hospital, 955-6175

HUP, 662-7300

There are also sleep disorder programs at:

Abington Memorial Hospital, 576-2226

CHOP, 590-1656

Southern Chester County Hospital, 869-1259

Sleep Disorder Labs are limited to diagnostic and treatment services for sleep-related breathing problems like sleep apnea. These include:

Holy Redeemer Hospital, 938-3448

Temple University Hospital, 707-8163

Cooper Medical Center, 609-342-3269

Pennsylvania Hospital, 829-3250

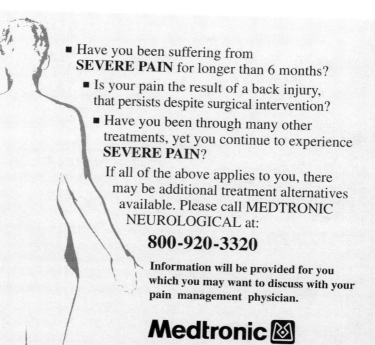

CHAPTER 18

The New Medicine

*How unconventional medicine can bring you
health, happiness and a longer life. Here's what
works and what doesn't, plus where to find who
does what*

A few summers ago I was bleary-eyed from popping
pills to relieve the worse-than-usual sneezing and itching from my annual bout with
hay fever. My daughter suggested that, if I was unwilling to resume allergy shots,
why not try acupuncture? It suddenly occurred to me how totally differently we
viewed health care. While I had an allergist, she had an acupuncturist. I would see
an orthopedist if I sprained my back from too much exercise; she, under the same
conditions, visited a chiropractor. She got massages to relieve stress; I got a mani-
cure. My standard treatment for a cold was around-the-clock antihistamines and
decongestants. She insisted I'd get better faster with a homeopathic remedy called
Alpha CF. I blithely chalked up our differences to the generation gap or new-age-
itis, a disease she'd caught after moving to California. That's until I realized that my
daughter had simply tapped into the hottest trend in the health-care industry.

Alternative medicine, once the butt of bad guru jokes, has poked much more
than its nose under conventional medicine's elitist tent. No longer confined to the
touchy/feely firmament of hippies and healers, alternative therapies attract conservative suburban matrons and busy executives who aren't the least bit embarrassed to
refer their friends to the chiropractor or acupuncturist who changed their lives. A
study recently published in the *New England Journal of Medicine* reports that in
1990, Americans made an estimated 42 million visits to providers of nonconventional therapies, where they shelled out approximately $10.3 billion from their own
pockets. While some alternative practices may be covered by health insurance, most
are not. Check your policy.

What's the appeal?

Why, with the brilliant achievements of modern medicine in full flower, are people
flocking elsewhere? A good part of the disillusionment seems rooted in the limita-

tions of conventional medicine and our love/hate relationship with medical technology. We love it when it works; we hate it when it doesn't work well enough to cure the problem. We're tired of endless testing with ambiguous results, and whatever happened to tender loving care? Patients are sick of often being seen as problems—the migraine in examining room B—instead of people. And they're sick *and* tired of traipsing around to specialists. They want a health practitioner who sees them as a whole person and not a body part, one who spends time with them, listens to their complaints and makes them a partner in their recovery. That is exactly what they find in alternative medicine, where the provider is less of an authority figure and more of a trusted friend. It's no accident that one of the buzzwords of the movement is *empowerment.*

Nobody disputes the value of conventional medicine in acute care situations—when you break your arm or need a cancerous tumor cut out or you're battling pneumonia. But the reliable pill-and-scalpel approach doesn't do much for the myriad ailments related to aging and lifestyle that drive most of us to see a doctor. Yet these very ills—things like back problems, anxiety, headaches, arthritis, high blood pressure, ulcers and chronic pain—are the meat and potatoes of alternative medicine, which treats them less invasively and less expensively. But its appeal is even broader. By emphasizing wellness and prevention, alternative medicine ties into the overall greening of America and its fascination with the newest twist in healing, the idea that the mind and body can work in concert.

Bad reviews from the critics

Alternative medicine's penetration into the mainstream hasn't silenced its critics, who rail that it is outright quackery, nothing more than the placebo effect and, they say with some justification, that most conditions it treats would improve eventually merely by being left alone. But who wants to wait?

Whether the naysayers are bad-mouthing something as far out as crystal healing or as old as homeopathy, the typical condemnation put forth by the establishment cites the lack of scientific proof. Where, they ask, are the standard double-blind clinical studies? What you've got instead, they argue, are books and papers full of endless anecdotes not worth decimating forests for the paper they're printed on.

Worth looking into

Some of those charges may soon be answered. At Temple University, the Center for Frontier Sciences is examining, under strict scientific criteria, a broad range of alternative topics. For example, what is the nature of the mind and what role does it play in other biological functions? How do electromagnetic fields influence health? How can we better understand the effects of the "soft medicines"—therapeutic touch, electro-acupuncture, etc.—without being able to use the traditional measures?

Even more significant in the push to give legitimacy to nonconventional approaches is the new, federally funded Office of Alternative Medicine in Washington. Limited to a mere $2 million budget—small change compared with

Philadelphia
MAGAZINE

Guide To
Good Health

Yes, I would like information from the following advertisers:

1	2	3	4	5	6	7	8	9	10	11	12	13	14	15	16	17	18	19	20
21	22	23	24	25	26	27	28	29	30	31	32	33	34	35	36	37	38	39	40
41	42	43	44	45	46	47	48	49	50	51	52	53	54	55	56	57	58	59	60
61	62	63	64	65	66	67	68	69	70	71	72	73	74	75	76	77	78	79	80
81	82	83	84	85	86	87	88	89	90	91	92	93	94	95	96	97	98	99	100

Please type or print the following. Please allow 6-8 weeks for processing. All requests fulfilled if received before December 15, 1995.

Name:_____

Address:_____

Telephone:_____ Age:_____ Male/Female:_____

If you have children, how many:_____

Requesting information for:_____

     Yourself:_____

     Parent:_____

     Other:_____

Where did you purchase this Guide Book?_____

Why did you purchase this Guide Book?_____
_____

What different topics would you like covered in the next edition of

PHILADELPHIA Magazine's Guide to Good Health?
_____
_____

I currently subscribe to PHILADELPHIA Magazine:_____

I would like information on becoming a subscriber to PHILADELPHIA Magazine:_____

the $10 billion bestowed on its parent, the National Institutes of Health—the mission of OAM dwarfs its size. "We'd like to find what conditions could be best helped by alternative medicine," says Dr. Joseph Jacobs, OAM's director. "For example, we could use better studies to show how chiropractic makes back pain more manageable. Some of these alternatives could be just as good, cheaper and safer than many of the drugs and treatments we now use."

At present, OAM is geared to fund ten two-year projects with $50,000 each; all are designed to show how a particular alternative treatment is equal to or better than standard therapies. Some scoff that this request for grant proposals will be a casting call for quacks. Dr. Jacobs doubts it. "If you turn over a rock," he says, "you don't necessarily find a snake. You may find something worth examining." Like bee pollen as an antihistamine or certain herbal medicines that may not be cures but might improve quality of life.

In the meantime, we all want the answers to two simple questions: What works? What doesn't? On the following pages you'll read about the most-accepted alternative therapies, along with a smattering of those beyond the fringe. Although the jury is still out on hard scientific data, I'm one of the thousands who's not waiting around for the verdict. I've now got a chiropractor I swear by. I take a homeopathic remedy, Oscillococcinum, at the first sign of a cold. And as the allergy season approaches, I'm seriously considering acupuncture. Who says a mother can't learn from her daughter?

Acupuncture
A little stab'll do ya

We can thank Richard Nixon for drawing attention to acupuncture. Among the press corps accompanying Nixon on his landmark visit to China in 1972 was the *New York Times'* James Reston, who underwent an emergency appendectomy in Peking. To his amazement, instead of pumping him full of painkillers after the operation, the local doctors stuck needles all over him. And it worked. On his return home, Reston wrote glowingly about his experience.

Since then, acupuncture has become one of the most popular alternative therapies. The World Health Organization recognizes more than 40 medical problems, from allergies to arthritis to AIDS, that it can help. Nationwide there are nearly 7,000 practitioners and 50 schools. Pennsylvania is one of 20 states that license or certify acupuncture. The American Association of Acupuncture and Oriental Medicine reports that 15 million Americans had acupuncture treatments in 1991. The needles hurt no more than tiny pins and the sensation they give is one of mild tingling. Afterward you're likely to feel relaxed.

Why acupuncture works is something of a mystery. It's rooted in a concept of energy, and to understand that, it's necessary to change the way we're accustomed to looking at sickness. Western medicine is based on complex electrical and chemical interactions that regulate metabolism. When something in the body goes askew, we search for the imbalance with laboratory tests—checking glucose levels, electrolytes, T-cell counts and the like. Then we try to correct the problem with drugs. By contrast, Eastern medicine barely measures symptoms. It views metabolism as a life force called Qi ("chee") that can't be quantified in a test tube.

Qi circulates through the body along a dozen pathways called meridians, which do not correspond to any physical map we learned in high school biology. The other key in the Oriental concept of disease is yin and yang, the interdependent, opposing forces of nature. The trick in all of life is to maintain the proper balance between yin and yang so that Qi can flow naturally.

Illness occurs when Qi is blocked. Health returns by restoring harmony, and that's where acupuncture enters the picture. The acupuncturist, who knows hundreds of points along the meridians, inserts three- to four-inch-long hair-thin needles at key places to stimulate or sedate the system. The needles help release whatever is obstructing Qi so that the body can heal itself.

Got all that? What's even more confusing is that there are different schools of acupuncture—traditional Chinese medicine, Five Elements, medical acupuncture, electro-acupuncture—all with somewhat different approaches to diagnosis and treatment. And don't ask for proof in the form of standard medical studies, because there isn't much. There's no placebo for a needle. But there is overwhelming anecdotal evidence that acupuncture is capable of some pretty remarkable things.

"I call that a miracle"

Consider the following patients of Dr. Ghodratolla Heidary, an Iranian-born anesthesiologist on the staff of Lankenau Hospital in Bryn Mawr. He first became interested in acupuncture for pain management. Proponents believe it releases endorphins, the body's natural painkillers. But today most of Heidary's patients come to him to stop smoking.

John Franzini, a 40-year-old Buick dealer, suffered for more than a year with a god-awful case of shingles that doctors treated with nothing but ointments and painkillers. The pain was so intense he couldn't even comb his hair. A customer told him about Dr. Heidary, and despite his skepticism, he was willing to try anything. He had three treatments in four weeks. Two or three days after the first one, the sores began to dry up and the pain lessened. Within a month, he was better. "He made me a believer," Franzini says.

Irene Varano, whose husband is a surgeon at Jefferson Hospital, has a son who was a two-pack-a-day smoker. When her niece suffered a smoking-induced mouth malignancy, she went on a crusade to get her son to throw away his cigarettes. "I call Lankenau and say, 'What can you do for smoking right away, one, two, three?' They tell me about Dr. Heidary. I think, What do I have to lose? I make my son go with me. He gets the acupuncture. He's never smoked again. I call that a miracle."

Dr. Robert Mitchell, a retired obstetrician/gynecologist, was wracked with recurrent sciatica that sent shooting pains down his leg. He'd been to a chiropractor and had had steroid injections from an orthopedist. After two treatments with Heidary, he was back on the golf course and hasn't had a problem since. When his wife was bedridden with the same problem, he persuaded her to try acupuncture. By the third visit, she was pain-free.

Dr. Scott Goldman, chief of heart surgery at Lankenau, had reached the end of his rope with his father-in-law, a four-pack-a-day smoker. After one session with Heidary, his 50-year habit ended. Goldman has since begun to refer to Heidary his postoperative thoracic patients who have painful incisions and don't want to get loaded with narcotics to cope.

Blending East and West

"In Eastern medicine there are connections between systems that in Western medicine we don't have models for," says Dr. Marshall Sager, a Bala Cynwyd physician-turned-acupuncturist. "Instead of treating symptoms, they look for underlying imbalance. It's the difference between treating the tree and the root." He became interested in acupuncture after watching his wife's quality of life destroyed by drugs given to her in a long and losing battle with cancer. "I decided there must be a less destructive way to heal."

He choose to study medical acupuncture "because after 4,000 years it had withstood the test of time," and enrolled in a special program for physicians at UCLA School of Medicine. He thinks acupuncture has made him a better doctor by increasing his treatment options. At the same time, his medical training makes him a better acupuncturist. "I was treating a man for fatigue with acupuncture and while he was making progress, my experience as a Western physician told me something wasn't right. I ordered tests and discovered he had leukemia. At a time like that, my dual training proved to be terribly important."

From migraines to skin rashes

Lots of licensed acupuncturists are not physicians, such as Germantown-based Nancy Post (438-2657), whose patients report great success with problems ranging from headaches to skin rashes that have not responded to conventional medicine's cures. In Center City, Cathy Lyn Goldstein (988-9898), a 32-year-old woman who studied acupuncture in China, is often asked, "What's a nice Jewish girl like you doing in a job like this?" She treats insomnia, chronic fatigue and yeast infections, and has had impressive success with PMS. A *Daily News* writer who goes to Goldstein for tune-ups first turned to acupuncture after a car accident put her out of work for a year. "At the time I actually thought about killing myself from the agony," she says. "The only choice I had was constant heavy medication, which I refused. Once I started acupuncture, I was able to get off drugs and resume a normal, relatively pain-free life." She's also used acupuncture to cure her migraines.

The range of problems responsive to acupuncture seems endless—veterinarians are even sticking animals. A New York dentist, Dr. Joel Friedman, uses it for the pain of TMJ. Its success in weight loss is spotty and, as with smoking, seems tied to motivation. One particularly promising area is addiction. It's most effective with substances like alcohol, heroin, cocaine and nicotine, least helpful with tranquilizers like Valium. Acupuncture eases withdrawal and reduces craving. More than 300 programs nationwide are following a model developed by Dr. Michael Smith at Lincoln Hospital in the Bronx that combines acupuncture with supportive counseling. One of them is at the North Philadelphia Health System (787-2000).

Acupuncture should not be used in place of standard medical examinations, nor should you expect it to cure diseases like cancer. In choosing an acupuncturist, find out if he or she attended an accredited school and is licensed or has been approved by the National Committee for the Certification of Acupuncturists. Make sure that only disposable, pre-sterilized needles are used. The American Association of Acupuncture and Oriental Medicine has a referral list of local certified acupuncturists and lots of free information (919-787-5181). In the Cherry Hill area, family physician Dr. Wan B. Lo practices acupuncture for pain control at 525 Route 73 South, Marlton (609-596-1005).

Homeopathy
Arsenic and old medicine

Francine Homer is a no-nonsense retired schoolteacher married to a professional skeptic, WWDB talk-radio host Irv Homer. For some nine years Francine had been plagued by painful, itchy skin eruptions caused by poor circulation. "My legs looked like raw meat," she says. "Mornings I'd have blood on my sheets from the oozing and scratching." The only treatment offered by the many doctors she'd consulted were cortisone ointments or injections that helped, at best, temporarily.

She reached the point where she'd try anything. Anything turned out to be Bensalem's Dr. Nand Gupta, recommended by a guest on her husband's radio show. "He took down my history and asked me a lot of strange questions, like whether I prefer sweet to sour flavors. Then he took out a vial of tiny sugar pills, put something on them from an eyedropper, shook the vial and sent me home with them. The itching subsided almost immediately. It took about six months for the rash to disappear. That was five years ago, and it's never returned." She has since sent many friends and used Dr. Gupta for other ailments. "It's really a shame," she says, "that more people don't trust this."

Less is more

Despite the often astounding results of homeopathic treatment, to trust it does require a rather grand leap of faith. Homeopathy was developed 200 years ago by a

German doctor, Samuel Hahnemann, for whom Hahnemann University Hospital is named. Distressed by the barbarian medical practices of his day, he started experimenting with natural medicines and formed a theory that became known as the law of similars: The same substance that in large doses causes an illness can cure that illness in small or infinitesimal amounts. This is like the fight-fire-with-fire idea behind vaccines and allergy shots, which use a speck of virus or allergen to produce an immune reaction.

The thing about homeopathy that drives scientists crazy isn't his like-cures-like principle, but its other core belief: Less is more. Hahnemann taught that the smaller the dose of the remedy, the stronger its effect. The 1,500 remedies in the *Homeopathic Pharmacopeia* (considered nonprescription, loosely FDA-regulated drugs) are so diluted that they frequently contain nothing more than a memory of their original ingredient.

Thierry Montfort, president of the U.S. branch of Boiron, the world's largest homeopathic pharmaceutical firm (whose American headquarters are in Delaware County), explains, "You start with a mother tincture of an animal, mineral or plant substance. Then you dilute it by putting one drop of tincture into one to 99 drops of a neutral solution like alcohol or distilled water. That's followed by a vigorous shaking called potentization, which activates the remedy—it then gets rediluted and potentized as many as 200 times." When the remedies are ready for market, there's often none there anymore, and that's what requires the leap of faith.

"People practicing homeopathy don't appreciate the enormity of what they're asking us to believe," says Joel Gurin, science editor of *Consumer Reports* and one of homeopathy's staunchest critics. "This law of infinite dilution, this notion that things are more powerful when they're not there, is a lot to take. This isn't alternative medicine, it's alternative science."

Back in style

Nevertheless, more and more people are flocking to homeopaths, who have regained much of the stature they enjoyed at the turn of the century. Philadelphia, in particular, was a hotbed of homeopathy until 1910. That's when a commission formed to evaluate American medical schools slapped a grade B status on the ones teaching homeopathy, effectively forcing institutions like Hahnemann to drop their homeopathic courses; by 1950 there were few American-trained homeopaths left.

However, the movement never lost steam in Europe. The Queen of England has a homeopath on her staff. In France, a third of family physicians practice homeopathy; in Germany, one out of every five. The resurgence in the United States dates to the early '70s, spurred by disaffected young doctors who wanted less toxic and more individual ways to treat their patients.

Today an estimated 2,000 physicians in America use homeopathy. Dr. Philip Bonnet, a Pennington, New Jersey, psychiatrist, switched to it after a career in nutritional medicine, because he felt traditional Western medicine was too narrow. "It sees the body as a machine, stopping at the skin," he says. "What about the spiritual

and energetic side?" He particularly likes not damaging people. "When I was prescribing psychotropic drugs I usually felt more like a warden than a healer."

The followers of homeopathy are legion, including Tina Turner, Vidal
Sassoon, Yehudi Menuhin, *Dallas* star Linda Gray and hordes of lesser-known folks
like Joan Leof, who once worked in PR at Graduate Hospital. Leof sought out Dr.
Lucy Nitskansky, a Russian-born homeopath in Philadelphia, to wean herself off
thyroid medication and to find a way to get through menopause without hormones.
"My first consultation lasted two hours," she recalls. "I filled out a 15-page family
and medical history, things like: Do you feel more uncomfortable with a tight collar
or a tight belt? What fears do you have? And: Give as many adjectives as possible to
describe your personality." Eventually, Leof left the office with an assortment of
remedies. (Classical homeopaths use only one at a time; others, a variety pack.)
"Since I started taking these medicines," she reports, "I feel like I'm 20. My body is
light and clear. My internist is floored that my thyroid has remained stable."

Do it yourself

Because the medicines used in homeopathy are nontoxic, people are encouraged to
become educated in self-treatment. Beth Rotundo is a practical nurse who is Eastern
Pennsylvania coordinator of lay study groups. She joined her first group as a student in 1978; today people all over the tri-state area are flocking to monthly meetings in homes, churches and schools. The study groups get their information from
workbooks provided by the National Center for Homeopathy as well as lectures
from invited health professionals.

"Our goal is to shift the emphasis from the doctor to the patient and to educate people about the remedies as well as their limitations," says Rotundo. "People
worry that they have to make a choice between allopathic and homeopathic medicine, but they're really complementary. Most of us are perfectly capable of handling
minor health problems—stuff like colds, flu bugs and sprains. We want to be in
control of our lives."

Perhaps that explains how Patty Smith could take two doses of Arsenicum
album to quell an agonizing attack of food poisoning and two hours later find herself in front of the refrigerator nibbling scallops in black-bean sauce. Smith, who
sets up homeopathic study groups in New Jersey, once badly burned her fingers in
an oven. "The pain was excruciating," she says. "I started sticking Cantharis
[Spanish fly] pellets under my tongue every 15 minutes for an hour and a half. Then
I spaced them out. By the next morning only one finger was pink. I could understand the pain going away, but the healing amazed me."

Where's the proof?

Much, but not all, of the evidence of homeopathy's efficacy is anecdotal. However,
in 1991 the *British Medical Journal* reviewed 107 clinical homeopathic studies and
found that 81 showed positive results, although the methodology of some of the
research was questioned. A double-blind study published in *Lancet* found that a

homeopathic remedy significantly reduced hay fever symptoms. Another study showed that flu sufferers taking Oscillococcinum had a quicker recovery than a control group given a placebo.

"We have plenty of clinical and anecdotal evidence that homeopathic remedies work, but we don't have a unifying theory why," says Jay Borneman, whose great-grandfather, grandfather and father were homeopathic pharmacists. "Still, the lack of an explanation doesn't make the phenomenon cease to exist." Borneman is vice president of Standard Homeopathic Company, the largest homeopathic drug firm in America. Like Boiron, whose sales have jumped 20-fold in the last decade, their business is booming. "I see this as science," Borneman says. "It's not new-age mysticism or religion. And it certainly shouldn't be used in lieu of conventional medicine, which saved my daughter's life. But we used homeopathic remedies before and after her heart surgery to help her wounds heal."

Nobody disputes its safety. Even critic Joel Gurin concedes, "I don't know anybody strongly harmed by homeopathy." But he does worry about people who might be hurt by discontinuing useful drugs in favor of homeopathic remedies. "There is something going on in all these cases of cures," Gurin will admit, "but the answer isn't in quantum physics. It may be in the mind/body connection." The lack of proof is one reason health insurers such as Independence Blue Cross do not endorse homeopathy and typically do not cover homeopathic services and supplies. Gurin suggests the secret to homeopathy is in the power of the placebo effect. But then how would he explain the success of homeopathic remedies with infants and animals? Our ignorance of *how* should not be considered acceptable proof against homeopathy. Until recently we hadn't a clue how aspirin worked as an analgesic. Which brings us full circle, to the leap of faith.

Homeopaths practicing in the area include:

Dr. Philip Bonnet, Pennington, 609-737-2700

Dr. Nand Gupta, Bensalem, 639-7363

Drs. Ira Cantor and Richard Fried, Kimberton, 923-4125

Dr. Lucy Nitskansky, Philadelphia, 698-1042

Mitchel Shapiro, P.A.C., Philadelphia, 566-7691

Dr. Howard Posner, Bala Cynwyd, 667-2927

George Hopkins, D.C., Devon, 688-8808

Active homeopathic study groups in the Philadelphia area include:

Bryn Athyn Study Group, 947-3265

Conshohocken Homeopathic Study Group, 610-828-7607

Delaware County Homeopathic Study Group, 610-876-3910

Homeopathic Study Group of Central Montgomery County, 610-828-3910

Meadville Homeopathic Study Group, 610-336-1141

In New Jersey, call Patty Smith (609-393-0702). The 7,000-member National Center for Homeopathy is an excellent information source (703-548-7790). Doctor's Choice, a health resource center at the Crossroads Shopping Plaza, Route 38 and Church Road, Cherry Hill, has homeopathic medicines and lectures as part of its full-service health education program supervised by Dr. William Block.

Laying On of Hands
A need to be kneaded

Most of us grew up thinking of massage in one of two ways. The sexy type meant being rubbed with scented oils by a scantily clad, curvaceous masseuse who'd willingly massage body parts that never see the light of day. The other scenario required someone with muscles like Popeye who wore a white coat and probably worked in a health club or a steam bath. What they did was called Swedish massage, a method of stroking and rubbing muscles and ligaments to get out knots. Alternative medicine looks at massage from a more health-oriented perspective. The preferred new-age term is *bodywork*. You're still allowed to enjoy the laying on of hands, but its purpose is decidedly therapeutic. And there's no shortage of evidence that human touch has physical and emotional benefits. It can increase blood flow, stimulate the nervous system, stretch soft tissue and relieve muscle spasms. Bodywork goes a step further by tying good health to proper alignment. "Bodywork is a gentle way to connect the mind and body," says Judah Roseman, whose specialty is shiatsu. "Who hasn't had pain or trauma in their lives? These tensions and memories get stored in the body and need to be unlocked."

One order of shiatsu, please

Shiatsu, as Roseman explains it, is a Japanese term for finger pressure. Using the hands and feet, the practitioner applies gentle but deep pressure along the same pathways as the acupuncturist and with the same goal: to balance and harmonize the movement of Qi. "Our lifestyle creates excesses and deficiencies," Roseman says. "Shiatsu can reduce the excesses and replenish the deficiencies." It's done without oils because they would interfere with the flow of energy, and the client wears light cotton clothing because it's a good energy conductor. "It's not merely a technique," Roseman explains. "It's two beings exchanging energy fields." Advocates of shiatsu believe that in addition to affecting the muscular and skeletal system, it regulates biological functions like digestion and circulation.

Roseman, who has a master's in educational psychology, is a member of the American Oriental Bodywork Therapy Association. With his wife, Ruth, he runs

Associates for Creative Wellness in Cherry Hill (609-424-7501), where yoga, meditation, stress management and cooking are taught. Many of their shiatsu clients are professionals whose complaints range from stress to stiff necks. He charges $50 for an hour in the office and $75 to $85 for home visits, depending on location.

Posture perfect

Rolfing, also known as structural integration, is designed to improve posture and repair the emotional and physical trauma trapped within our bodies. Created by Dr. Ida Rolf, who had a Ph.D. in biochemistry, rolfing stretches and separates major muscle groups and the soft tissue that connects them. Rolfers reorder the head, shoulders, chest, pelvis and legs into vertical alignment, which results in proper posture and minimizes the negative effects of gravity. Upon completion of a typical ten-session program, people report feeling physically, emotionally and spiritually enhanced. The cost, $800 to $1,000, is not covered by insurance.

Interior designer Sue Goldstein Rubel was rolfed by Robert Toporek, a local practitioner who focuses much of his practice on infants and children, especially those with disabilities like cerebral palsy, arthritis and brain injury. Because her own experience with rolfing was so positive, Goldstein subsequently sent to Toporek every member of her family—from her young son, whose asthma was cured, to her 75-year-old father-in-law. "I no longer go into neck spasms that I used to get from an auto accident," she says. "I'm much more aware of stress and strain in my body and the pain caused by bad posture. People think if you're rolfed, you're weird, but it's changed my life."

Certified rolfers in Philadelphia include Toporek (875-0930), Linda Grace (985-1263) and Rebecca Carli-Mills (848-4739).

Reflex on this

For pure pleasure, nothing beats **reflexology**. There are some 7,000 nerve endings in the foot, which reflexologists view as control panels to the rest of the body. By applying gentle pressure to certain points (which supposedly connect to various organs), the practitioner disperses metabolic waste that's clogging the circulatory and nervous systems. Paul J. Nathan, a Wyndmoor foot reflexologist at the Whitemarsh Chiropractic Center (825-6363), says reflexology reduces stress, cleanses the body of impurities and revitalizes the immune system. Randy Rodgers of Northeast Reflexology Associates, 4644 Tacony Street (533-9350), has used reflexology, he says, to break up blockage in arteries in the legs. He claims that by increasing circulation, patients have avoided bypass surgery, which may be a bit of a tall order. Perhaps more reliable are the promises made by psychologists and WWDB talk-show hosts Yvonne Kaye and Murray Needleman. They simply tout foot reflexology for being energizing and relaxing. In most cases, that's quite enough.

Just the right touch

The **Feldenkrais Method**, developed by an Israeli engineer/physicist, rests on a complicated brain-body theory that connects muscular movement with the entire nervous system. It retrains the brain to unlearn the muscles' bad habits. The "teacher" gently moves and lifts parts of the body in a way geared to freed them from the stress of gravity. Those who have tried the method, especially dancers, actors and athletes, report feeling light and graceful afterward. It purports to be helpful for MS and stroke patients. In Philadelphia, workshops are conducted by Bob Chapra (732-9173).

The **Alexander Technique** evolved around the turn of the century from the work of a Shakespearean thespian interested in the principles underlying movement. Many of its current adherents are actors. During the nearly hour-long sessions, a certified instructor coaches participants on exploring their movement history, identifying its problems and improving coordination. Supposedly that leads to less muscle tension and stress. In Philadelphia, workshops and training are given by Bruce and Martha Fertman at the Alexander Foundation (844-0670).

Some exercise techniques transcend body-building and are considered holistic health programs by their proponents. One is **Pilates**, favored by Candice Bergen, skater Kristi Yamaguchi and local sports medicine orthopedist Dr. Nicholas DiNubile. It's done on a spring-loaded platform bed that looks like a cross between an exercise machine and a torture rack. Pilates promises increased strength, flexibility and endurance, plus improved posture, alignment and balance. It's offered along with Kripalu yoga, hatha yoga, the Alexander technique, the Feldenkrais method and T'ai Chi at Alternative Health and Fitness Concepts, 2016 Walnut Street (5674969), which also provides massage therapy and cranio-sacral therapy.

Hellerwork is a method developed by aerospace engineer Joseph Heller, a student of Ida Rolf. He felt that rolfing lacked a strong mind-body connection, so he combined many of its physical principles—proper posture, balance and muscle manipulation—with a focus on self-actualization. Sharon Butler, a Hellerwork practitioner in Berwyn (889-9795), says she's been working recently with carpal tunnel syndrome and sees a 75 percent improvement in the first session. A complete program lasts 11 sessions at $70 each.

Trager is the creation of a physician who believed that if there's tension in your body, it's because your emotions are holding your muscles hostage. It uses gentle rhythmic body massage to carry the mind to a relaxed, meditative state. Practitioners claim it's helpful for physical problems related to nerve impairment like multiple sclerosis, muscular dystrophy and Parkinson's disease. It's done locally by Robert McLaughlin, a licensed physical therapist (745-4025).

Chiropractic
The master manipulators

If you are one of those skeptics who still think alternative medicine will never be anything but just that, consider the case of chiropractic. Within the last two decades it has moved from being viewed by most people as weird and even dangerous to a position of relative acceptance by both the medical and lay communities. Chiropractic is now the third-largest primary health-care profession in the Western world, led only by medicine and dentistry. There are some 45,000 licensed chiropractors and 14 accredited chiropractic schools in the United States, offering four- or five-year programs that incorporate much of what's taught in medical schools. Chiropractic's shift into the mainstream may serve as a bellwether for other non-conventional disciplines like homeopathy and acupuncture, which are still nibbling on the fringe and still plagued by the problem that bedevils most alternatives: While the results may be extremely helpful, the premise can be awfully hard to swallow.

For example, chiropractic attributes almost every health problem, from gastric disorders to hormonal imbalance, to something called "subluxations." (Someone likened them to a unicorn: sounds great but nobody's ever found one.) These minute misalignments of the spine supposedly irritate the nerves along the spinal cord, and that in turn lowers the body's defenses against illness. Chiropractors are taught that by relieving pressure on those nerves through spinal manipulation, health will be restored. Maybe so, maybe not. But if you limp into a chiropractor's office with shooting pains in your leg and you walk out straight and pain-free, do you care that the doctor believes he can use the same technique to cure a cold?

Relief from back pain prompts nearly half of the visits to chiropractic offices—one in 20 Americans takes his or her backache to a chiropractor. There is ample evidence that spinal manipulation and adjustment can be extremely effective for lower-back pain. Last year the Rand research institute in Santa Monica reviewed 67 studies and articles and nine books examining the validity of spinal manipulation for back pain and concluded that chiropractic is helpful and appropriate.

All it's cracked up to be

"But who the hell wants their back cracked? That word has gotten us into more trouble—I don't like my staff to use it," says Dr. Basil Snyman, a very busy Center City chiropractor who remembers starting his practice when "everybody thought we were a dangerous cult."

Today the majority of his patients arrive with a back problem—more often from too much exercise rather than too little. By the time they reach him they've been through the medical mill and are fairly desperate. To their surprise, although not his, they often wind up getting help for a complaint other than the one that brought them in to start with. For example, he's cured a reflex problem through manipulation that relieved the nerves impinging on the esophagus; quelled anxiety attacks by easing chest pressure that's causing shortness of breath; and decreased pain from TMJ.

What Snyman gives his patients, after X-rays, a history and an examination, is a program of spinal manipulation (sometimes combined with electrotherapy and ultrasound) along with diet, exercise and nutrition suggestions. His fee for an initial consultation, examination, treatment and X-rays runs $170; office visits are $35. "Now that Blue Cross will pay chiropractors," he says wryly, "people are beginning to think we're okay."

But is it safe?

Consider that chiropractors pay less than $3,000 a year in malpractice insurance, which is a good indicator that they're not often sued. (Orthopedic surgeons, on the other hand, pay $50,000.) There is the remote risk of a stroke from neck manipulation, but it happens in two to three cases per million treatments, compared with 150,000 cases of paralysis per million neurosurgical neck operations. (Chiropractors are not permitted to operate or prescribe drugs.) There is also the chance that a serious condition might go misdiagnosed, but such reports are hard to find.

When should you visit a chiropractor? Probably before you agree to back surgery—since adjustment may keep you out of the operating room—or afterward for maintenance. Periodic manipulation may stave off degeneration from osteoarthritis. Other conditions successfully handled by chiropractors include neck pain and headaches. An Australian study showed that all 30 patients randomly chosen for chiropractic treatment from a group of 85 with a long-term history of migraines improved radically within seven visits.

If you aren't seeing some improvement after a half-dozen treatments, try something else. The best way to choose a chiropractor is on the recommendation of a satisfied friend. In Pennsylvania chiropractors are multiplying like rabbits; 3,500 have been licensed here in the last 15 years. If you can't find one from a personal reference, call the Pennsylvania Chiropractic Society hotline (717-232-5762).

Hypnosis
You are getting healthy

What else could it be but magic? There on the stage, a tiny, 100-pound woman has just been hypnotized—and she's lifting a 200-pound man in the air! While demonstrations like this make for dramatic entertainment, they've given the public a distorted view of hypnosis. "You can't make anyone do things under hypnosis that they would not do under normal circumstances," explains Clorinda Margolis, Ph.D. (592-8165), a psychologist who frequently uses medical hypnosis with her clients. "It's not a deep sleep and it's not a control thing. It's focused concentration, and you can always bring yourself out of a trance."

About half the people Dr. Margolis treats in her Center City practice have some kind of health problem—from folks who want to stop smoking to cancer and AIDS sufferers. She considers hypnosis a form of training that gives people control of their lives. "You can use the mind and imagery," she says, "to alter the way the body responds." The kind of control she's talking about takes at least six training sessions, strong commitment and lots of practice at home with a tape she provides. Her work is so absorbing, she sometimes goes into a light trance herself.

"It's not a quick fix"

Dr. Margolis' faith in hypnosis is validated by a large body of research showing that hypnosis promotes healing, boosts the immune system and regulates addictions like smoking and eating. "But it is not a quick fix," cautions Ron Pekala, Ph.D., president of the Greater Philadelphia Society of Clinical Hypnosis. "It's a coping mechanism, not a cure, and it works best as an adjunct to therapy. I can give you hypnotic suggestions to stop using drugs, but it will be hard to maintain them if you keep hanging out with your druggie friends."

Hypnosis is also an excellent tool for managing chronic pain. Unlike acute pain, which comes on suddenly as a warning, long-standing pain doesn't conform to a medical model—often its cause is unknown and standard treatment doesn't alleviate it. But in training pain-sufferers how to change the way they respond to their environment, hypnotism may afford effective relief.

Don't confuse hypnosis with currently popular techniques like deep relaxation, guided imagery and meditation. These are indeed excellent means for letting go of stress, but zoning out is not the same as the altered state of being reached in a hypnotic trance. "Hypnosis can put you in contact with a part of your experience that's completely separate from your conscious awareness," explains psychologist Linda Shrier, Ph.D. She means the part of your mind that automatically presses the gas and steers the car while you're talking or listening to the radio—the same part that monitors the edge of the bed while you're sleeping so you don't fall off.

Altered states

This other level of consciousness is where messages are imprinted during hypnosis. For some reason, the automatic pilot part of us accepts things differently, and orders given to it have a greater impact than things we're told in an alert and aware state. These messages tend to be most powerful when they are in the form of images rather than intellectual commands. For example, you might not easily salivate at the count of three, but a hypnotist can build an experience such as eating a lemon that becomes so real you will salivate as if you'd bitten into the tart fruit. Because imagery is so central to hypnosis, the best subjects are often people who get lost in daydreams and have the capacity to become so absorbed in a book that when the phone rings, they'll jump from fright. The breadth of what hypnosis can persuade people to do ranges from overcoming the fear of flying to decreasing drug dependency for chronic pain.

At St. Christopher's Hospital, Dr. Carlton Dampier oversees two hypnosis pilot programs. One teaches kids suffering from sickle-cell anemia how to hypnotize themselves in order to control their pain with less medication. The other prepares young cancer patients for difficult procedures like bone marrow transplants and spinal taps so that they'll require less anesthesia. Hypnosis even has applications for AIDS. One small study showed a slower decline in the immune system of a group of AIDS patients who'd had hypnosis along with counseling compared to a group that received counseling alone. Dr. Steven M. Rosenberg (782-8414), an Elkins Park board-certified medical psychotherapist, uses hypnosis in conjunction with behavior modification to help people stop smoking and also to treat insomnia, obsessive/compulsive behavior and concentration problems.

Given the proven value of hypnosis, it's no wonder the English now consider it part of conventional medicine. When choosing a hypnotist, it's wise to select a health professional like a physician or a psychologist. The Greater Philadelphia Society of Clinical Hypnosis has a referral service (386-5288).

Mind/Body Connection
The barriers are down

What a day! Your mother is in the hospital recovering from surgery. You got a royal chewing out from your boss. Your son just called to tell you he's fine, but he smashed up the car. And to top it off, your mind is gossiping with your body about how awful you feel. Chemicals from your brain are racing hither and yon delivering messages about your emotional turmoil to cells in your endocrine and immune systems. That may explain why a few days later you wind up in bed with a god-awful cold.

Such is the premise of a relatively new medical specialty called **psychoneuroimmunology** (PNI), which has established definite links between the brain, behavior and immunity. Dr. Robert Knobler, a neurologist at Thomas Jefferson Hospital, says, "It's now universally accepted that emotional conditions alter hormonal responses, which in turn affect the immune system." He saw it happen in a study he conducted in which patients given a placebo to treat multiple sclerosis exhibited similar responses to another group given a real experimental drug.

We've long known that hope is powerful medicine, and now we're beginning to understand the links between psychological and biological activity. This is a radical shift for Western medicine, which has traditionally viewed the mind (the nervous system) and the body (the immune system) as independent entities. What a shock to find laboratory evidence that thoughts actually have biochemical counterparts. In fact, the body has a whole drugstore of peptides, neurotransmitters, amino acids and the like that translate beliefs and attitudes into physiological changes. Anxiety can affect the gastrointestinal system, contributing to ulcers and colitis. Anger may drive up blood pressure.

Hello—this is the body calling the mind

Now that the links have been established, the hot debate is over how important these connections are and what they mean. *The Harvard Mental Health Letter* reports studies showing that depressed people are more vulnerable to physical illness than those not depressed; that five years after a spouse dies, death rates for widows and widowers are higher than for the still-married; that unhappily married women have fewer of certain immune cells than happily married women; that exercise, relaxation and stress management increased the number of T cells 10 percent in a group of men infected with HIV; that in a group with both highly stressed and relaxed people exposed to cold germs, a much higher percentage of the former got sick; and on and on and on.

Long before research validated the mind/body connection, people like the late Norman Cousins already knew it existed. He's the writer who, after being stricken with arthritis, laughed himself back to health by watching comedy movies. About a dozen years ago he wrote a book, *Anatomy of an Illness as Perceived by the Patient,* that many ridiculed as nonsense. A decade later he'd become the guru of a movement supporting the medical power of positive thinking. It has spawned many of the mind/body interventions used throughout alternative medicine.

In California, Dr. Dean Ornish teaches people to reverse heart disease through diet and lifestyle changes. Harvard cardiologist Dr. Herbert Benson touts the **relaxation response**, widely used to keep stress at bay. At the University of Massachusetts there's a popular eight-week physician-referred course in Buddhist meditation for people with chronic pain and stress-related illnesses. **Transcendental Meditation**, popular in the '60s after the Beatles' encounter with Maharishi Mahesh Yogi, has been learned by more than a million Americans, who use it for everything from hypertension to stress reduction. Research into TM shows that its users have a 56 percent lower hospitalization rate than the norm, that it cuts alcohol and drug abuse, and that it reduces asthma and muscle pain. While critics assail the softness of the studies, TM continues to attract followers. Local TM centers are located at 234 South 22nd Street (732-8464) and 505 Cottman Avenue (745-3925).

Cancer victims in particular seem to benefit from mind/body therapies, especially **guided imagery**, in which hypnotherapists help them (and AIDS patients as well) fight their disease by entering into a light trance. Other imagery therapy teaches patients to imagine a warrior leading an attack march through their body and killing diseased cells.

No one disputes that these techniques improve the quality of life and maybe even prolong it. But the right attitude doesn't *cure* anything. People who've been told that they can think themselves well are prone to feeling like failures when their disease progresses. That is one psychological burden nobody should bear.

Biofeedback and biology

The connection between the mind and the immune system has barely been scratched. Much further along is our understanding of how the mind can be brought to control certain parts of the body. We cannot, for example, lower our blood pressure or slow our heartbeat on command. But we can be trained to recognize when those systems are speeding up and "think" them down. That is the premise behind **biofeedback**. It takes advantage of our ability to manipulate our thoughts so we can create physical changes and control involuntary behavior. Remember Pavlov's famous experiment, in which a dog "learned" to salivate when a bell sounded? Or the way you taught the muscles in your hand to write your name, doing it so many times it became automatic?

That skill can be harnessed with the use of a machine and the help of a mental health professional, usually a psychologist. The patient sits in front of a computer screen with electrodes and sensors placed on his or her fingers and body. These measure internal activity like heart rate, muscle tension and temperature, which show up on the screen like a line on a graph or as tones. When the patient thinks calm, pleasing thoughts, the line flattens out. Yet with the stress of something as simple as trying to remember a phone number, the line leaps up and down like a jumping bean. With the coaching of a therapist, patients develop the ability to control the line and change these automatic responses on their own.

Biofeedback has changed a great deal from the early days, when it was believed that lowering temperature and relaxing the muscles in the forehead would improve just about any problem, from stress to debilitating pain. Today the thrust is toward specific tasks for specific symptoms. A woman who had residual pain after surgery from a pinched nerve in her neck, for example, was taught to relax by raising the temperature in her finger. But because she was relaxing the wrong thing, it didn't work and she considered biofeedback a failure. When she gave it another try and learned breathing control and neuromuscular relaxation, she got relief.

Biofeedback isn't easy. "It's not a massage," says Linda Schrier, a Ph.D. in psychology who runs a program at 1015 Chestnut Street (592-8165). "You have to do the work and be motivated. The machine just tells how you're doing." After a dozen sessions you should know if you're getting anywhere.

What's around?

For an excellent overview of this subject, see *Mind/Body Medicine: How to Use Your Mind for Better Health,* edited by Daniel Goleman, Ph.D., and Joel Gurin for Consumer Reports Books. In addition, the Mastery Program, with main headquarters at 700 South Henderson Road, King of Prussia (337-4550), does a souped-up form of biofeedback that has been successful in treating problems as diverse as alcoholism, depression and chronic pain. A psychological program in stress and chronic-pain management has just been started at Friends Hospital. At the Valley Forge Medical Center, Tracey Vawter uses biofeedback to treat alcohol, drug and gambling addictions (539-8500).

Macrobiotics

What it is

Based on the philosophical foundation of yin and yang, macrobiotics is not merely a diet but an entirely new way of living. The goal of adherents is for the body to achieve balance with the environment, which may necessitate giving up all things chemical or synthetic (including commercial cosmetics and polyester clothing) as well as household appliances that emit low-level radiation (such as microwaves and television sets).

True followers of macrobiotics devote at least half of their fairly limited menu to whole grains, 20 to 30 percent to vegetables and the rest to soups, beans, sea vegetables (such as kelp) and some fish. The preparation of meals, which are made in a pressure cooker or steamed on a gas stove, is meticulous and time-consuming—even the way the food is cut influences its nutritional value. Proponents also pay great attention to where it is grown, seeking out food that is organic and local to keep in tune with the environment. For instance, people who live in New England would eat more apples than oranges; in Florida, the opposite.

The emphasis is on unprocessed products; refined sugar is verboten. "The food you eat has a powerful energy," says Robert Pirello, publisher and editor of *MacroNews*. "Your blood, your bones, your mind all are created from what you put in your body. The effect is not just physical, but spiritual and emotional."

Does it work?

Macrobiotic literature is rife with anecdotal cases of sick people who put up with the rigors of this plan because they believe it's responsible for reversing chronic or deadly diseases such as cancer. John Denver and Dr. Benjamin Spock are among its adherents, and its success stories range from reports of increased energy and stamina to a decreased dependency on drugs for ailments such as diabetes and hypoglycemia.

Dr. Howard Posner, a homeopathic physician practicing nutritional therapy and internal medicine in Bala Cynwyd, says that a macrobiotic diet can be beneficial, but only when used sparingly: "B-2, B-6, B-12 and vitamin D deficiencies often occur with this program, leading to anemia, rickets and possibly nerve damage."

This lifestyle is difficult to maintain, which may be why so many people quit. But used for short periods in moderation, macrobiotics appears to have benefits. Even Posner admits it can "really clean out the system, and is much better than the garbage the average American eats."

Macrobiotic workshops and cooking classes are conducted through the offices of *MacroNews* (243 Dickinson Street; 551-1430). If you want to sample macrobiotic food, try the lunch counter at Essene Cafe and Natural Food Market (719 South 4th Street), or take home prepared macrobiotic meals from Zagara's (501

Route 73 South, Marlton, NJ). For a good introduction to macrobiotics, try Michio Kusbi's *The Macrobiotic Way*.

Herbalism

What it is

In certain hospitals in China, patients get their medication delivered at the crack of dawn in a thermos bottle. Inside is a foul-tasting tea that's been tailor-made from a concoction of herbs. China isn't alone in relying on herbal medicine: People in most Third World nations still use plants, a medicinal source since the earliest days of mankind, in lieu of drugs. After a woman we know caught a cold in Belize, her guide walked into the rain forest, pulled some leaves from a plant called jackass bitters and steeped them in a tea that cured her in two days.

Unlike an all-purpose antibiotic that a Western doctor is likely to give every patient with a sore throat, therapeutic herbs are highly individualized treatments geared to assisting natural healing. True Chinese herb doctors are scarce in Philadelphia, so your best bet is to find an acupuncturist who knows the tradition. Laila Wah (731-0177) is an all-purpose Oriental healer who includes among her techniques acupuncture, herbology and shiatsu massage. Wah reports particular success treating complaints like PMS, high blood pressure, stress and back pain with a clientele that includes many business and professional people. "I only want to treat those who come to me to be empowered to take care of their own health," she says.

Does it work?

It all depends what for. There's no good argument for treating a serious infection with herbs instead of antibiotics. On the other hand, there's ample reason to look into herbs for treating the ailments of modern society for which there are no cures—things like fatigue, indigestion and the stuffiness of colds. Some herbs, such as echinacea, are known immune-boosters; many herbs contain the same active ingredients found in conventional drugs, yet are far gentler. But do be careful— some herbs can be quite toxic and should not be taken without guidance.

The American Association of Acupuncture and Oriental Medicine furnishes referrals for local acupuncturists and information about Chinese herbs for a $5 charge. Send a written request to 4104 Lake Boon Trail, Raleigh, N.C., 27607.

Informed Consent

Keep in mind that alternative medicine is best used as a complement to allopathic medicine, not a substitute. Before you jump in, consider the following:

Don't seek an alternative for something that should be treated conventionally—acute diseases, a serious infection, broken bones, a malignancy. You could do yourself great harm this way.

Ask how many treatments it will take to feel some improvement, and if you don't get it within that number, move on.

If the cost seems exorbitant or a large outlay of cash is required up front, be careful. Charlatans are skilled in duping people desperate for cures.

Natural isn't synonymous with safe. There are herbs that can be quite toxic. As soon as you experience side effects, stop treatment.

Check out the practitioner's credentials. Don't be shy asking about things like educational background, licensing, certification, accreditation. A string of initials after someone's name doesn't make him a professional. Many alternative therapies have state or national associations that can provide information. Call them!

Be appropriately skeptical and leery of anybody who promises something that only a magic wand could conjure. Watch out for "brand new," unproven treatments, astounding claims and secret discoveries, especially those invented by people with no medical background. If a therapy promises the moon and sounds ridiculous, it probably is. Remember Laetrile?

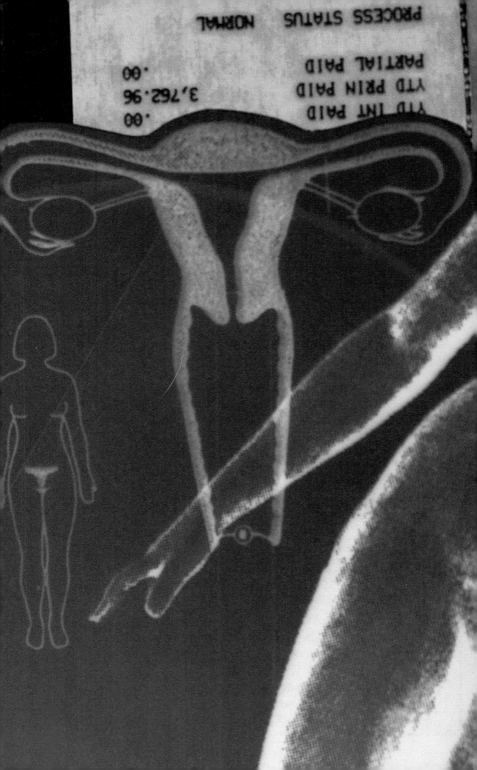

5

The Healthy Woman

Good Health Made Simple

At the Center for Women's Health, we believe each facet of your health is part of the whole—so why get your health care in fragments? We've brought together in one location a team of health care professionals who provide comprehensive health care for women of all ages, with special attention to menopause and the years after.

For more information or an appointment, call 1-800-PRO-HEALTH.

CENTER *for* WOMEN'S HEALTH
MEDICAL COLLEGE OF PENNSYLVANIA

City Avenue and Presidential Boulevard
Philadelphia, Pa.

Offering care and programs in:
Gynecology • Internal Medicine • Obstetrics • Menopause • Breast Health •
Weight Management and Nutrition • PMS • Psychological Counseling • Osteoporosis •
Incontinence • Gynecologic Oncology • Plastic Surgery • Repetitive Pregnancy Loss •
And More!

In Sickness and in Health

Finally, women's diseases and conditions are getting the attention they deserve

For too long, women have gotten the shaft from the male-dominated medical establishment. Consider just this one example: Back in the '60s, epidemiological studies suggested that the hormone estrogen helped protect women from heart disease. So what did the government do? It spent millions on two huge studies investigating the effects of estrogen on the heart—*in men!*

This exasperating story is but one example of the way research dollars have favored men, giving scant attention to women's diseases and producing treatment models of questionable relevance to 51 percent of the population. But in recent years women have gotten smart and turned militant, demanding their fair share. As a result, in 1993 the government launched the Women's Health Initiative, which will spend $625 million over the next 14 years testing prevention and treatment strategies for three major diseases affecting older women: osteoporosis, heart disease and cancer.

Suddenly women's health is not only the hot spot in medical research, but the cutting edge in hospital marketing. Providers are busy setting up special women's centers and competing for women's medical business. Despite these gains, women must be careful not to forget the lesson that came out of all those years of being ignored: educate yourself. The closest guarantee to good medicine is an informed patient.

To help you along, here is an overview of the diseases and conditions affecting all those with birth certificates marked *female*.

Hysteria Over Hysterectomy

Here's a *Jeopardy* question I'll bet most of you will miss. The answer is: the second-most-frequent major surgery in the United States. Did you guess gallbladder? Nope. Mastectomy? Heart bypass? Laminectomy? All wrong. The correct response: What is hysterectomy?—a far-too-frequently performed operation that removes a woman's uterus and/or ovaries. (Cesarean sections are in first place.) An estimated 650,000 hysterectomies are performed annually in the United States, five times the rate in Europe. By age 60, more than one-third of American women have bid their reproductive organs goodbye. Typically the surgery occurs around age 43. By contrast, only 4 percent of European women in their 40s have had the same experience.

The uterus is one of the few organs that gets taken out even when it's not diseased. The criteria for recommending a hysterectomy have been about as flexible as a Slinky. At least two of them—cancer prevention and birth control—are not valid. And with increased information that the uterus plays a lifelong role in certain hormonal activity, it can no longer be viewed as being nothing more than a fetal residence. The question a woman facing a hysterectomy ought to be asking isn't whether she needs her uterus, but whether she needs to undergo major surgery from which 25 to 50 percent of patients experience some complications, albeit usually minor.

What's behind the American love affair with hysterectomy? There are a variety of reasons ranging from economics (it's a great income-producer for doctors) to acceptance (because doctors do so many, they've become relatively safe) to attitude (many still consider the uterus a useless organ, post-childbearing) to a lack of viable alternatives. But all these traditional arguments for hysterectomy have begun leaking like a torpedoed water tower. More and more gynecologists, joined by the voices of women's health consumer groups, are railing against using hysterectomy as a routine answer to the common female problems of benign tumors and excessive bleeding.

When is it necessary?

Thomas Jefferson University gynecologist Marty Weisberg says there are only a handful of legitimate grounds for performing hysterectomies. From a doctor's point of view they are: cancer—the kind that can be cured by taking out the uterus; fibroid tumors that are so large they're impinging on other organs; anemia from excessive bleeding; massive infections that don't respond to antibiotics. That's it. From a patient's perspective, the surgery may be a valid option if the woman has intolerably heavy periods that turn her into a menstrual cripple, unusually painful menstrual cramps that aren't amenable to any other treatment or very large fibroid tumors that make it impossible for her to button her skirts. "For a doctor, the decision usually relates to life-threatening issues," says Weisberg. "For the patient, it may be more to improve the quality of life than to save it."

At the very least, no woman should agree to a hysterectomy without getting a second opinion. Keep in mind that surgeons like to operate. As Dr. Francis Hutchins, a gynecological surgeon at Graduate Hospital, puts it, "If your only tool is a hammer, every problem looks like a nail." Questions you want to raise include: Do I have a disease? Is it serious? What are the consequences of doing nothing? What are my treatment options?

Ask about a myomectomy

A woman with fibroid tumors, a benign condition responsible for about one-third of all hysterectomies, may consider an operation called a myomectomy if she's of childbearing age and/or doesn't want to lose her uterus. This operation, often performed by fertility specialists, cuts out the tumors but leaves the uterus functional. Depending on the size or placement of the tumor, a myomectomy can be done by opening the abdomen or with a minimal incision using a laparoscope or through the vagina using a hysteroscope. Dr. Hutchins says, "Myomectomy is best used in selected cases with few tumors of moderate size. Though once considered more complicated than just removing the uterus itself, today we have improved techniques with drugs and certain instruments that can reduce the blood loss, and that's key to reducing complications." Myomectomies, which are popular in Europe, require a high level of technical skill—more than a standard hysterectomy—so choose your surgeon carefully and ask how often he/she does this procedure.

On the other hand, a woman approaching menopause who has fibroid tumors that aren't causing pain or a bulging belly may want to try to sweat it out with hormonal treatments, because the growth of these tumors depends on an estrogen supply. As that hormone level dwindles, the tumors shrink.

Help for heavy bleeders

As for excessive bleeding, the other common cause for a hysterectomy, that can be handled medically by either birth control pills or a variety of hormones that turn off the ovaries temporarily—or surgically. A new version of an old technique called endometrial ablation is gaining attention to counteract heavy bleeding, but it's still considered investigational by some insurance carriers. Essentially it destroys the lining of the uterus while leaving the organ intact. Hutchins used it recently for a thirtysomething executive whose periods were so bad that she once had to excuse an entire group of people from a meeting and call her secretary to help her mop up the blood stains on her suit. "Her choice," he explains, "was a hysterectomy with a six-week recovery or a one-day outpatient procedure that kept her uterus whole."

Endometrial ablation should be done only by someone who does it often and very well. "It's not easy," says Weisberg, "until you learn to do it." It's one of a number of procedures done through the increasingly popular hysteroscope, which is inserted into the vagina. When equipped with lights and lenses, this is a terrific diagnostic tool, especially to examine the uterus, perhaps take a biopsy and determine the cause of pain or bleeding.

Old vs. new

Speaking of gadgets, your surgeon may offer a new way of doing hysterectomies through the vagina using a laparoscope instead of a big incision in the abdomen. In the right hands and under the right circumstances, this can be a very good operation that leaves only a tiny scar and substantially reduces recovery time. But proceed cautiously before accepting this option, because it's being heavily promoted by companies who make the equipment and used as a marketing tool by doctors who don't have enough experience in its usage.

In short, don't get talked into a hysterectomy without exploring other possibilities and don't get lured into a new-fangled technique by somebody who is eager to use your body as a classroom.

Plugging the Leak: Incontinence

God is a man, after all.

That seems an inescapable conclusion if you look at a diagram illustrating why ten women have trouble controlling their bladders for every man similarly afflicted. When God made women, he gave them poorly developed bladder-control muscles. A woman's bladder rests on a trampoline-like muscular sheet called the pelvic floor, which holds it in place above the vagina—an arrangement with a certain amount of give that is unique to women. If the pelvic-floor muscle stretches or tears—as often happens in childbirth or at menopause—the bladder can fall in on the vagina, and the delicate pressure-transmission system that regulates urine flow through the urethra is disrupted. That's when you may have to depend on Depends.

As many as 10 million women in the United States suffer from incontinence, a problem compounded by feelings of shame and embarrassment that can cause sufferers to withdraw from normal activity and avoid seeking help. It's tragic, because most incontinence is treatable and much is curable.

The most common of several types is stress incontinence, in which some kind of impact—such as a sneeze, laughter, walking or reaching up—can cause displacement of the urethra and leakage of urine. It affects a small number of young women, especially in aerobics classes. About 30 percent of middle-aged women leak to some degree. And after menopause causes the pelvic floor to weaken and the tissues of the urethra to shrink, about one-third of all women experience incontinence.

Risk factors

Gender, age and childbearing are the main risk factors associated with incontinence. Most physicians believe that exercises developed in the '40s by a California gynecologist, Arnold Kegel, can not only help incontinence without resorting to surgery but also prevent the condition. Some even think these exercises should be taught to all pregnant women, because about 15 percent of new mothers experience stress incontinence after delivery; the number declines naturally to about 5 percent within three months. Kegels are fairly simple to do: The woman flexes the pelvic-floor muscles for ten minutes three times a day. It's an subtle regimen that can easily be combined with driving, watching television or conversing. For further instruction, speak to your doctor. Most women attempting Kegels have trouble locating the proper muscles. They're the ones that resist when a woman pulls out a tampon, and the ones stimulated during orgasm—which brings to mind a fringe benefit of the exercises!

Incontinence is often the result of an anatomical change. With aging, things get out of place; angles shift. When Kegel exercises don't help, surgery may be a route worth considering to restore the proper anatomy. There are several surgical approaches available—through the vagina, through an incision in the abdomen and through a laparoscope. The latest development is an injectable substance that provides support around the urethra. Discuss your options with your gynecologist, and if surgery is suggested, get a second opinion from a urologist.

On Again, Off Again: PMS

The old jokes about women getting out of whack when their monthlies come along are no longer considered funny now that PMS (premenstrual syndrome) has been recognized as a very real and chronic problem for as many as half of all women in their reproductive years. The symptoms encompass a broad range of emotional and physical responses that occur between ovulation and menstruation. This cyclical pattern and timing is critical in diagnosing the problem because the varied symptoms—things like mood swings, food cravings, angry outbursts, breast tenderness, fluid retention, migraines, anxiety, backaches, tension—mimic other disorders.

The causes are unknown but thought to be related to hormonal changes. Sometimes diet helps, but when PMS begins to interfere with work and relationships, a more aggressive medical approach may be in order. The Women's Health Connection, an organization devoted to holistic education and research in women's health, reports significant success in treating PMS with natural micronized progesterone. This is a substance derived from plants that is reportedly an exact chemical duplicate of what the ovaries produce, compared to synthetic progesterone, which is similar but not identical. The vast majority of the medical literature doesn't support the improved effects of natural progesterone, but it seems to help many women and may be worth examining.

More promising is the discovery that the antidepressant drug Prozac effectively relieves the anxiety, depression and food cravings associated with PMS. It has become a frontline treatment for the problem. Hormonal treatments are also used as a last resort, as are oral contraceptives.

PMS is a debilitating syndrome and should not simply be endured as a curse of being female. While finding the right treatment make take some trial and error, looking is worth the trouble.

For additional information

HUP operates the respected PMS Clinic under the direction of Dr. Steven Sondheimer (662-3329). Other hospitals that maintain women's health centers, such as Hahnemann, MCP and Graduate, can also be helpful.

PMS Access (1-800-222-4PMS) is a national information hotline for education as well as referral to support groups and physicians who specialize in PMS treatment.

Women's International Pharmacy (1-800-279-5708) is affiliated with the Women's Health Connection. They will answer questions about natural progesterone and PMS, as well as other holistic medicines for treating menopause, infertility, postpartum depression and thyroid and adrenal disorder. They also send detailed information packets free of charge.

The Reason for Pap Smears: Cervical Cancer

After years of stressing that cancer is not contagious, scientists now suspect that one kind—cervical cancer—can be transmitted after all. No, it doesn't spread through sneezes or handshakes, but intimate contact is very much the point. Since the 19th century, doctors have pondered the fact that prostitutes often get cervical cancer and nuns rarely do. Research published in 1980 convinced most doctors that the human papilloma virus (HPV) is the culprit that spreads the disease. HPV has more than 60 subtypes, including one that causes the common finger wart and four associated with genital cancer. Scientists can neither culture HPV nor cure it, and often no visible symptoms appear, but sometimes it shows up as a cauliflower-like wart or as dysplasia, an area of abnormal cell growth on the cervix that is always treated when discovered, because it can lead to cancer.

About 13,500 new cases of cervical cancer were diagnosed in the United States last year, and 4,400 women died from it. The women most likely to be stricken fall between the ages of 20 and 40, have been sexually active since the age of 17 and have had many sex partners. Even intercourse with just one partner—male or female—can mean a high risk of exposure to HPV if that partner has had multiple sexual contacts. Women who smoke more than four cigarettes a day and those whose immune systems are suppressed by AIDS or other medical conditions are also at increased risk.

Preventive measures, as with any other sexually transmitted disease, are pretty obvious: Limit your number of sex partners and use a condom even if you're on the pill. Be advised, though, that when it comes to HPV, "safe" sex is not completely safe because the virus can be spread through contact between the genitals, not just through semen. The most important prevention by far is for women to have a yearly Pap smear starting at age 18 or when they become sexually active. This inexpensive test, while sometimes inaccurate, helps doctors to identify cell abnormalities before they become cancerous and has contributed to a high overall survival rate of 66 percent within five years of detection.

Sex and STDs

While HPV is the only sexually transmitted disease associated with cancer, other STDs—chlamydia, gonorrhea, syphilis, trichomoniasis, genital herpes, genital warts—cause other dangerous infections that lead to all kinds of dire complications of the reproductive tract. The Guttmacher Institute reports that each year women come down with over a million cases of pelvic inflammatory disease, just one complication of a particular STD that may lead to anything from chronic pelvic pain to infertility.

At present the best protection against STDs are latex condoms. Some are curable with antibiotic treatment. Herpes, one of the viruses, can be controlled with the drug acyclovir. If you have vaginal discomfort or sores, see your doctor immediately.

No Prevention or Cure: Ovarian Cancer

The statistics on this are worse than grim: One in 70 women in the United States will develop ovarian cancer; 21,000 new cases were diagnosed last year and 13,000 women died from it—61 percent of them within five years of diagnosis. Ovarian cancer usually strikes after menopause, with incidence peaking in the early 60s and then subsiding. Women who have never been pregnant and women who enter early menopause also appear to be at increased risk. Studies have implicated high-fat diets and the use of talcum powder on sanitary pads or genitals, but those results are not universally accepted. Use of the birth-control pill appears to provide a measure of protection.

Ovarian cancer is almost never found early, in part because its symptoms—indigestion, fullness and pain in the lower abdomen—occur late. At least 75 percent of its victims are already in the third of four stages of cancer when they are discovered, which means that the tumors have spread. In 1989, after comedian Gilda Radner died of ovarian cancer at the age of 42, her husband, Gene Wilder, launched a television advertising campaign to persuade more women to seek a trio of tests that can help screen for the disease. One of them is CA-125, a tumor byproduct secreted into the bloodstream. It was developed to help manage patients with known ovarian cancer, which is its only FDA-approved use. The CA-125 test has an enormously high rate of false positives and is not a reliable screening tool.

There are three types of ovarian cancer, but 85 percent are of the epithelial variety, affecting the surface of the ovary where the egg breaks free once a month, creating opportunities for abnormal cell transformations. A 1990 Italian study suggested that about 5.8 percent of ovarian cancers occur in women whose family members have a predisposition to the disease, and tends to strike them in their 30s or 40s.

Women attempting to assess their risk should determine whether at least two first-degree relatives—mother or sisters—had ovarian cancer. But it is not at all clear what the next step should be. Little is known about the risk. Some high-risk women opt to have their ovaries removed, but there are cases of ovarian cancer occurring in the peritoneal cavity even in the absence of ovaries. For most women in 1994, medical science offers virtually no effective screening method and no preventive measures.

Dem Bones, Dem Bones: Osteoporosis

Osteoporosis, the scourge of the elderly, is in a sense a childhood disease, because the scene is set early in life for trouble later on, when osteoporosis causes thin, weak bones to fracture, sometimes spontaneously, crippling bodies and curbing independence. Building strong bones between ages 11 and 24 is essential so that a woman has a full deck when she reaches her peak bone density, in her early 30s. From then on, according to current medical research, she only discards bone mass and can never draw more.

Some 25 million Americans suffer from osteoporosis, and that number is expected to swell to epidemic proportions as the population lives longer and baby boomers age. Aside from demographics, data shows that between 1955 and 1983, for unknown reasons, bone-fracture rates increased. Osteoporosis affects more than half of all women over 65. In their 50s, six women suffer from osteoporosis for every man; by their 80s, the proportion is two to one.

Scientists believe that estrogen protects women from bone loss until menopause, which ushers in a five-year period of rapid decline (as much as 20 percent of bone mass) followed by a continuing loss of 1 to 3 percent per year until death. Although osteoporosis is not in itself deadly, geriatric hip fractures often force women into nursing homes, and complications are fatal 20 percent of the time.

Risky business

Gender and advancing age are the main risk factors for osteoporosis. Caucasians and Asians are more likely victims than blacks. Thin women with small frames are at a disadvantage, although height itself is not a predictor. Poor nutrition, a sedentary lifestyle, smoking, excessive caffeine and boozing—especially in youth—are all associated with osteoporosis. Excessive exercise and abnormal menstruation—as is common among anorexics—can permanently disrupt the formation of bone mass, as can some drugs, including corticosteroids, anticonvulsants and thyroid hormones that suppress the pituitary gland. Family history appears to be relevant as well.

The calcium connection

Calcium builds strong bones, just as your mother told you, and after age 55, it actually helps to retard bone loss. Premenopausal women should ingest 1,000 milligrams per day; after menopause, when the ability to absorb calcium diminishes, 1,500 milligrams is preferred. Foods that are rich in calcium include milk (an eight-ounce glass provides about 300 milligrams) and some other dairy products; green leafy vegetables like broccoli, collard greens and spinach; oysters, salmon, sardines and tofu. Vitamin D helps the body absorb calcium. It's available, along with calcium, in tablet form; the antacid Tums is a good source.

The estrogen connection

Increasingly, doctors are prescribing estrogen (along with progesterone) for menopausal women at high risk of osteoporosis. The hormone retards bone loss and reduces the risk of both fractures and heart disease by 50 percent. The doctors interviewed about osteoporosis for this chapter were against the routine prescription of hormone replacement therapy for *all* women, but believed it to be beneficial for many. One indicator would be a measure of bone density. The $170 test is not cost-effective for all premenopausal women, but worth considering for those in the danger categories.

The guaranteed no-risk prevention for osteoporosis is weight-bearing exercise—important for bone health throughout life, but crucial for the elderly. (See Chapter 2, *Barbells Are Not for Dumbbells.*) For additional information, contact the National Osteoporosis Foundation in Washington at 202-223-2226.

Priming the Pump: Heart Disease

Concern—and anger—about heart disease in women exploded onto the American scene two years ago after new studies showed that certain diagnostic tests are not as accurate in women as in men and that women do not fare as well as men in certain kinds of heart surgery. Moreover, statistics show that 39 percent of women die with-in the first year after a heart attack, compared with only 31 percent of men. Clearly, heart problems of women need to be treated differently from males'.

We know that women often wait longer than men to seek treatment after a heart attack, possibly because their symptoms don't fit the familiar male pattern of a crushing sensation in the chest spreading toward the left side. Women's symptoms tend to be less specific, may involve discomfort in the stomach or upper abdomen and, instead of pain, they experience fatigue, sweating and nausea.

Heart attacks tend to strike women ten to 20 years later than men. It's thought this is because estrogen helps to protect women until menopause, perhaps by lowering bad cholesterol (LDL) and raising good cholesterol (HDL), or perhaps by protecting the walls of the blood vessels. But after age 65, one in three American women suffers from cardiovascular disease.

Calculate your risk

High blood pressure (140/90 or higher) puts women at heightened risk for heart disease. Diabetes appears to diminish the advantages estrogen bestows on women. High-fat diets and cigarette smoking increase risk, but moderate alcohol intake of one or two drinks a day may actually lower it. Black women are 24 percent more likely to die of heart disease than white women, and for all women, a family history of premature coronary disease (before age 60) is a red flag. Other contributory factors are a couch-potato lifestyle and apple-shape obesity (large midsections) as opposed to the pear-shape type (with large buttocks and thighs). Who knows why? A history of yo-yo dieting, stress and use of birth-control pills may also add to your risk.

Doctors had been in a dither about the dangers of cholesterol until new studies suggested that while too much cholesterol is indeed harmful, too little may leave a person vulnerable to many noncoronary diseases, including some cancers, strokes, and lung and liver disease. In general, anything above 240 is considered high and should be discussed with your doctor. But more important than the total number is the good (HDL) to bad (LDL) ratio. HDL carries cholesterol out of the cells into the liver, where it's excreted. LDL carries it into the bloodstream, where it decorates the artery walls.

Women who want to ward off heart disease should not smoke, should consider hormone therapy after menopause and should exercise for 20 to 30 minutes three or four times a week. Even a brisk walk raises the heartbeat. A low-fat diet is also important. Avoid eating a lot of animal fat, especially pork and beef, and remove skin from chicken. Fry as little as possible and when you do, use vegetable or olive oil, not palm or coconut oil. Skip cheeses, substitute yogurt for sour cream, and drink low-fat milk. More than any other malady, the prevention of heart disease forces a woman to take a sober look at her lifestyle and perhaps make basic changes that may require forming new habits. Like we said at the beginning, knowledge is power—and the key to good health.

Look for Lumps: Breast Cancer

Perhaps no disease that afflicts women has generated more lore, myth or wishful thinking than breast cancer. One cancer surgeon who is fed up with theories about ear wax and breast size as risk factors—and macrobiotic diets and laughter as cures—says, "I think when somebody has the disease, it's biology that determines the outcome. I have lots of patients who have great attitudes who are doing real crummy."

The facts are these: The chances of a woman getting breast cancer have more than doubled since 1940, according to the American Cancer Society. One in eight women is now likely to be stricken. But the percentage of those who die—roughly 46,000 a year—has remained constant. The glimmer of good news is that the five-year survival rate of women with breast cancer *that is found early* is 92 percent. There is no better prevention than early detection. Most breast lumps are found by women themselves, a strong argument for monthly self-examination. Mammographies are also critical. The guidelines are in a state of flux, but, in general, a baseline study between 35 and 40 is advised, followed by bi-annual mammograms from 40 to 50 and annual ones thereafter. Very high-risk women, in particular those with breast implants that may be defective and leaking, should consider an MRI, which is more effective than a mammogram for diagnosing abnormal breast tissue.

Risk factors

Heredity looks like a prime risk factor: 15 percent of breast cancer seems to be genetically linked. Women are at increased risk if one or more of their close relatives—mother, sisters and grandmothers—have had it. The history of the mother's side of the family appears to be more important than that of the father's side, and the younger the relatives were when the disease struck, the more likely it is that the cancer will be passed on.

Hormonal cycles, too, seem to have an impact. Early onset of menstruation (the average age for American girls is 13) and late onset of menopause (the average age is 50) are associated with increased risk, while breast-feeding is associated with reduced risk. Obese women and those who have never had a full-term pregnancy are probably also at increased risk, as are women who have used birth-control pills for more than six years and before childbirth. Estrogen replacement therapy is thought by some to increase the incidence of breast cancer in certain women. (See Chapter 20, *A Change of Thought on Change of Life.*) The cause and effect of alcohol and a high-fat diet have yet to be determined, although preliminary evidence points to some connection between breast cancer and a high intake of either one. Studies are currently under way examining a link between breast cancer and pesticides, as well as other environmental factors.

The incidence of breast cancer rises with age, and women who have had it once are more likely to get it again. Benign lumps are not predictive of cancer, but they can complicate its detection.

The preventive value of the drug Tamoxifen is being studied in depth along with the identification of a genetic marker for predicting who will get certain other cancers. But until research comes up with definitive answers, screening, self-exams and awareness are as good as it gets.

Breast cancer resources and services

The following organizations provide a range of help to breast-cancer patients and their families:

Breast Health Institute
1015 CHESTNUT STREET; 627-4447

A nonprofit center dedicated to raising money for breast-cancer research. Provides advocacy, educational seminars and research grants. Gives vouchers to uninsured, low-income women for mammography services at Hahnemann University Hospital. Sponsors the Race for the Cure, a well-attended fund-raising event for research money held annually on Mother's Day at the Philadelphia Art Museum.

Linda Creed Foundation
118 SOUTH 11TH STREET; 955-4354

Dedicated to the early detection and treatment of breast cancer, this is a nonprofit organization sponsored by Jefferson Hospital, offering seminars, advocacy and referrals. Operates free mammography services and free breast-cancer screenings at Jefferson Park Hospital, Methodist Hospital and Jefferson Hospital. Provides educational programs through businesses and high schools on breast self-examination, risk factors and disease protection. Also runs a 12-week support workshop for breast-cancer patients.

Living Beyond Breast Cancer
P.O. Box 92; NARBERTH, PA 19072; 610-668-1320

Nonprofit organization established by radiation oncologist Marisa Weiss. In collaboration with various hospitals, it sponsors periodic educational conferences for survivors as well as physicians, featuring noted authorities as speakers. Call to be put on mailing list.

The Joan A. Karnell Women's Cancer Center
AYER BUILDING; 800 SPRUCE STREET; 829-7584

The center provides group and individual therapy for women and their families, cosmetology services and patient educational programs. Also specializes in cancer of the reproductive organs. A resource library is open, free of charge, from 9 to 4:30 on weekdays.

Support Groups

A New Beginning
ABINGTON HOSPITAL; DIXON BUILDING; HORACE
AVENUE; ABINGTON; 646-4954

A self-help support group for victims. Families and friends are welcome. A member of the National Breast Coalition.

Breast Cancer Support Group
MONTGOMERY CANCER CENTER; 1330 POWELL STREET,
SUITE 308; NORRISTOWN; 270-2700

Two-hour programs that teach individuals how to cope with breast cancer are held once a month.

Note: Check hospital listings for additional breast-cancer support groups.

Therapeutic Services

Breast Cancer Physical Therapy Center
1905 SPRUCE STREET; 772-0160

Pre- and post-surgical physical therapy, particularly to restore movement in the arm and shoulder area after mastectomy. The center is especially noted for its work in minimizing and controlling lymphadema.

External Reconstruction Technology
4835 BENNER STREET; 333-8424

An alternative to surgical implants for mastectomy patients. Creates highly individualized breasts, adhered with adhesive, to match patient's skin tone and body contour.

Women's Services

Alpha Pregnancy Services
735-6028

Birthright
877-7070

Childbirth Education Association of Greater Philadelphia
828-0131

Choice Hotline
985-3300

Covenant House
844-1020

Health clinic for infants and adults, pre-natal care; payment on a sliding scale.

Elizabeth Blackwell Center for Women
923-7577

A full spectrum of health services, including primary care with a feminist perspective, gynecology, confidential HIV testing, counseling.

HERS Foundation
667-7757

Hysterectomy educational resources and services that focus on alternative options as well as the consequences of surgery.

Interim House
849-4606

Six-month treatment facility for women recovering from substance abuse.

Lamaze Educators of Southeastern Pennsylvania, Inc.
1-800-368-4404

My Sister's Place
727-1640

One-year residential substance abuse rehab for pregnant women and women with children up to four years of age. Must be on medical assistance.

Planned Parenthood
351-5560

Pregnancy Hotline
829-5437

Resolve
849-3920

For couples with infertility problems.

Spectrum Health Services
471-2750

Comprehensive services including medical, counseling and education.

WATS—Women's Anonymous Test Site
246-5210

Anonymous, free HIV testing and counseling.

WOAR—Women Organized Against Rape
985-3333

Counseling and support services for children and adults, education for groups and schools, 24-hour hotline.

Women Coping With Chronic Physical Illness
762-6660

A support group for women with chronic medical conditions. Meets weekly at Hahnemann University Hospital.

Women's Diagnostic Services
667-6634

Breast care for women, low-dose mammographies and self-examination training.

Women's Recovery Center
110 NORTH ESSEX AVENUE, NARBERTH, PA; 664-5858

Intensive outpatient programs for women with eating disorders including bulimia, anorexia, binge eating and compulsive overeating, with special attention to cross-addictions. Small groups meet three times a week and use a variety of treatment modalities, including movement therapy, drug and alcohol counseling, support groups, nutritional advice and educational workshops.

Women's Suburban Clinic
647-1344

Gynecological care.

Domestic Abuse

Domestic Abuse Project of Delaware County
565-4590

Counseling, case management, support groups, employment services, safe house, 24-hour crisis hotline.

Domestic Violence Program
SPANISH HOTLINE, 235-9992
ENGLISH HOTLINE, 739-9999

Free counseling, legal referrals, G.E.D. classes, employment counseling/training, teen-parent program.

Lutheran Settlement House
426-8610

Up to 30 days residency for victims of domestic violence; affiliated with Domestic Violence Program.

Women Against Abuse
386-7777

Shelter for battered women and children, legal center, transitional housing.

Women in Transition
751-1111

Composed of four interrelated services: 24-hour hotline, counseling and advocacy, peer support groups, and prevention education and community outreach.

PARTNERSHIPS DO WORK!

J ust ask one of the 14,000 children who have leaned on the Caring Foundation, Independence Blue Cross and Pennsylvania Blue Shield.

Nearly four years ago, Independence Blue Cross and Pennsylvania Blue Shield took the lead in addressing the needs of uninsured children in our region. They created the Caring Foundation of Southeastern Pennsylvania to provide health care insurance for children whose parents made too much for government assistance but not enough to buy the insurance themselves.

Already, more than 14,000 children have gone to the doctor's office and emergency room, had blood tests, immunizations, eye exams and much more because of the Caring Foundation. All at no cost to their families.

The Foundation's success is in its partnerships. The leadership of Independence Blue Cross and Pennsylvania Blue Shield makes this initiative work, along with the involvement of other funders, health care providers, state and local government and the community-at-large.

Last year, Governor Casey selected the Foundation to run the Children's Health Insurance Program (CHIP) of Pennsylvania in this region. With the Governor's recent expansion of that program, the Caring Foundation can now insure thousands more children.

Now, more children than ever can lean on us.

The Caring Foundation...the answer for uninsured children!

The Caring Foundation
OF SOUTHEASTERN PENNSYLVANIA

To become a partner, call
1-800-464-KIDS

A charitable foundation affiliated with

**Independence
Blue Cross
Pennsylvania
Blue Shield**

® Registered Marks of the Blue Cross and
Blue Shield Association, an association of Independent
Blue Cross and Blue Shield Plans.

CHAPTER 20

A Change of Thought on Change of Life

For years menopausal women worried about the risks of hormone therapy. Now they're talking about the benefits

s it warm in here or is it me?" asked one of the four women at the table, fanning herself furiously with the menu. Her three companions, all successful career women closing in on their 50th birthdays, nodded sympathetically at the classic symptom of a hot flash.

"Aren't you taking hormones?" one of them asked.

"No. I've read too much about the risks of breast cancer and I'm afraid," she replied. "I'm trying to tough it out, but I don't think I can last. I haven't had a full night's sleep in months. I wake up two or three times; my nightgown's soaked. And talk about moody! I'm up and down like a yo-yo."

"Well, I think you're nuts," her friend said. "I've been on estrogen for four years. It took a while to get the dosage adjusted, and I'm not thrilled with getting my period every month, but I must say, I feel terrific. It's kind of like slowing down the aging process." She grinned. "And that includes getting my sex drive back."

The third woman had been listening intently. "I need to be convinced that hormones are safe," she said. "My sister gained weight when she started. She complains to me about feeling bloated half the month, and she gets headaches she never had before. Her doctor swears by hormones, but my doctor has some reservations. How do you know who to believe?"

To take hormones—or not to take them. That is the question plaguing millions of middle-aged women caught in the hormone conundrum. Having reached that transition stage once quaintly labeled "change of life," women want assurance that it's safe to take manufactured replacement hormones to augment their body's declining production of estrogen and progesterone. What they're getting, however, is a very mixed message. One day the media hype the risk of hormones; the next they tout the benefits. Studies seem to conflict in their findings. Medical professionals are either enthusiastic or cautious. One group of hormone users raves about the results; another rails against the side effects. Instead of helping women make a decision, the abundance of information is just making them more confused.

When the available data are examined, the benefits of HRT (hormone replacement theory) outnumber what most people call "the risks"—but what Dr. Marie Savard more appropriately prefers to call "the uncertainties." Two of these are significant. One is the issue of breast cancer, which has jumped from striking one in 22 women in 1977 to one in eight women in 1993. Estrogen has been established as a growth factor in breast tumors, *but not as a cause.* More about that later. The other cloudy area is the role of progesterone in HRT. Nearly all the data collected thus far come from women taking only estrogen. Except in cases of endometrial cancer, where progesterone clearly eliminates the problems caused by estrogen, any positive or negative effects of combined hormone therapy are yet to be firmly established. There are some studies coming from the University of Georgia that suggest that the addition of progesterone reduces the chance of cancer. If that finding is supported by other studies, it might shift the balance in present attitudes.

What is menopause?

The term *menopause* technically refers to a woman's last menstrual period. The several years during which she cycles from erratic periods to none at all are called perimenopause; the time after her periods cease is called postmenopause. Approximately one-third of all premenopausal women in America are surgically thrust into instant menopause by hysterectomies. The rest gradually begin the hormone descent sometime in their 40s, when the ovaries start putting out less and less estrogen and progesterone. The uneven spiking of hormone levels causes the symptoms of perimenopause—the hot flashes, mood swings, irregular bleeding, night sweats and vaginal dryness that send women to their gynecologists shrieking for relief. At this point, many doctors will commence HRT based strictly on the woman's symptoms, or on the results of a simple blood test that measures an increase in her follicle-stimulating hormone (FSH) level. The rise of that pituitary hormone signals the beginning of the end.

Aged before its time: Premature menopause

For most women, menopause is a natural phase of life that comes on with graying hair and reading glasses. But for thousands of women in their childbearing years, nature's timetable speeds up. The result is premature menopause, also known as premature ovarian failure, a disorder *not* related to the normal aging process, which has exactly the same symptoms.

For a woman who hasn't completed or even started her family, the diagnosis can be devastating. She may have put off having kids, thinking she had lots of time. Then she learns that it's too late, and it feels as if something has been erased from her life without her permission.

Doctors once believed that women in premature menopause had no eggs left at all; now, they know that some dormant but potentially fertile eggs might remain despite the lack of estrogen. What isn't certain is how long the opportunity to activate these eggs lasts. Dr. Jerome Check, an Elkins Park fertility specialist, works with many women suffering from premature menopause. With new techniques he's able to help about 20 percent of them become pregnant and about 8 percent give birth—unfortunately, there's a high miscarriage rate with the procedure.

Most women diagnosed with premature menopause are between 35 and 40. The rest are in their early 30s, and some are even as young as their 20s. And though no one has collected data that proves the incidence has increased, doctors report they're seeing more cases now than ever before. Although some cases can be explained by an obvious factor, such as damage to or surgical removal of the ovaries, most of the time the cause is a mystery. Indeed, the largest category is called idiopathic, a fancy way for doctors to say "We just don't know."

But research is beginning to yield answers. One strong possibility is heredity: About 13 percent of women with premature menopause report their mothers and sisters had the same pattern. Another promising area of research suggests that the disorder may be caused by an out-of-control immune system: Antibodies mistakenly view the egg follicles as "foreign" and set about destroying them.

Any young woman who suffers from premature menopause should pay attention to the disorder, because lacking estrogen at an early age puts her at high risk for a variety of medical problems. If you've got premature ovarian failure and you're not on hormone replacement, then you're not getting the proper treatment.

The case for HRT

Today some 43 million American women are candidates for hormone replacement, an option that was not available to most of their mothers. A Gallup poll conducted for the North American Menopause Society found that fewer than half the women eligible for HRT have ever tried it. Many complained that they hadn't gotten sufficient information from their physicians.

In the narrow view of some HRT opponents, the mere fact that women now live far beyond menopause is no reason to mess with Mother Nature. Nora Coffee, director of HERS (Hysterectomy Education Resources and Services), says, "You can't improve on what nature gave you. The idea that women need hormone substitutes suggests we are somehow deficient and should have been born with an estrogen pump." Jerome Check, a reproductive endocrinologist, counters with the more popular position: "Just because women are living longer doesn't mean that deterioration is appropriate."

In-depth research into hormones dates back only to the 1940s. By the mid '60s, doctors were actively writing estrogen prescriptions at five times the dosages used today. The first sign of trouble came with the release in 1975 of a major study that reported a four-fold increase in endometrial cancer among women taking estrogen by itself. Estrogen causes changes in the lining of the uterus that can lead to cancer. It has since been proven that adding progesterone to the hormone package causes a monthly sloughing of this lining, and completely eliminates the danger. Nevertheless, this widely reported study planted a fear of hormones in women and gave rise to persistent misunderstandings of the links between hormones and cancer.

"Endometrial cancer is the only cancer ever unequivocally validated at a cellular level to be related to *unopposed* estrogen," says Dr. Winnifred Cutler, president of the Athena Institute for Women's Wellness and author of several books on women's health and sexual function. An advocate of combination hormone therapy, Dr. Cutler has examined 3,500 studies on women's health and hormones and published 30 papers of her own. She says, "Those who suggest hormones cause any other cancers are not in labs studying cells, where to date there has been no cause and effect established."

How to interpret the research

The whole area of hormone-therapy research does a disservice to women. At present there is an appalling absence of solid, double-blind scientific studies comparing hormone takers with matched control groups. Two new long-term studies recently launched by the National Institutes of Health should provide this much-needed information, but not for several years. In the vacuum, organizations like the Washington-based National Women's Health Network remain cautiously critical of HRT and supportive of only short-term (one- to three-year) hormone replacement for menopausal complaints.

What's not well understood by the general public is that the bulk of research data about hormones comes from epidemiological studies. These are statistical compilations—not standard clinical tests. The results measure only the rate at which a disease occurs in a particular group.

Within a data base of 36 epidemiological studies performed over the past decade examining the link between HRT and breast cancer, 32 showed no effect, and four found a minimal increase in the risk. Not long ago, the Center for Disease Control lumped together a slew of major studies in a trendy new procedure called meta-analysis and arrived at an overall 1.3 percent increase in breast cancer among women taking estrogen for 15 years or longer—but no increase in risk among five-year users.

What do these figures amount to? Not much more than a minor warning in the jargon of epidemiologists, and even less than that, according to Dr. Lila Nachtigall, a respected New York reproductive endocrinologist who has been working in the field of hormone replacement for 22 years. She says, "So long as the figures for estrogen and breast cancer hover at 1.1 to 1.3 percent, that's too low for the likelihood it's a carcinogen. For an obvious cancer link, the incidence would be three, four or five times greater, like it was with endometrial cancer."

Estrogen and cancer growth

While nobody has any proof that hormones trigger cancer, it has been definitely found that estrogen does speed up the growth of some breast tumors. This is the reason hormones are generally not prescribed for women with a family history of breast cancer. Among the important questions yet to be answered: Does estrogen precipitate the tumors, or does it only accelerate the growth of certain already present lesions? What is the effect of progesterone? And if hormones make small cancers grow to the point where they can be detected and treated, is that all bad?

For a cancer specialist like Presbyterian Medical Center's Dr. Donna Glover, the "growth factor" alone is enough to give pause. "I wouldn't tell all women not to take hormones," she says. "I'd tell them to weigh the risks, since estrogen is definitely known to be a growth accelerator with ovarian, endometrial and breast cancer." She advises women on HRT to be extremely conscientious about monthly breast self-examination, and to have yearly mammograms. She says, "If you discover a breast lump and it doesn't disappear after your period, get a mammogram. Then get an excisional biopsy that cuts out a piece of the lump for a pathologist to examine. Conversely, if the mammogram indicates the lump is benign, don't go home and forget about it. Verify the diagnosis with either an ultrasound or a needle aspiration to see if the lump is a cyst or a solid mass that should be removed."

At this point, the worry about hormones and breast cancer stems more from what we don't know than from what we do. For now, bear in mind that the cancer risks, on paper, are relatively small. That certainly doesn't mean hormone replacement is for everybody. In addition to a personal or family history of breast cancer, there are other contra-indications. Dr. Bernard Eskin, professor of obstetrics and gynecology in reproductive endocrinology at the Medical College of Pennsylvania, would not give hormones to anyone with liver disease, a history of phlebitis or thrombosis, cardiac disease of unknown origin or uterine bleeding problems. A sliding scale of personal risk factors, including fibrocystic disease or cancer in a sibling or parent, should be discussed with your doctor.

Health benefits of HRT

In the view of many doctors, the compelling case for the important health benefits of HRT far outweighs the hue and cry against it. Dr. Mona Shangold, director of the Sports Gynecology and Women's Life Cycle Center at Hahnemann University Hospital, is often asked by her patients if it's safe to take hormones. "I tell them it's safer to take them than not to take them," she says. At least 25 studies, including a recent look at 48,000 nurses over a ten-year period, have shown that women who take estrogen can expect a 50 percent reduction in heart disease, which kills more than twice as many women as all forms of cancer combined. Another massive problem for older women is osteoporosis, which 40 percent of them develop. Many never recover from falls or fractures. Although calcium and exercise can reduce the peak bone loss that accompanies menopause, neither is as effective as estrogen.

(You can get a bone-density test that will determine if you're at risk for fractures.) If you decide not to take hormones for heart disease or osteoporosis, be sure to discuss alternative options with your doctor.

In addition to its protection against heart disease and osteoporosis, HRT combats the psychological and intellectual problems of menopause. The midlife woman can be a walking complaint department. Where has her sex drive gone? Why is she so irritable and moody? What the hell is wrong with her memory? All these changes are related to estrogen, which regulates sexual desire, enhances mood and even affects brain chemistry. For many women, HRT restores lost balance and provides a sense of well-being associated with feeling young and vigorous.

Will I gain weight?

In some women, taking hormones creates its own set of problems: breast tenderness, nausea, bloating, fluid retention, headaches. Often these can be eradicated by changing pills, dosages or regimens. Most doctors recommend taking a combination of estrogen and progestin, because that mimics the natural production of the menstrual cycle. Don't be alarmed if your doctor has to juggle the formula for several months before finding what works for you. Because our bodies produce highly individual levels of hormones, there is no single right way to take the replacements. Some women never adjust to the pills, and quit. Others put up with several months of mild weight gain and then stay on hormones without trouble for years.

Of the myriad estrogen preparations on the market, the three most popular oral pills in the United States are Premaran (.625 dose), Ogun and Estrace. Some women prefer the estrogen patch, which provides continuous-release estrogen through the skin. As yet, it has no proven benefits over the oral dose, and some women get an allergic rash from it. Provera is the most commonly used synthetic progestin. Some women find that synthetic progestins make them irritable and headachey. As an alternative, the Woman's International Pharmacy (1-800-279-5708) markets a natural micronized progesterone made from plants like yams and soybeans in both pill and cream form. They claim this natural product eliminates the aggravating symptoms of the synthetic form. The newest addition to the hormone package is estrogen combined with androgen, which is normally produced by the ovaries. However, its level drops as much as 50 percent after menopause. There's research indicating that androgens have a positive effect on mood, memory, concentration and sex drive.

There is no proper time to start hormones—let your symptoms be your guide—and no fixed time to stop. Shangold says, "There is no evidence at present that taking it forever is harmful." Those in the more cautious school would set a five-year limit.

You may prefer to treat the symptoms of menopause with natural remedies. Among those tried but unproven are such things as acupuncture, biofeedback, large doses of vitamin E, herbs, garlic and ginseng, a Chinese medicinal plant that may contain estrogen-like compounds. Herbal supplements taken in moderation won't

One woman's story

"Life is just too hard now"
-Liz

Eating Disorders. Abuse. Depression. Anxiety. If you are overwhelmed by any of these problems, we can help.

One woman's center

The Renfrew Center is exclusively dedicated to helping women with their struggles discover new ways of living. We offer educational programs, group and individual therapy throughout the area as well as residential programs at our site located near Chestnut Hill.

Call 1-800-RENFREW for information on any of our programs.

THE
RENFREW CENTER

Empowering Women To Reclaim Their Lives

1-800-RENFREW

be harmful, but in excess they can cause damage. Talk to your doctor.

The hormone debate is likely to rage for years to come. Obviously, no drug is risk-free—even aspirin can be dangerous. But until the gray areas of HRT are cleared up, women may have to rely on something besides research data to decide whether HRT is right for them. "Women know how they feel with hormones and without them," declares Marie Savard. "It's a quality of life issue, and nobody talks enough about that."

For Your Information

For a fine layman's approach to this problem, we suggest the revised and expanded new edition of *Menopause: A Guide for Women and the Men Who Love Them*, by Dr. Celso Ramon-Garcia and Winnifred Cutler, Ph.D. (Norton, $20). The concerns about HRT are well explored in the paperback *Women's Health Alert*, by Dr. Sidney Wolfe and the watchdog Public Citizen Health Research Council (Addison-Wesley, $7.95).

The Athena Institute for Women's Wellness (642-3073) periodically holds workshops on women's health. Call for a schedule. The Sports Gynecology and Women's Life Cycle Center directed by Dr. Mona Shangold at Hahnemann University Hospital can be reached at 246-5183.

Dr. Jerome Check (635-4400), who has offices in Cherry Hill and Elkins Park, has succeeded in developing viable pregnancies for a number of women stricken with premature menopause in their child-bearing years.

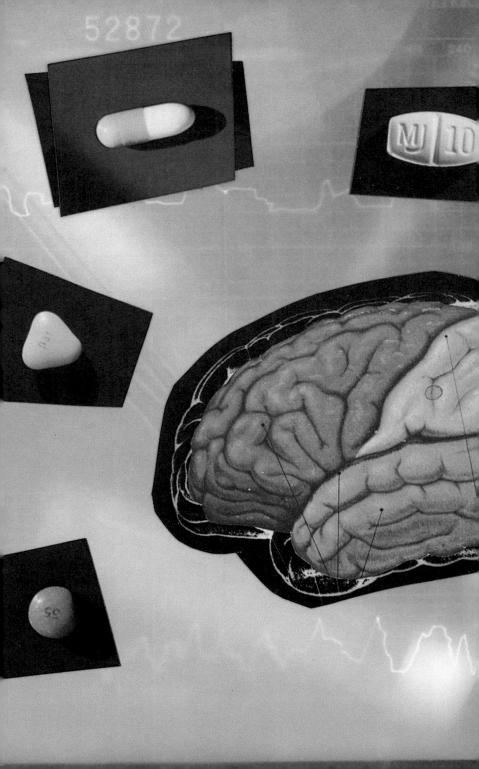

6

Mind Over Matter

CHAPTER 21

High Anxiety

*While you are reading this, some 20 million
Americans may be having an anxiety attack.
Makes you nervous, doesn't it?*

The attack—the Big One, as Bob now calls it—arose out of
nowhere. True, he'd been wrestling with scattered episodes of anxiety for nearly five
years, but the others had been minor by comparison. A wave of fear would wash
over him briefly in class and his hand would shake so hard he couldn't take attendance. Or he'd walk down the street, bump into an acquaintance and his mind
would click off. He'd make a fast excuse that he had an appointment and dash off,
absolutely certain that he could no more carry on a simple conversation than play
quarterback for the Eagles. This time, it was different. This time he was sure he was
going to die.

It happened on the Pennsylvania Turnpike when he was coming back from a
visit to his parents. He was feeling guilty because he'd given in to his sick mother's
insistence that she didn't need a doctor. Suddenly he felt like he was sucking in too
much air and couldn't catch his breath. He began to pant like an overheated dog on
a 100-degree day. His hand shook so violently that he could barely steer. And he
couldn't stop because his right foot froze on the pedal. The speedometer read 55.

"I knew it was the end," he says. "I thought to myself, This is it. In my
mind's eye I had this image of an awful wreck. I saw the car hitting the guardrail at
the right front end, swerving and then fishtailing so that my side would get
smashed."

"I can't stop the car!" he yelled to his wife, who did not know how to drive.
"I can't move my foot."

Somehow he managed to slide his left foot onto the brake while she pried his
right foot off the gas pedal. Providentially, they were near an exit, and able to inch
into the service area. There they sat for two hours, until he calmed down.

What happened to this high school teacher was neither rare nor inexplicable.
He had an anxiety attack, a horrifying experience that will strike an estimated one in

12 Americans sometime in their lives. While most anxiety attacks are not so life-threatening, they can make life a horrible ordeal.

The symptoms of anxiety sufferers run the gamut from ongoing states of low-level jumpiness and hyper-vigilance to periodic panic attacks that hit with hurricane force. Some have phobias that compel them to avoid anything from cats to airplanes. Others (agoraphobics) live as prisoners in what they believe is the only safe haven: their own home.

"Nature favors anxious genes"

The problem of anxiety is nothing new; it harks back to a prehistoric era when the anxiety mechanism was a crucial factor in survival. What we label anxiety today was originally a primitive alert system that warned early man (and probably animals) of impending danger. Built into our subconscious is something that takes over our bodies and drives us to fight back, flee, freeze in our tracks or faint until danger passes. This "flight or fight" response, protected by evolution, tended to err on the side of over-vigilance—which is certainly preferable to an alert system that, in an ambiguous situation, would miss the danger entirely. "Nature," says University of Pennsylvania psychiatrist Dr. Aaron Beck, "favors anxious genes."

Even today, in the 20th century, our bodies are still roaming the savanna. "Our environment has changed," says Beck, "but we haven't." In many ways, that's good. Anxiety is still a valuable survival tool, one that helps us assess situations and quickly react to potential dangers. Like pain, anxiety is an attention-getter that screams *something is wrong! Correct it!* A primitive suspicion of the unknown or unfamiliar is still an important checking system.

If anxiety were triggered only in the face of real danger, as intended by nature, it would pose no problem. Instead, it's become a double-edged sword. The sense of insecurity that worked so beautifully to keep our ancestors from taking risks in the wild becomes an impediment rather than an aid when it's activated at the wrong time in contemporary life; certainly it's no help at all when it blocks normal performance.

Where do these feelings come from?

Sometimes, anxious feelings are caused by a real "danger," and abate when the danger passes. Why is it that one person reacts to anxiety-producing situations within normal response limits and another loses hold of reality? Over the years, several theories have emerged for what's behind "free-floating anxiety." Psychoanalysts tend to follow Freud's lead and say that anxiety is aroused by the threat of a forbidden unconscious impulse breaking into conscious awareness. The treatment mode in this model focuses on gaining insight into the fear, which should lead to controlling it. Behaviorists take another view. They believe that anxiety is a conditioned reflex that occurs when a particular place or thing is paired with some real or imagined threat. Their cure involves desensitizing the patient through repeated visits to the feared place. Then there are the medical researchers who are convinced that anxiety (panic attacks in particular) is caused by an imbalance in the body chemistry.

Dr. Aaron Beck disagrees with all of the traditional explanations. His theory, simplistic as it may sound, is quite revolutionary, although Beck himself hardly fits the stereotype of an iconoclast. An affable man with short thick hair the color of whipped cream, a slightly bent posture and a shuffling gait, the septuagenarian Beck is a giant in the field he pioneered: cognitive therapy.

I think, therefore I worry

Cognition means thinking: Beck says anxiety is the result of thinking we are in danger, and the key to treating it is to unlock the automatic thoughts and spontaneous visual images that produce an anxiety attack. Forget probing into childhood memories; forget that the dizzy feeling triggering a fear of fainting may be due to low blood sugar. What's more important in controlling anxiety, Beck says, is to understand how the anxious distort reality by *misreading* signals. Thus, the anxious think that the wind rustling the blinds is an intruder breaking in; that a salesman who is preoccupied with a headache intentionally ignored them. The leap from the distorted thought to the visual image to the first stir of panic takes but a split second. A graduate student prone to anxiety attacks described how she could be crossing the street and the light would change. Suddenly she'd imagine all the cars rushing at her; she'd be trapped, and she'd think, I'm going to die without anyone to help me.

These mental pictures are so powerful they become reality. Anxiety patients believe their fantasies are actually happening; no matter how preposterous the images may be, they can't turn them off. And while the mind races with fearful thoughts and images, the body simultaneously begins sending its ancient defense signals. A nervous boy rings the doorbell for a blind date. He visualizes the girl looking at him contemptuously and his palms begin to sweat and his heart feels like it's exploding in his chest. His mind goes blank, and when she opens the door he can't even say hello.

Anticipating the worst

Once Beck understood the role of automatic thoughts and images in producing anxiety, he had no trouble getting patients to describe the attacks in great detail. A male patient who falls apart when he has to make a speech describes how he actually sees himself crumbling on the podium and collapsing in a heap. Soon all his colleagues are standing over him asking how this could have happened to such a top guy. Another sees himself at a meeting where he is about to speak, bursts into tears and runs from the room. He is mortified and thinks, It's all over. I blew the job. My career is dead.

Armed with these insights, Beck declared the old notion of free-floating anxiety to be nonsense. Anxiety, he claims, is an emotional response to the fearful thought that something awful is going to happen. That thought could be the fear of an internal physical disaster, the fear of a mental breakdown or the fear of some social disgrace. The anxious overestimate the degree of real danger (which increases fear) while they underestimate their ability to cope (which increases anxiety).

It's typical for the anxious to focus on the signals that possibly indicate danger (a stomachache, for instance) while they ignore the possible cause of the signal (having just wolfed down a huge meal, say). Regardless of how distorted the anxious person's perceptions are, they seem perfectly reasonable—and terrifying—to him. In cognitive therapy, the anxious are taught to zero in on their fear-producing thoughts, test them against reality and look for reasonable alternative explanations. In short, they learn to think the way the rest of us do when we get a stomachache.

The perfectionist syndrome

Beck has found that the anxious among us share a number of characteristic thought patterns. Considered individually, their misperceptions are not all that uncommon. But collectively, they create a twisted view of life's perils. A core belief of anxiety-sufferers is the need to be perfect at everything. While perfectionism is generally an asset on the job and a positive factor in career advancement, it also creates a special vulnerability to anxiety attacks. The anxious feel insecure about one area of their lives and dramatize that particular flaw. Perhaps they are competent in business but fall apart on dates. Or they're great in one-to-one relationships but a dud at parties. Whatever their weak link is, they'll dwell on it, magnify its importance and minimize the strengths they do have. This makes them particularly anxiety-prone, because each error is seen as a harbinger of impending disaster, a catastrophe waiting to happen.

Although anxiety has many faces, general anxiety victims fall into two categories. Either they dread some kind of physical harm—an attack, an accident, a disease—or they are threatened by their social environment. Social anxiety is the harder of the two to visualize. While it may relate to personal encounters or career concerns, Beck says that all social anxiety stems from an underlying fear of negative evaluation. "People are universally afraid of being judged poorly by others," he says. "They're worried about measuring up." Social anxiety is extremely widespread, but not always crippling. At a workshop he conducted for 500 therapists, Beck asked how many had ever experienced some anxiety based on negative evaluation. Every single person raised his hand. "The pros worry they won't be good enough," Beck says, "and the amateurs worry they'll look as inexperienced as they really are."

The burden of keeping anxiety in check is exhausting for those who suffer from it. Unlike depression victims, who are often immobilized, people with generalized anxiety are out there struggling from moment to moment to keep a grip on their lives. For many of them, cognitive therapy as practiced by Beck's disciples holds great promise. It seems to succeed when all else fails by teaching people to give everything a second thought.

CHAPTER 22

The Drug Zone

*Move over, Dr. Freud. The prescription pad may
be the answer to depression, anxiety and other
problems once reserved for the shrink's couch*

As cataclysmically as the ruminations of Sigmund
Freud, a revolution is taking place in the field of psychiatry that has changed the
way doctors view mental illness. One out of every eight prescriptions written in the
United States is for a drug to combat an emotional problem we used to take exclusively to a therapist's couch. That's still where many family and personal issues are
best resolved. But Freud did not have the advantages of modern science, which has
made astounding discoveries about the physiology of the brain, in particular the
chemicals that affect mood and behavior. No longer is it generally accepted that, if
you could only stop hating your mother or learn to love yourself even though you
flunked out of college, you would cure your depression or reduce your anxiety. It's
now understood that these and more serious mental disorders as diverse as panic
attacks, bulimia and chronic depression can be treated by addressing a chemical
imbalance in your brain.

Sophisticated technology has made it possible to see actual chemical changes
taking place in the brain during a panic attack. And we now know the brain isn't
really much like a computer; it's more like the hurly-burly floor of the stock
exchange, with neurons shooting electrochemical messages to each other hither and
yon. Scientists have established that psychotropic drugs work by affecting either the
chemistry of these messages (the neurotransmitters) or the sites where the messages
are received (the receptors).

The earliest psychotropic drugs arrived on the scene when very little was
known about the brain; their discovery was as much accident as design. The first antidepressant, for example, was stumbled upon back in the '50s when doctors noticed
that tuberculosis patients treated with the drug iproniazid became inexplicably cheerful. Someone shrewdly deduced that their exuberance might be drug-related, and that
launched the use of one of the first mood elevators, the MAO inhibitors.

These were followed by a larger group of antidepressants known as the tricy-clates—drugs like Elavil and Tofranil—which, while effective in relieving depression, had a variety of unpleasant side effects ranging from dry mouth to constipation. The latest antidepressants, a group of drugs called SRIs (seroronin re-uptake inhibitors is the pharmacological jargon) are cousins to the tricyclates. They produce fewer side effects, however, because they act on fewer chemical systems. As many as 30 percent of the patients who did not respond to the older drugs—or wouldn't take them— seem to benefit from these second-generation antidepressants.

The pros of Prozac

The most successful of these SRIs to date is Prozac. Much of the earlier controversy it generated has justifiably died away, and currently an estimated 15 million people worldwide are taking Prozac. Most of the negative press came from the fact that a statistically small number of people who took the drug killed themselves while on it—an act that, unfortunately, is not uncommon among the depressed. A few on Prozac have even killed other people. Nonetheless, the cause-and-effect evidence linking the drug to these aberrant behaviors is quite sketchy.

It appears that the attack on Prozac has been orchestrated by the Church of Scientology as part of its campaign to discredit psychiatry. Despite the horror stories once trotted out on TV talk shows like *Donahue*, most of the psychiatric communi-ty steadfastly supports the safety and efficacy of Prozac. Some people report experi-encing jitters and restlessness as a side effect, but that is quite different from violent behavior. Recently it's been found that patients complain less of "feeling wired" when their dosage is reduced from the standard 20 milligrams a day to ten. While Prozac has the lion's share of the market, its cousins—Zoloft and, to a lesser degree, Paxil—are gaining popularity. Zoloft in particular seems to produce fewer side effects than Prozac in some people. A new antidepressant, Effexor, has just been approved by the FDA. It works on two chemical systems, serotonin and norepi-nephrin, and the double-barreled effect may help those who don't respond to Prozac and Zoloft.

Is it a good idea to take a drug simply because every season of the year feels like the winter of discontent? A recent bestseller, *Listening to Prozac*, raised some provocative questions about the popular antidepressants, which are increasingly being prescribed for milder problems as a sort of personality pill. How does the doctor draw the line between illness and normal, if unhappy, behavior? When does drug therapy turn into drug abuse? Are we entering an era of cosmetic psychiatry, where a pill can make you calmer and better able to cope?

On the plus side, there's no evidence to suggest that the new antidepressants are dangerous. They're nontoxic, nonaddictive and, because they don't produce a "high," have little incentive for abuse. But, as they haven't been around for decades, some experts worry about the unknown long-term effects. Another concern is that drugs will become a substitute for examining very real problems in our lives, thus robbing us of an opportunity to make worthwhile behavioral and emotional changes.

While these are interesting philosophical issues, there is no denying that Prozac and its relatives have brought unprecedented relief to people with serious emotional problems. Dr. Joseph Mendels, executive director of the Philadelphia Medical Institute and a nationally known psychiatrist who specializes in psychopharmacology, says, "It's my view that someone who has suffered from a depression that persists for more than several weeks, one that is present more than half the time and interferes with general living, ought to be evaluated, preferably by a psychiatrist."

Help without dependency

Today nearly every kind of emotional disorder is being studied in the laboratory. Anxiety, once considered an emotional maladaptation of our flight-or-fight response to danger, may in some cases be due to a problem in a part of the brain that secretes a tranquilizer-like chemical. Genetic studies have traced an inherited predisposition—like that of diabetes or cancer—to anxiety, and physiological research has identified an area in the midbrain, no bigger than a pinhead, that actually controls it.

Armed with this information, researchers have actively embarked on a search to find new substances to treat anxiety, in particular a drug that has the relaxing effect of Valium without the sedation and dependency that creates Valium abuse. One of them, Buspirone, is part of a group referred to in the trade as non-benzodiazepines to distinguish them from traditional tranquilizers. While these newer anti-anxiety medications have the advantage of being nonaddictive, they have the disadvantage of a delayed response—unlike Valium, they don't create an immediate feeling of relaxation. Where most tranquilizers are prescribed on an as-needed basis—take one when you feel anxious—Buspirone must be taken on a regimented program of so many pills every day, and two or three weeks might pass before there's an effect.

That explains why the non-benzodiazepines have had a rough time gaining popular acceptance, despite the fact that they're much less dangerous. Dr. Karl Rickels, a professor of psychiatry at the University of Pennsylvania Medical School, says, "We have to re-educate people to be patient with these new drugs that work slower and may even cause agitation the first few days. But they have fewer side effects. After four weeks patients do as well as on Valium and after six months they show no dependency problems."

Some anxiety-sufferers have difficulty focusing. Diverted by a forest of activity, they can't zero in on the important tree. They're now being treated with Ritalin, a drug typically used (with some controversy) for children diagnosed with attention deficit disorder (ADD), or hyperactivity. In adults who may well have been ADD kids, it improves concentration and keeps the roving mind on a set path.

Participating in a drug trial

The recent advances in psychotropic drugs, remarkable as they seem, represent a period of scientific refinement rather than discovery. The really exciting work in psychopharmacology is a good five to ten years away from appearing on prescription pads. The only way the public can get its hands on the wonder drugs of tomorrow today is by participating in the investigative drug studies that precede FDA approval. You'll often see ads in newspapers recruiting participants for a drug study at one of the university hospitals. This isn't nearly as dangerous as it sounds—often some 500,000 people nationwide participate in these trials, and the drugs involved have all passed extensive safety testing and are being examined chiefly to see if they perform as promised. The Philadelphia Medical Institute (PMI), one of a handful of private organizations around the country that evaluate and develop medical treatment for psychological disorders, has conducted trials involving more than 10,000 people, and only once has there been a serious side effect from an investigation of a drug.

Most drug-trial drugs are free, because the research is funded by either the FDA or the pharmaceutical company. Often the drugs are already marketed in other countries or are available here for a different purpose. For instance, a drug under investigation at PMI for its potential to improve memory is already used by millions as a blood-pressure medication. And several studies are exploring new possibilities for existing antidepressants. Bulimics have shown substantial improvement when treated with an antidepressant, although the drug has no effect on anorexics, which suggests that these eating disorders may not be opposite sides of the same coin. People suffering from unmanageable cravings—foodaholics, alcoholics, cocaine-abusers, chain-smokers—who are highly motivated to kick their habits also have been aided significantly by antidepressants.

Don't panic!

Panic disorders, too, are now being successfully controlled by drugs. Once considered a severe form of anxiety, these attacks now appear to be something quite different, with a separate trigger that responds to chemical manipulation. The jury is still out on whether drugs are the best way to treat panic disorders, because many well-respected studies have shown that cognitive therapy (see Chapter 21, *High Anxiety*) is as effective in conquering panic as drug therapy.

There's also a good bit of evidence that obsessive-compulsive disorders respond to drugs. These illnesses can actually be observed in PET scan pictures, where they show up as markedly different from normal brain activity, an indication that drugs may help the problem. A case in point is Jim, a married man in his 40s who participated in one of the drug trials at PMI. He'd gone from being a neat, orderly young man into someone so obsessed with cleanliness that he spent two hours each morning and three each night cleaning himself. It got so bad that he made his children wear gloves to touch him. He knew his behavior was crazy, but

he couldn't stop. After ten weeks on chlorimipramine, an antidepressant sold in
Canada and Europe, he was back to being bearably meticulous. Dr. Joseph Mendels,
director of PMI, admits that nobody understands why many of these drugs work,
although it's speculated that they have something to do with regulating seratonin,
the chemical system that plays a role in behaviors as diverse as appetite, sleep and
sex.

As we move forward through the '90s, there will hardly be an emotional
problem that's not susceptible to altering through drugs. Researchers at Columbia-
Presbyterian Hospital in New York are trying a drug called Nardil on people overcome with intense shyness and hyper-sensitivity. Beta blockers normally used for
heart patients and high blood pressure are being given to certain performers to
combat stage fright (Carly Simon should be happy to hear about that). And scientists at UC Irvine are excited about BPD, a drug that improves memory in rats and
is ready for human trials.

Can we talk?

Will psychotropic drugs someday put the talk therapy of psychologists out of business? Absolutely not. There are all kinds of emotional problems that cannot and
should not be treated with medication. One of the men who makes a strong argument in support of other approaches to curing mood disorders is Aaron Beck, the
University of Pennsylvania psychiatrist regarded as the father of cognitive therapy.
Beck and fellow travelers like Dr. David Burns, author of the best-selling *Feeling
Good*, believe people get depressed because they view themselves negatively and
magnify the extent of their problems. Cognitive therapy adjusts negative thinking to
fit a more positive reality.

The psychological and the biological approach are not mutually exclusive,
but often different sides of the same coin, and there is plenty of data to support
both. Beck has research to support his contention that, while many anxious and
depressed people respond to drugs, they also respond to cognitive therapy. In one
study comparing the two, drug treatment helped more people with severe, immobi-
lizing biological depression than situationally triggered psychological depression.
"But," Beck notes, "cognitive therapy helped both groups equally well." There's
even evidence that cognitive therapy produces chemical changes, just as drug therapy produces psychological changes. No doubt as we move forward into the '90s
with an increased understanding of the brain and behavior, the line between psychology and biology will shift and blur even more. But in the meantime, there's
plenty of help available whether you choose to take a pill or talk it out.

The warning signs of depression

How do you know whether you're a candidate for antidepressant medication? Ask
yourself: Do I feel sad, blue, hopeless, down in the dumps or irritable, and am I getting less pleasure from the things I normally enjoy? If the answer is yes, then look at

whether you have had any four of the following symptoms for at least two weeks:

1. Poor appetite and weight loss or increased appetite and weight gain.

2. Sleep disturbance, especially early-morning wakefulness.

3. Thoughts and actions slowed down or speeded up.

4. Loss of interest in normal activities and decreased sex drive.

5. Loss of energy; fatigue.

6. Diminished ability to think and concentrate; difficulty making decisions.

7. Feelings of worthlessness, self-reproach or inappropriate guilt.

These symptoms of biological or clinical depression often happen to people who have no reason to be depressed, yet they find they just aren't enjoying life like they once did and they are physically pooped. If this describes how you're feeling, you might want to visit one of the clinics listed in this chapter for an evaluation.

The warning signs of anxiety

There are three major categories of anxiety disorders. First are the phobias, such as fear of flying, fear of cats, fear of closed spaces, etc. Phobias do not respond particularly well to drugs. Second are panic disorders, the sudden onset of explosive, overwhelming feelings of terror, as if the body's alarm system were ringing for no apparent reason. The third and largest group is generalized anxiety. Someone with this condition can be treated with tranquilizers in concert with therapy; consider getting medical advice if three of the four following signs persist for at least one month.

1. Motor tension: shakiness, tension, aching muscles, inability to relax, jumpiness, fatigue.

2. Uncontrollable body sensations: sweating, heart pounding, clammy hands, dry mouth, dizziness, light-headedness, hot and cold flashes, upset stomach, lump in the throat, diarrhea, pallor or flushed face.

3. Apprehensive expectation: fear, worry, rumination, anticipation of misfortune to self or others.

4. Vigilance and scanning: constant hyper-attention that makes it difficult to concentrate and leads to irritability, impatience, insomnia and always feeling on edge.

While not as easily treated as depression, anxiety disorders are significantly improved by drugs and/or psychotherapy 75 percent of the time. The Center for Psychotherapy Research (349-5220) at the University of Pennsylvania has low-cost programs with experienced therapists for people prone to worry.

If You Need Help

The Philadelphia Medical Institute
1015 CHESTNUT STREET; 923-2583

A for-profit organization whose sole purpose is conducting drug studies. Their work is paid for by the companies who want the studies done, so you pay nothing. It is medically managed with great care and all patients undergo a complete medical examination before becoming part of any research program.

The University of Pennsylvania Psychopharmacology Treatment Unit
UNIVERSITY SCIENCE CENTER, 3600 MARKET STREET, SUITE 872; 898-4301

This outpatient clinic provides free evaluation and treatment in a variety of research programs designed to help patients suffering from panic and other anxiety disorders, as well as depression and social phobia. Both standard and investigational medications, some not yet otherwise available in the United States, are used in treatment. The clinic also sponsors research programs designed to help persons who are physically dependent upon tranquilizers such as Xanax, Ativan and Valium to stop using them.

Freedom From Depression
DEPRESSION RESEARCH UNIT, UNIVERSITY OF PENNSYLVANIA MEDICAL CENTER, 3600 MARKET STREET, 8TH FLOOR; 662-3462

This clinic is devoted to the treatment and investigation of biological depression. Each patient goes through a thorough psychiatric and medical evaluation, and those not considered appropriate are referred elsewhere. Treatment may combine antidepressant medication with supportive psychotherapy. A donation of $50 is requested for the Jack Warsaw Fund for research in biological psychiatry; otherwise it's free.

Center for Cognitive Therapy
HUP, 3600 MARKET STREET, 7TH FLOOR; 898-4100

This program uses the behavioral concepts pioneered by Dr. Aaron Beck, which are based on the premise that anxiety and depression come from distorted ways of thinking. The therapy seldom uses drugs, relying instead on teaching how to recognize distorted thinking and change it. It has an excellent reputation and a high success rate. The sliding-scale fee is based on income.

Mood and Anxiety Disorders Program
MEDICAL COLLEGE OF PENNSYLVANIA/EPPI, 3200 HENRY AVENUE; 842-4242

Comprehensive clinical outpatient treatment programs for individuals having problems with depression, anxiety, anger, aggression, shyness. Treatment options include individual/group psychotherapy, cognitive/behavioral therapy and medication therapy. A sliding-scale fee (based on income) is available to eligible individuals. Treatment associated with participation in sponsored clinical research programs is provided at no cost to eligible individuals.

The Belmont Center for Comprehensive Treatment

4200 MONUMENT ROAD; 877-2000

Belmont provides outpatient and day-program treatment of depression and anxiety-based disorders, including panic disorder and obsessive-compulsive disorders. Special programs are available for adults, women and deaf persons. The anxiety and affective-disorders inpatient unit provides intensive biological, psychological and social treatment of mood and anxiety disorders. Fees may be covered by insurance. Belmont Center for Comprehensive Treatment is a member of the Albert Einstein Healthcare Network.

Mood Disorders Program

THE INSTITUTE OF PENNSYLVANIA HOSPITAL, 111 NORTH 49TH STREET; 471-2542

Specializing in inpatient and outpatient treatment of mood disorders such as major depression, manic depressive or bipolar disorder, seasonal affective disorder, postpartum depression and chronic "blues." Institute clinicians specialize in working with patients who have not responded to medications, are experiencing recurrent depression or who have complex co-existing conditions, such as addiction and anxiety. A combination of individual, group and family, pharmacologic and rehabilitation therapies is used to help patients recover from painful symptoms and better cope with the challenges of daily living.

Child and Adolescent Anxiety Disorders Clinic

TEMPLE UNIVERSITY, WEISS HALL, 13TH STREET AND CECIL B. MOORE AVENUE; 204-7165

Dedicated to children 9 to 13 whose anxiety interferes with daily functioning. Children acquire and practice behavioral skills in 16 to 20 individual sessions. Treatment is free.

Just What the Doctor Ordered

The following chart contains information about the most commonly prescribed psychotropic drugs. Before beginning any kind of drug therapy for a psychological problem, always discuss with your doctor your complete medical history, any other medication you're taking, risks if you're pregnant or nursing, and the interactive effects of alcohol with your prescription. A variety of side effects other than those noted may occur in vulnerable individuals, so you should carefully discuss your health profile with your psychiatrist.

Anxiety

Chemical Name: alprazolam
Brand Name: Xanax

Used For: Generalized anxiety disorder. Panic disorder.
Do Not Use If: You have a history of alcohol abuse or other misuse of addictive drugs. Be sure to tell your doctor if you have ever had any allergic reactions to medication, or if you have liver, kidney or lung disease, or a history of seizures.
How Long Until It Works: Some relief within an hour. A week for patients with generalized anxiety disorder. Two to four weeks for patients with panic disorder.
Common Side Effects: Drowsiness. Gastrointestinal disorders. Heightens the effect of alcohol. Bitter taste in mouth, dry mouth or excessive salivation. Headache. Nausea. Nervousness. Excessive sweating. Withdrawal symptoms, especially if stopped abruptly.

Chemical Name: buspirone
Brand Name: BuSpar

Used For: Generalized anxiety disorder.
Do Not Use If: You are taking a monoamine oxidase inhibitor (MAOI) or any other medication that would cause oversedation.
How Long Until It Works: About four weeks.
Common Side Effects: Nausea. Headache. Dizziness. Nervousness. Weakness.

Chemical Name: diazepam
Brand Name: Valium

Used For: Generalized anxiety disorder. Sometimes, to treat muscle spasms.
Do Not Use If: You have a history of alcohol abuse or other misuse of addictive drugs. Be sure to tell your doctor if you have ever had any allergic reactions to medication; if you have liver, kidney or lung disease; or a history of seizures.
How Long Until It Works: 30 minutes to an hour. Substantial improvement within a week.
Common Side Effects: Drowsiness. Dizziness. Heightens the effect of alcohol. Gastrointestinal disorders. Withdrawal symptoms, especially if stopped abruptly.

Chemical Name: lorazepam
Brand Name: Ativan

Used For: Generalized anxiety disorder. Also, for calming agitated patients with mania or schizophrenia.
Do Not Use If: You have a history of alcohol abuse or other misuse of addictive drugs; you are taking any other medication that might cause oversedation.
How Long Until It Works: Some relief in about an hour. Much improvement within a week.
Common Side Effects: Bitter taste in mouth, dry mouth or excessive salivation. Drowsiness. Loss of appetite. Nausea, sweating or vomiting. Heightens the effects of alcohol. Withdrawal symptoms, especially if stopped abruptly.

Attention Deficit Disorder

Chemical Name: methylphenidate
Brand Name: Ritalin

Used For: Commonly used to treat children with attention deficit disorder, it is increasingly being prescribed for adults with ADD who have difficulty focusing or concentrating.

Do Not Use If: You are taking an MAO inhibitor, hypertension medication, oral anticoagulants or anticonvulsants.

How Long Until It Works: Two to three weeks.

Common Side Effects: This drug is related to amphetamines and may occasionally be habit-forming. Complaints include restlessness, mild dry mouth, headache, insomnia.

Bipolar Affective Disorder
(Manic Depression)

Chemical Name: lithium
Brand Names: Lithonate, Lithane, Eskalith, others

Used For: Acute and long-term treatment of bipolar affective disorder. Helps prevent extreme highs and lows.

Do Not Use If: You have kidney disease; you are taking diuretics for high blood pressure; you use anti-inflammatory drugs like Motrin.

How Long Until It Works: Hard to pinpoint. Usually the doctor observes the patient over a period of time for signs of lessened mood swings.

Common Side Effects: Gastrointestinal disorders. Metallic taste in mouth. Increased frequency of urination and increased thirst. Weakness. Drowsiness. Weight gain and bloating. Acne. Trembling of hands.

Depression

Chemical Name: amitriptyline
Brand Names: Elavil, Endep, others

Used For: Major depression.

Do Not Use If: You have a history of seizures, glaucoma, cardiovascular disorders, drug or alcohol abuse, and/or are taking thyroid medication or an MAOI.

How Long Until It Works: Two to six weeks.

Common Side Effects: Dry mouth. Gastrointestinal disorders. Blurry vision. Difficulty urinating. Increased sensitivity to the sun. Dizziness when standing up quickly. Weight gain. Sleepiness. Increased sweating.

Chemical Name: doxepin
Brand Names: Adapin, Sinequan, others

Used For: Major depression.

Do Not Use If: You have a history of glaucoma, an enlarged prostate, cardiovascular disorders.
How Long Until It Works: Two to six weeks.
Common Side Effects: Dry mouth. Constipation. Blurry vision. Difficulty urinating. Increased sun sensitivity. Dizziness after standing quickly. Weight gain. Sleepiness. Increased sweating.

Chemical Name: fluoxetine
Brand Name: Prozac
Used For: Depression and several anxiety disorders, also for PMS.
Do Not Use If: You have severe insomnia or you are dangerously underweight.
How Long Until It Works: Two to four weeks.
Common Side Effects: Loss of appetite. Insomnia. Nausea, diarrhea or stomach cramps. Headaches. Nervousness. Sexual dysfunction.

Chemical Name: imipramine
Brand Names: Tofranil, Janimine, others
Used For: Major depression. Also, some anxiety disorders.
Do Not Use If: You have a history of glaucoma, an enlarged prostate or cardiovascular disorders.
How Long Until It Works: Two to six weeks.
Common Side Effects: Dry mouth. Constipation. Blurry vision. Difficulty urinating. Increased sensitivity to the sun. Dizziness after standing up quickly. Weight gain. Increased sweating. Drowsiness.

Chemical Name: nortriptyline
Brand Names: Aventyl, Pamelor
Used For: Major depression.
Do Not Use If: You have narrow-angle glaucoma, an enlarged prostate or certain heart-rhythm irregularities.
How Long Until It Works: Two to six weeks.
Common Side Effects: Anxiety. Blurred vision. Dry mouth. Difficulty urinating. Gastrointestinal disorders. Sweating. Weakness. Weight gain or loss. Increased sensitivity to the sun.

Chemical Name: paroxetine
Brand Name: Paxil
Used For: Depression.
Do Not Use If: You have severe insomnia or you are dangerously underweight.
How Long Until It Works: Two to four weeks.
Common Side Effects: Weakness, sweating, nausea, decreased appetite, dizziness, insomnia, nervousness. Sexual dysfunction.

Chemical Name: sertraline
Brand Name: Zoloft

Used For: Depression.
Do Not Use If: You have severe insomnia or you are dangerously underweight.
How Long Until It Works: Two to four weeks.
Common Side Effects: Gastrointestinal disorders. Dizziness. Insomnia. Headache. Sweating. Dry mouth. Sexual dysfunction.

Chemical Name: venlafexine
Brand Name: Effexor

Used For: Depression.
Do Not Use If: You are taking an MAO inhibitor or other antidepressant; if you have a history of high blood pressure, discuss first with your doctor.
How Long Until It Works: Two to four weeks.
Common Side Effects: Possible rise in blood pressure, nausea, headache, insomnia.

Schizophrenia

Chemical Name: clozapine
Brand Name: Clozarile

Used For: Severely ill schizophrenic patients who fail to show an acceptable response to standard antipsychotic drugs.
Do Not Use If: You cannot comply with the need to have weekly blood counts.
How Long Until It Works: Two to four weeks.
Common Side Effects: Sedation. Increased salivation and drooling. Rapid heart rate. Dizziness caused by lowered blood pressure. Nausea and vomiting. Constipation. Dry mouth.

Chemical Name: fluphenazine
Brand Names: Permitil, Prolixin

Used For: Psychosis associated with schizophrenia, mania, severe behavioral problems.
Do Not Use If: Use carefully if you have a history of seizures.
How Long Until It Works: Two weeks.
Common Side Effects: Blurred vision. Dizziness. Fatigue. Gastrointestinal disorders. Dry mouth. Jitteriness. Weight gain.

Chemical Name: haloperidol
Brand Name: Haldol

Used For: Psychosis associated with schizophrenia, mania or depression.
How Long Until It Works: Two to four weeks.
Do Not Use If: You have a history of seizures.
Common Side Effects: Muscle stiffness. Tremors. Jumpiness. Weight gain.

Chemical Name: thioridazine

Brand Name: Mellaril, Millazine, others

Used For: Psychosis associated with schizophrenia, mania and severe behavioral problems.

How Long Until It Works: Two weeks.

Do Not Use If: You are taking any other drugs that may cause oversedation.

Common Side Effects: Blurred vision. Gastrointestinal disorders. Dizziness. Drowsiness. Restlessness. Weight gain.

Chemical Name: trifluoperazine

Brand Name: Stelazine

Used For: Psychosis associated with schizophrenia, mania or depression.

Do Not Use If: You are taking any other drugs that may cause oversedation.

How Long Until It Works: The patient will probably become calmer and somewhat less violent after a few doses, but complete relief may take up to four weeks.

Common Side Effects: Sedation. Low blood pressure and dizziness. Dry mouth. Constipation. Difficulty urinating. Blurry vision. Muscle stiffness. Weight gain. Increased sensitivity to the sun.

CHAPTER 23

Where to Go for Help

Sometimes, the doctor's office isn't enough

When emotional problems require more attention than regular visits to a therapist's office, it may be necessary to check into a hospital for inpatient or daily outpatient care. As these listings show, there are treatment programs tailored to every kind of psychological disturbance from stress to incest to obsessive-compulsive disorders to schizophrenia. Some psychiatric hospitals also treat mental retardation. In addition to the specialty facilities listed in this section, check Chapter 12 for those local hospitals that have psychiatric departments offering both in- and outpatient care.

Psychiatric Facilities

Belmont Center for Comprehensive Treatment

4200 Monument Road; 877-2000, 456-8000 (*program information*), 581-3774 (*admission*), 581-3757 (*Woodside Hall addiction treatment program*). Doctors on active staff: 176 (*80% board-certified*); number of beds: 147; 2.3 RNs per bed; accreditation: JCAHO, National Association of Psychiatric Health Systems.

Emergency room services: access to psychiatric emergency at Albert Einstein Medical Center.

Special treatment units: inpatient, outpatient and comprehensive day treatment programs for alcohol, chemical and gambling addictions, dual diagnosis for adolescents and adults, Anxiety/Affective Disorders, Adolescent Treatment Program, Deaf Treatment Program, Obsessive-Compulsive Disorders Program, Eating Disorders Program, Family Center, Forensic Mental Health Service, Senior Recovery Program,

Woodside Hall Addictions Treatment Program, Women's Center, CAREER®
Intensive Outpatient Addictions Program.
Physical rehab services: physical medicine and rehab.

Belmont Center for Comprehensive Treatment is a private, nonprofit psychiatric
hospital and a member of Albert Einstein Healthcare Network.

Center for the Family, Inc.

CORPORATE HEADQUARTERS: 14 WASHINGTON ROAD, SUITE 702, PRINCETON JUNCTION, NJ.
OTHER SITES: 1002 EAST GREENVIEW EXECUTIVE CAMPUS, MARLTON, NJ, AND 1911 MANNING
STREET, PHILADELPHIA. STAFF COMPOSED OF LICENSED BOARD-CERTIFIED PSYCHIATRIST AND
MASTER-LEVEL THERAPISTS; ACCEPTS ALL MAJOR INSURANCE.

The Center for the Family provides innovative outpatient treatment to patients
with eating disorders, adolescents with emotional and behavioral problems and
those with drug and alcohol problems, and handles general mental health issues
such as depression, marital counseling and attention deficit hyperactive disorder.
Services include an intensive outpatient program, partial hospitalization program
and outpatient treatment. The center addresses the causes of the problems and
emphasizes early and intensive intervention to break the cycle causing the problem.
All significant individuals and social systems that have an impact on the patient are
involved in treatment. The center is regarded as the primary point in service for difficult patients who need expert care in a warm and caring environment.

The Charter Fairmount Institute

561 FAIRTHORNE AVENUE, ROXBOROUGH; 487-4000. STAFF COMPOSED OF MULTIDISCIPLINARY
TEAM, INCLUDING PSYCHIATRISTS, PSYCHIATRIC NURSES, PSYCHOLOGISTS, ALLIED THERAPISTS
AND SOCIAL WORKERS; NUMBER OF BEDS: 169; ACCREDITATION: JCAHO; LICENSED BY DPW
AND ODAP; ACCEPTS MOST INSURANCE.

Specialized treatment programs: geriatric unit, adolescent program (ages 12-
18) including substance-abuse services and a school program, adult dual-diagnosis,
adult special-care program (ages 18 and older) for those suffering from acute psychiatric disorders, residential program.
Outpatient health and wellness: partial hospitalization day treatment.
Charter Fairmount, established in 1926, provides a variety of therapy programs,
including recreational, music, art, family and other ancillary services.

Eastern Pennsylvania Psychiatric Institute (EPPI)

 E

3300 HENRY AVENUE; 842-4100. EPPI IS THE PSYCHIATRIC ARM OF MEDICAL COLLEGE
HOSPITALS, A MEMBER OF THE ALLEGHENY HEALTH SYSTEM. IT HOUSES SEVERAL PSYCHIATRIC
UNITS, THE SLEEP DISORDERS CENTER, THE MID-ATLANTIC REGIONAL EPILEPSY CENTER, THE

CIBA-GEIGY RESEARCH UNIT AND THE PEDIATRIC NEURODEVELOPMENTAL PROGRAM. STAFF COMPOSED OF: 44 PSYCHIATRISTS (*95% board-certified*), 19 PSYCHOLOGISTS AND 15 SOCIAL WORKERS; NUMBER OF BEDS: 117; 2.29 RNS PER BED; ACCREDITATION: JCAHO.

Specialized psychiatry treatment programs: Behavioral Therapy Clinic; Center for the Treatment and Study of Anxiety, Child and Adolescent Depression Clinic; Child and Adolescent Psychiatry Outpatient Clinic and Inpatient Services; Crime Victims Program; Family/Couples Therapy Clinic; Family Coping Skills Workshop; Group Psychotherapy Clinic; Marital and Family Therapy Clinic; Mood, Anxiety and Personality Disorders Clinic; Preschool and School Age Partial Hospitalization Program; a therapeutic nursery for preschoolers with neurodevelopmental delays; Psychiatric Consultation-Liaison Service; Psychotherapy Clinic; Schizophrenia Diagnostic Center; Psychiatric Emergency Service for the clients of community mental-health centers throughout Northeast and Northwest Philadelphia. In addition, EPPI maintains a General Psychiatric Unit, an Affective Disorders Unit, which treats patients with severe mood disturbances, an Adult Psychiatric Intensive Care Unit, a Psychiatric Step-Down Unit, a Neuropsychiatric Unit, a Children's Unit and an Adolescent Unit.

Friends Hospital

4641 ROOSEVELT BOULEVARD; 831-4600, 831-4870 (*for general information or referral, Monday to Friday 8:30-4:30*). STAFF COMPOSED OF 29 PSYCHIATRISTS (*90% board-certified*), SIX LICENSED PSYCHOLOGISTS, 15 REHABILITATIVE THERAPISTS AND 13 SOCIAL WORKERS; NUMBER OF BEDS: 192; ONE RN PER 2.5 BEDS; ACCREDITATION: JCAHO, DPW.

Specialized treatment programs: Young People's Unit (treating 13-to-21-year-olds with emotional, behavioral or psychiatric problems); Adolescent Dual Diagnosis Program (treating young people with addiction and psychiatric diagnoses); Supportive Care Unit, partial hospital programs (see outpatient); the Greystone Program (residential services), pain/stress management, addictions recovery, Focus Program (evaluation and brief-stay program for adults); Geropsychiatry Service (for those with issues related to aging, loss or illnesses); horticultural, recreational, expressive, vocational and occupational therapy.
Outpatient programs: The Passage (partial hospital program for adolescents), the Day Program (for adults), The Garden (for older adults), Friends Recovery Center (intensive addictions recovery), Clark Clinic (services offered on a sliding fee scale). Additional outpatient treatment available in West Chester, King of Prussia, Linwood (N.J.), Philadelphia and Bucks County.

Founded in 1813, Friends is the first private, not-for-profit psychiatric hospital in the country. Located on a beautifully landscaped 100-acre site, it offers a full range of in- and outpatient services for adults, adolescents and the elderly. A Guide to Staff is available.

Hampton Hospital

650 RANCOCAS ROAD, RANCOCAS, NJ; 609-267-7000, 1-800-345-7345 (*referral and assessment*).
STAFF COMPOSED OF FOUR PSYCHIATRISTS AND TWO PSYCHOLOGISTS; NUMBER OF BEDS: 100;
1.8 RNS PER BED, 1.8 SOCIAL WORKERS PER PATIENT; ACCEPTS ALL TYPES OF MAJOR INSURANCE;
DETOX AVAILABLE.

A private psychiatric hospital offering treatment, research, education and diagnosis for adults of all ages and adolescents with emotional problems. Composed of five independent specialty units: the Adolescent Psychiatric Treatment Program, the Adolescent Dual Diagnosis Treatment Program, the Adult Psychiatric Treatment Program, the Adult Dual Diagnosis Treatment Program and the Geropsychiatric Treatment Program. Concentrates on dual-diagnosis patients (those who are diagnosed with both a mental disorder and a substance-abuse problem). Offers outpatient services at Hampton Counseling Center sites at Greentree Commons, Suite 8001 B, Route 73, Marlton, NJ, (609) 596-5333; and 368 Lakehurst Road, Suite 205, Toms River, NJ, (908) 914-9036. Services include intensive day programs for adolescents and adults of all ages, intensive drug and alcohol programs, short-term therapy, co-dependency programs, early intervention programs for adolescents, after-care programs, neuropsychiatric evaluations, medication management, intervention programs, family and marital counseling.

The Horsham Clinic

722 EAST BUTLER PIKE, AMBLER; 643-7800, 800-237-4447 (*Assessment and Referral Center*).
STAFF COMPOSED OF 22 PSYCHIATRISTS (*100% board-certified/board-eligible*), 12 PSYCHOLO-
GISTS, 15 SOCIAL WORKERS; NUMBER OF BEDS: 138; 1.73 RNS PER BED; ACCREDITATION: JCAHO;
ACCEPTS MOST INSURANCE.

Specialized adult-treatment programs: adult in- and outpatient dual diagnosis; psychiatric inpatient care, partial hospitalization and Short-Term Assessment and Treatment Unit available for those 18 and older who require brief, focused treatment; adult intensive day treatment program with a bio-psycho-social treatment model, psycho-educational and skill training groups; women's programs providing individualized treatment include: Women's Evening Intensive Partial Program, Women's Recovery From Trauma for Sexual Abuse Survivors, women's groups in the Adolescent and Adult Partial Hospitalization units.
Specialized adolescent and children's programs: Young Adolescent Unit for ages 11-13, Older Adolescent Unit for ages 14-18 and Children's Unit for ages 5-12; outpatient counseling, day treatment program, inpatient treatment, family counseling.

The Horsham Clinic is a private, psychiatric hospital situated in a distinctive, 55-acre setting in suburban Philadelphia.

The Institute of Pennsylvania Hospital

111 NORTH 49TH STREET, PHILADELPHIA, 471-2000. STAFF COMPOSED OF 260 LICENSED PSY-
CHIATRISTS, PLUS SOCIAL WORKERS, PSYCHOLOGISTS AND ADDICTION COUNSELORS; NUMBER
OF BEDS: 234; ONE RN PER TWO BEDS; ROOM COST: $984; GOURMET FOOD SERVICE: $19 PER
DAY; ACCREDITATION: JCAHO, ACGME, DPW.

Emergency room service: access to psychiatric emergency at Pennsylvania
Hospital.

Specialized treatment programs (in- and outpatient): substance-abuse treatment for adolescents and adults, including dual-diagnosis care, evaluation services,
brief intensive treatment, anxiety disorders, dissociative disorders, young adult, geriatric psychiatry, Kirkbride Apartment Program, Mill Creek School (a licensed high
school for inpatients and day students).

Psychiatric rehab services: in- and outpatient life-skills and social-rehab programs, occupational therapy, therapeutic, leisure and recreational activities, creative
arts therapies, adventure-based programs, pre-vocational rehab and career counseling.

Outpatient health and wellness programs: Speaker's Bureau; Family Night
Coping Skills Workshop (for families of the mentally ill); Outpatient Clinic (child,
adult and couples therapy offered on a sliding fee scale); access to day treatment
programs for all age groups.

The Institute of Pennsylvania Hospital was opened in 1841 to offer expanded,
humane services to mentally ill patients of Pennsylvania Hospital, the nation's first
hospital. Today, The Institute is a private, nonprofit facility serving adolescents and
adults on a short and long-term basis.

Mount Sinai Hospital

4TH AND REED STREETS, PHILADELPHIA; 339-3456. DOCTORS ON ACTIVE STAFF: 45 (*91%
board-certified*); NUMBER OF BEDS: 220; ONE RN PER 2.2 BEDS; ACCREDITATION: JCAHO, CAP.

Inpatient programs for adolescents, adults and older adults; partial hospital program and sub-acute psychiatric program. Also offers adult substance-abuse rehab
program, detox unit, outpatient substance-abuse programs and services for the
dual-diagnosed. Mt. Sinai is part of Graduate Health System.

Northwestern Institute

450 BETHLEHEM PIKE, P.O. BOX 209, FORT WASHINGTON; 641-5300. STAFF COMPOSED OF 45 PSYCHIATRISTS (*90% board-certified*), FOUR PSYCHOLOGISTS AND 20 SOCIAL WORKERS; NUMBER OF BEDS: 146; 2.24 RNS PER BED; SEMIPRIVATE ROOM COST: $775-$1,000; ACCREDITATION: JCAHO; FOR MORE INFORMATION, CALL 800-344-NWIP.

Specialized adult programs: dissociative disorders; Older Adult Program (for dealing with the loss of a spouse or longtime friend or emotional problems resulting from retirement); Adolescent Program (for youngsters 13-18 with emotional or behavioral problems); Children's Program (for 6-to-12-year-olds suffering from hyperactivity, depression, psychosis, trauma or abuse); Women's Unit (to help women over 18 cope with depression, sexual, physical or emotional abuse, codependency and sexual dysfunction).

Unique treatment unit: the Sanctuary Program, a 22-bed voluntary inpatient protected environment organized for adults who've experienced abuse or psychological trauma as children and as a result find themselves suffering from depression or self-destructive, obsessive behavior. The treatment uses a multidisciplinary staff of psychiatrists, social workers, dance and art therapists and nurses in an integrated approach to healing.

Outpatient health and wellness programs: a broad spectrum of community education seminars.

A private psychiatric hospital offering in- and outpatient treatment as well as a partial hospitalization program for those who need inpatient services without overnight hospital stays.

Philadelphia Child Guidance Center

34TH STREET AND CIVIC CENTER BOULEVARD, 243-2600 (*evening crisis hotline: 243-2888*); CHILD ASSIST NETWORK REFERRAL SERVICE: 243-2702. STAFF COMPOSED OF PSYCHIATRISTS (*91% board-certified*), PSYCHOLOGISTS AND SOCIAL WORKERS; NUMBER OF BEDS: 38; ONE RN PER THREE BEDS; ROOM COST: $865; ACCREDITATION: JCAHO.

Specialized treatment programs: Day Hospital Program, two residential apartment units for families undergoing intensive inpatient treatment.

Outpatient programs: assessment; individual, group and family therapy; medication clinic; intensive family/home-based program; therapeutic preschool program; drug and alcohol treatment; therapeutic foster homes.

The Philadelphia Child Guidance Center, a comprehensive mental health organization serving children and adolescents with emotional/behavioral problems, is internationally known for expertise in family therapy, eating disorders and psychosomatic illness. It is a teaching hospital affiliated with the University of Pennsylvania School of Medicine and the Children's Hospital of Philadelphia.

The Westmeade Centers

8765 STENTON AVENUE, WYNDMOOR, 836-9600; AND 1460 MEETINGHOUSE ROAD, HARTSVILLE (*Bucks County*), 491-9400. ATTENDING STAFF COMPOSED OF 12 PSYCHIATRISTS AND 25 PSYCHOLOGISTS; STAFF TO PATIENT RATIO: 1:1; NUMBER OF BEDS: 50; ACCREDITATION: JCAHO

Specialized programs: adult center for individuals with post-traumatic stress, borderline personality disorder, severe depression and other severe clinical symptoms and personality disorders; adolescent center for those 11-18 with acute psychiatric problems, including depression, impulsive behavior, psychotic disorders and attention-deficit disorders. Both programs offer treatment for dual diagnosis and eating disorders.

Outpatient health and wellness programs: Intensive Daily Outpatient Program and Home Care for patients who were recently discharged and no longer require 24-hour supervision, but still need daily therapy.

These private psychiatric inpatient facilities provide short-term, acute care for voluntary patients in a residential, noninstitutional setting, which gives them an opportunity to develop the skills to manage their problems in an environment similar to the one they will return to in their everyday lives.

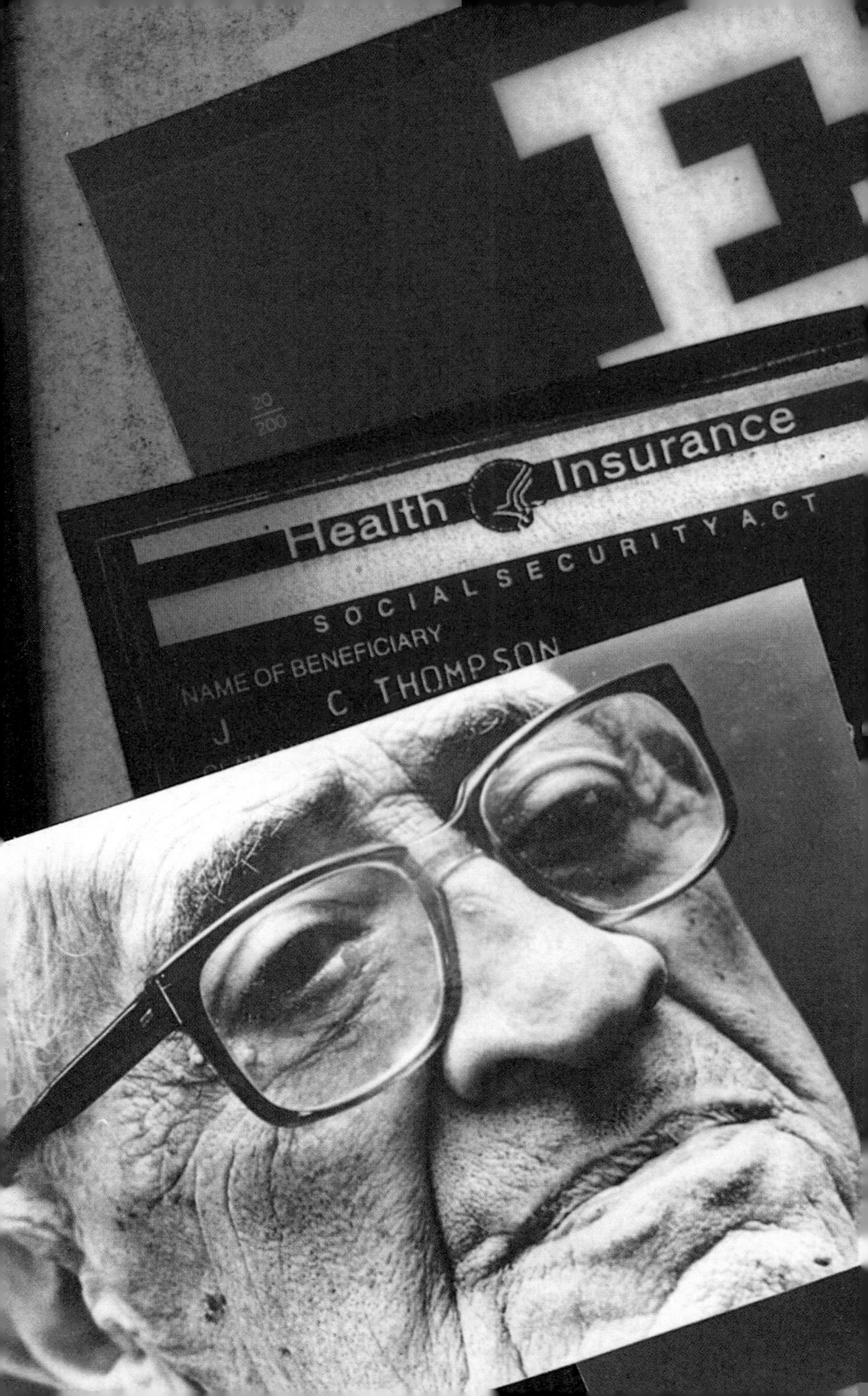
20/200
Health Insurance
SOCIAL SECURITY ACT
NAME OF BENEFICIARY
J C THOMPSON

7

Wisdom
for the Aging

Bishop White Lodge
The Skilled Nursing Facility
at
Cathedral Village

VISIT OUR NEW ALZHEIMER'S UNIT

The opening of our new Alzheimer's Unit allows us to offer a very special program of care to residents with memory impairment.

Our Alzheimer's program combines twenty-four hour nursing care, activities and personal attention. Experienced staff members understand the problems encountered by both the resident and family when memory impairment exists.

The warm home-like environment of the sun room in the Alzheimer's Unit is the center of daily life where a full schedule of daily activities promotes social and physical stimulation.

Skilled and Intermediate nursing care will always be available at Bishop White Lodge but as caregiver for one whose needs are very special, we invite you to visit our new Alzheimer's Unit.

Call or visit Monday through Friday for information and a tour.
If you need a weekend visit, please call for an appointment.

Bishop White Lodge

600 East Cathedral Road
Philadelphia, PA 19128
(215) 487-1300

CHAPTER 24

Remembrance of Things . . .

What happens when we forget to remember

Memorize the following 15 grocery items for 30 seconds. Don't cheat. Then take a piece of paper and write down as many as you can remember:

hot dogs	honey	chestnuts
toilet paper	canned ham	tomatoes
cereal	spaghetti	soda
detergent	milk	yams
cheese	ketchup	potato chips

If you're under 40, you should have remembered ten items. From 40 to 50, the norm is nine; from 60 to 69, eight, and over 70, seven.

Now read these following names, then cover them with a piece of paper and fill in the blanks below:

Harold Smith	Andrew Kelly
MaryAnne White	Amy Pott
Louise Parks	David Benson

_____ Kelly

_____ Smith

_____ Parks

_____ Benson

_____ Pott

_____ White

Under the age of 50, you should have remembered at least two of the first names; over 50, at least one.

Regardless of how well or poorly you scored (it's your secret), I'm willing to bet my next week's salary that if you are over 35 and reading this, you've forgotten something within the last few days. Maybe it was the name of a person you met or the whatyamacallit in your tool kit or kitchen drawer that fixes the whoosit you were holding in your hand. Perhaps it was whatever task sent you from the bedroom to the living room and then eluded you when you got there. Possibly you just forgot where you left your car keys. No matter what it was you couldn't remember, I'm willing to sweeten my wager with a second week's salary and bet that forgetting things upsets you a lot more than you'd like to admit. You may have even reached the point where you're covering up the problem by joking that you're suffering from that new disease, CRS—Can't Remember Shit.

None of us expects to age without certain inevitable deteriorations. Our eyesight gets dimmer, our hearts get weaker; our muscles grow flabbier. It becomes harder to run for the train, chase the tennis ball, drink and dance until the wee hours. For some reason, we accept these physical signs of winding down with reluctant resignation. But when our memory slackens even slightly, we panic—could this be, God forbid, the start of Alzheimer's disease? Let me reassure you, it probably is not; casual memory lapses happen to teenagers as well as to their grandparents. When you're 25 and forget to fill the gas tank, you're simply considered thoughtless. But when you're 55, the same carelessness takes on different implications.

Age-associated memory loss

Fortunately, most memory problems are a perfectly natural part of aging. Some are attributable to what's frequently labeled "benign forgetfulness," which is caused mainly by not paying enough attention. People in this category, when asked to memorize three names, will have no trouble recalling them five minutes later. However, another kind of memory deficiency is the result of age-related physiological changes in the brain. Since 1986, this condition has been recognized by the National Institute of Mental Health (NIMH) as Age-Associated Memory Impairment (AAMI). Most experts believe AAMI, which kicks in after age 55, is a separate phenomenon from Alzheimer's, which strikes about 5 percent of those over 65.

Since the answer to any problem in America other than the economy seems to come from the drugstore, it's not surprising that in recent years, drug companies such as Searle have been pouring mega-dollars into finding a pill that will halt or reverse AAMI. With the graying of our population and an emphasis on jobs that require intellectual skill as opposed to physical strength or the mindless repetition of the assembly line, people are increasingly worried about normal memory decline. The pharmaceutical house that discovers a pill to combat spotty memory the way Valium masks anxiety or Prozac fights depression will make a fortune.

Thus far the drugs that look promising are still in the testing stage and available to the public only at places where clinical drug studies are done, such as the for-profit Memory Institute in Philadelphia. Since the drug researchers foot the bill, there's no charge to the participants.

The new families of drugs currently under investigation bear no resemblance to any of the existing compounds for treating emotional problems. One group called cognitive enhancers affects the way the brain uses glucose, since sugar is known to be a kind of mind fuel. Other test drugs enhance the activity of neuro-transmitters (the brain's messengers) or act on the receptor sites. In the latter case, the drugs seem to affect the ability to retrieve information, which differs from the filing part of memory. Also in the pipeline is a drug that's been successful in improving the learning ability of laboratory rats. Psychiatrist Joseph Mendels, medical director of the Memory Institute, says that within the decade a drug to restore lost memory function will be on the market. "But how dramatic that drug will be," he adds, "only time can tell."

Just a simple little test

I'll have to wait like everybody else for that pill because I scored too high on the Memory Institute's evaluation to qualify for its drug trials. Like most of the several hundred people who've gone there to be tested over the past few years, I was pretty nervous when I sat down for what they call the pen-and-pencil part of the exam, and at first I found it hard to concentrate. The test-giver began by telling me a story chock-full of details and asking me to repeat as much as I could remember. When she said I didn't do badly, I relaxed a bit and did even better on the second story. By the time she got to the paired-word section, I could actually feel my attention improving, and it showed. The vocabulary portion was a breeze; years as a writer didn't hurt. By now I was on a roll, and even managed to score above average on the section where I had to reproduce the shapes flashed on cards for a brief ten seconds. That surprised me, because I barely made it through geometry and rank down there with five-year-olds on those spatial-relation quizzes.

The second part of the test took place on a computer screen and involved recalling names, faces, telephone numbers and objects placed in rooms. I've always been lousy at remembering the names of people at parties, and everybody on this test looked alike—I swear there were three women with reddish hair named Jane or Janet. The only person I consistently recalled was a white-haired guy named Carl. He reminded me of my father.

Had my test results fallen below the norm for people my age, I would have been put through an arduous, no-cost physical examination: Tumors, thyroid conditions, Parkinson's disease, head injuries, alcohol and drugs can all affect memory. If those problems were ruled out and I was accepted into the program, I'd have been put on either a drug or a placebo for several months, then retested periodically to measure improvement. People on the placebo are eventually given the experimental drug too.

Memories are made of this

Scientists don't know exactly how memory works, but they do know that it's a combination of separate abilities, operating in different parts of the brain, that appear to be coordinated by a small curled organ called the hippocampus. Much of the information about conscious memory has been furnished by a man known only as H.M., whose hippocampus was surgically removed to treat his epileptic attacks. Minus the hippocampus, H.M. has retained his intellectual powers but has no conscious memory. For instance, he can read a newspaper and understand it, but 20 minutes later he can't recall having read the paper at all. Or he can master a new skill—in his case, mirror-reading—and have no memory of having done so.

Research has shown that over the years the brain, which can be likened to a piece of electrical machinery, shrinks. Past the age of 50 we start losing circuits. Large amounts of neurons die, and the activity of neurotransmitters diminishes. The changes are thought to be influenced not only by normal senescence, but by such factors as stress, environmental pollution, genetics and even medication. By age 65 most people will experience a decline in what's called explicit memory—the ability to recall the things, people and events stored in our brains over the years. The major area of distinction in memory between the young and the old is the ability to manage and retain new information, along with the speed of processing it. On the other hand, the accumulation of general knowledge—the so-called wisdom of age—gives us the skill to work around these changes.

It's also widely accepted that the emotions play a role in memory. Among the elderly especially, much of what presents itself as a memory disorder is frequently depression, says Dr. Mendels. He estimates that 10 to 20 percent of the elderly who appear to have the symptoms of Alzheimer's are actually suffering from clinical depression. "If you treat them for depression and ignore the Alzheimer's, many will get better. My position is, when in doubt, a therapeutic trial of antidepressant isn't a bad idea."

Even the way we store information is influenced by emotions. When something is linked to intense feelings, it's more likely to be remembered. That may be why so many wives have the unique ability to repeat every awful thing their husbands said in arguments 15 years earlier. Other emotions—anxiety in particular—block out memory, which explains why you can't find your glasses when you're in a hurry to make a plane or can't remember a phone number until you stop forcing yourself to think about it. If you've ever noticed that your mind gets clearer as you relax, it's because anxiety interferes with concentration and makes recall more difficult.

Signs of Alzheimer's disease

I left the Memory Institute pleased that my memory lapses were related more to anxiety than brain death and relieved that I didn't have what people jokingly refer to as premature Alzheimer's. Memory loss may be one of the markers of Alzheimer's disease, but it's by no means an absolute precursor to it. With Age-Associated

Memory Impairment you can easily forget where you left your car keys; with Alzheimer's disease you forget what the keys are for. There are other important differences as well. Those with AAMI have difficulty recalling names of people, places and things, but when they're given a clue, the forgotten items return. Let's say you can't remember a restaurant. If someone jogs your memory with its location or what you ate or with whom you dined, it will come back to you. But clues offer no assistance for Alzheimer's patients who also have very spotty recall of old data. One day they can remember their address; another day they can't.

"The common rule of thumb to use is that people who think they have Alzheimer's usually don't," says Dr. Chris Clark, director of Graduate Hospital's Memory Disorder Service. "Most people with Alzheimer's are brought in by a concerned family member. They act somewhat confused and aren't aware they have a memory problem." By contrast, people with normal memory loss due to aging bring the problem to a doctor of their own volition, often spurred by embarrassment. They'll complain they're afraid to take on new tasks at work because they may not be able to retain the information. Socially they find themselves turning down invitations because they can't remember the names of fellow guests. They're uncomfortable telling stories and talking about movies they saw or books they read, because they can't remember the details. And they're self-conscious in conversation because they have to fish around for words.

There is no single, diagnostic test for Alzheimer's disease, but it is important to consider the possibility of other problems that mimic it. Depression, drug and alcohol dependency, thyroid or nutritional deficiencies, brain tumors, stroke and head trauma can present with similar symptoms. And the interaction of medications can aggravate the condition.

Don't forget to remember this

Until a magic pill shows up on Memory Lane to deal with our remembrance of things past, there are techniques to fight forgetfulness that really do work—but you have to practice them.

Get in the habit of writing things down. That's why Post-Its were invented.

Be aware that distractions impair memory. Maybe kids can do homework plugged into a Walkman, but senior citizens are likely to have trouble remembering a phone number given while they're watching TV.

Play the association game. I always remember that the boating term "port" means left rather than right because port and left both have four letters.

Change your routine. Some people put their wristwatch on backward to remind themselves of a task. I've gotten into the habit of moving a jar of hand cream from my bedside table to the floor at night if I want to remember something in particular in the morning.

Use it or lose it. Research proves there is a correlation between memory and intellectual activity. If you figure your learning days are over at 65, you'll make less effort to retain information and feel more forgetful. Retirees who become couch potatoes tend to have more severe memory problems than people who find ways to stay alert.

Invent codes as reminders. Back in sixth grade everybody depended on the word HOMES as an acronym to remember the five Great Lakes. Of course, with aging you may have difficulty recalling the code word. Ultimately that's the test of whether or not you're suffering from CRS—and if you can remember what that means without referring back to the first page, rest easy. You don't have it.

For Your Information

The Memory Institute at 1015 Chestnut Street (923-8378) is looking for trial participants. You must be over 50, in good health and not taking psychotropic drugs. You must also believe you have a memory problem. The Institute's definition of "problem" is an awareness of a steady decline in your memory over the past decade that's come to interfere with things you consider important and seems to be worse than what your peers are complaining about. There is no charge for their service.

SCHEIE EYE INSTITUTE

Ophthalmologists at Scheie Eye Institute are world renowned for advancing knowledge about vision, eye diseases, and the prevention of blindness. As faculty members of the **University of Pennsylvania School of Medicine,** they have developed many new treatments that dramatically improve and preserve vision.

Scheie Eye Institute's ophthalmologists often use a team approach to provide comprehensive diagnosis and treatment for all eye conditions, including:

- *General ophthalmology*
- *Cataract and lens implant surgery*
- *Contact lenses*
- *Cornea transplants*
- *Diabetic retinopathy*
- *Glaucoma*
- *Infections*
- *Low vision*
- *Macular degeneration*
- *Muscle and eye movement surgery*
- *Neuro-ophthalmology*
- *Ocular genetics*
- *Plastic surgery*
- *Pediatric ophthalmology*
- *Radial keratotomy*
- *Retina and vitreous diseases*
- *Tumors of the eye*
- *Vision impairments of aging*

Diagnostic Technology
State-of-the-art diagnostic technology:

- Fluorescein Angiography
- ICG Angiography
- Ultrasound
- Laser Surgery
- CT and MRI Scanning
- Electro-diagnostic Testing

For information about our services, physicians, or to schedule an appointment, please call:

Scheie Eye Institute
215-662-8121

University of Pennsylvania Medical Center

Presbyterian Medical Center of Philadelphia

Diagnostic Centers
Alzheimer's Disease

For support groups, see Chapter 27.

Abington Memorial Hospital, 881-5640

Albert Einstein Medical Center, 456-8256

Ambulatory Geriatric Evaluation Service, 402-9890

Alzheimer's Association, 568-6430

Crozer-Chester Medical Center, 447-2030

Doylestown Hospital, 345-2200

Graduate Hospital, 893-2446

Hahnemann University Hospital, 246-5100

Institute of Pennsylvania Hospital, 471-2862

Thomas Jefferson University Hospital, 955-8033/955-8780

Jeanes Vital Age, 663-0875

Medical College of Pennsylvania, 842-4070

Paoli Memorial Hospital, 648-1206

Pennsylvania Hospital, 829-3000

Philadelphia Geriatric Center, 456-2900

Prime Health Medical Offices, 333-3500

Quakertown Hospital, 536-6016

St. Mary's Hospital, 757-5800

Temple University Hospital, 707-8902

University of Pennsylvania Medical Center Cognitive Neurology Program, 662-3606

University of Pennsylvania Medical Center King of Prussia Facility, 337-8882

University of Pennsylvania Medical Center
Foerderer Evaluation Program, 662-2746

CHAPTER 25

Services for the Aging

How to manage the crisis before it occurs

U sually it takes a crisis to get us thinking about our elderly parents' changing needs. Only then—after Dad has a stroke or Mom falls and breaks a hip—do we gather around the kitchen table to thrash out the options and make hurried decisions.

Granted, it's painful even to acknowledge that a parent who seems so vigorous now could someday become frail and helpless. But it's essential to overcome your hesitation and talk to your parents about future options while they're still of sound mind and body.

"Most healthy parents want to talk about those things with their children," says Vivian Greenberg, a Princeton-area clinical social worker and co-author of *Should Mom Live With Us: Is Happiness Possible if She Does?* "It's part of living. We're all going to grow old; we're all going to die. It's a matter of sitting down now, perhaps, and saying, 'What are your expectations for me in case you become sick, in case you become disabled? What is it you would like from me?'"

Although medical advances have helped us to live longer—today, life expectancy at birth is 72 for males and 79 for females—that doesn't necessarily translate into improved quality of life. It simply means more people are old longer, enduring chronic ailments such as heart disease and diabetes. "We have been very good at eliminating death due to acute illness," says Avalie Saperstein, vice president of the York House of the Philadelphia Geriatric Center. "We have not substantially changed the age that chronic illness begins."

When we think of elderly care, a nursing home is the first option that pops into our minds. Indeed, researchers report that nearly half of those Americans who turn 65 this year will spend some time in a nursing home before they die. At any given time, though, most of the nation's elderly do live in the community. Many are staying with relatives—studies suggest as much as 80 percent of the care given to the nation's elderly is provided by families.

Typically it's a daughter or daughter-in-law who becomes the primary caregiver—a stressful burden. People who care for their parents report high levels of depression and other emotional and physical problems. Part of the "sandwich generation," they feel pulled between the demands of their parents, their own children and spouse, and their careers.

"It does take a toll on you on all kinds of levels, physically as well as emotionally," says Orien Reid, WCAU-TV's consumer reporter, who looked after her mother for two years, until Octavine Alexander's Alzheimer's disease required nursing-home care. "It's going to take its toll on you professionally, too, because you're just not going to have the kind of time to devote that you had in the past," notes Reid, who serves on the board of the Alzheimer's Association of Greater Philadelphia. "It will change your whole life."

As the population ages—by the year 2030, more than one-fifth of the population will be 65 or older—demand will soar for every level of elderly health service, and already tight social service programs will be stretched even further. Earlier this year, the Philadelphia Long-Term Care Task Force warned that the city, even now experiencing a shortage of nursing-home beds, will need 7,000 more by 1995.

Nearly a quarter of those on waiting lists for nursing homes in Philadelphia now die in hospitals or at home without ever getting off the lists, according to Ed Ratajczak, director of long-term care services for the Philadelphia Corporation for the Aging. Some overwhelmed families even turn to "granny dumping," abandoning their relatives at emergency rooms when the burden of care gets to be too much.

But as bad as the nursing-home crisis is, the biggest local need in coming years will be affordable in-home care, which includes nursing visits and, even more important, custodial care.

"Most elderly who need some kind of assistance in the home don't need health care," says Lynne Kotranski, vice president for research and evaluation at the Philadelphia Health Management Corporation (PHMC), a nonprofit research organization. "They need someone to come in and help with cleaning and cooking and doing errands."

While policymakers debate how society is going to pay for the long-term care of its elderly, most of us are left to confront such questions on a strictly personal level: Does Aunt Rose need a nursing home or is there a way to keep her functioning independently? How do I find help for Grandpa when he lives 2,000 miles away? Who can tell me what to expect if my parents move in with us?

Here are some answers to those kinds of questions.

Money Matters
Paying the bills and protecting the nest egg

Long-term care is incredibly expensive. A nursing home can cost $25,000 to $70,000 a year; home care ranges from $50 to $200 a day.

"It's good to see mom smiling again."

Depression and memory loss in the elderly can and should be treated.

The Wills Geriatric Psychiatry Program is specially designed to treat the emotional, psychological and neurological needs of older people. The Program's staff is guided by a medical director named among the country's "best mental health experts" in *Good Housekeeping* magazine.

These dedicated, sensitive professionals of Wills and Jefferson hospitals provide expert care and support in a comfortable, homelike environment.

For help with depression, memory loss, anxiety and age-related physical and social losses, call **1-800-JEFF-NOW.**

WILLS GERIATRIC PSYCHIATRY PROGRAM
Wills Eye Hospital • Thomas Jefferson University Hospital
900 Walnut Street, Philadelphia, PA 19107

The biggest misconception is that Medicare pays the bills. Medicare, the federal health-care program for those 65 and older, covers doctors' bills and major hospital costs, but provides little help with long-term care. Under certain circumstances the program will pay for a part of up to 100 days of nursing care after a hospital stay, but it doesn't cover custodial care, the level most commonly needed by chronically ill elderly people. And its coverage of home health care is minimal.

"Medigap" insurance isn't the answer either. Sixty-five percent of Americans over 65 buy Medigap, which is designed to fill in the holes in Medicare coverage for doctor and hospital bills. But it doesn't cover most long-term care needs.

Medicaid is the big payer when it comes to nursing-home care; the health-insurance program established for poor Americans now pays nearly half of nursing-home expenses nationwide. When the cost of care exceeds a patient's ability to pay, making him or her "medically needy," Medicaid kicks in.

Nursing homes that accept Medicaid patients are reimbursed at rates set by the state. The industry claim the rates cover only three-fourths of their costs, so some homes refuse Medicaid patients outright and take only "private pay" clients. (Yes, they can do this.) Those on Medicaid can encounter long waiting lists.

The average Medicaid patient in Pennsylvania is a white woman age 80 or older who has exhausted more than $45,000 of her own money on nursing-home expenses, according to a 1988 study by the Pennsylvania Department of Insurance. This process is known as "spending down," and it can be a sorrowful one, since it forces people to eat up the portfolio of assets they took a lifetime to accrue.

To qualify for Medicaid, a person 65 or older must meet an income test. Generally, a single person may qualify when his or her countable assets are less than $2,400. Uncounted assets include a family home and household goods, a car, some life insurance, a burial fund and a cemetery plot. Your county assistance office can tell you if you are eligible.

A growing number of middle-class families are hiring "Medicaid planners," who can help shift assets so Grandma's nursing-home bills won't wipe out Grandpa's life savings—or your inheritance.

An irrevocable trust is one approach. Typically, a married couple puts all their assets into such a trust, which gives them interest income but no principal. If either spouse enters a nursing home, the other still gets the income. At the death of one or both, the principal goes to the survivors.

Critics say Medicaid planning is just an upscale version of welfare cheating. (The lobbying group AARP, among others, is uncomfortable with it.) Some of them call Medicaid planners "poverty planners."

"That's garbage," says Philadelphia lawyer Stephen A. Feldman, who specializes in estate planning and health law. "People have the right to make sure they can afford to maintain their lifestyles. These people have worked hard all their lives, they've paid their taxes, and they're entitled to benefit from the system as much as anybody else is."

Asset-shifting won't answer every problem. It used to be that qualifying one spouse for Medicaid meant impoverishing the partner. Now the mate who stays at home is allowed to retain some resources, but not enough, critics say. One local couple structured their assets to pay for the husband's care in a Bucks County nursing home. Now the wife, who is arthritic, needs to find a way to pay out of her own pocket for round-the-clock companion care for herself. But with her husband receiving Medicaid, her monthly income isn't allowed to exceed $1,200. That's what she lives on—and her rent is $600.

Shifting assets can trigger a waiting period of up to 30 months for Medicaid benefits, so Feldman says Medicaid planning should be a last resort. He recommends long-term care insurance for people in their late 50s and early 60s who are planning for early retirement. Buy such a policy for your parents now, he exhorts baby boomers; it could save you a lot of money later.

For many, the financing of long-term care is becoming an integral part of financial planning. It can be approached through several alternatives: reverse home mortgages (also called home equity conversion mortgages), life insurance policies with a living benefit for long-term care expenses, annuities and long-term care insurance itself. The latter is a relatively new type of insurance that typically covers nursing-home bills and/or home care. Most policies offer several levels of benefits and an option for increases pegged to inflation. The premiums vary according to the buyer's age at time of purchase, and, as might be expected, younger people pay less. But these policies are not cheap. A policy for a 65-year-old can cost around $1,000 a year, and someone 75 might pay twice as much.

They're not easy to plow through, either. *Consumer Reports* evaluated 94 policies last year, and found they vary widely and can be so confusing that even the agents misunderstand and misrepresent them. Moreover, not everybody who applies for the insurance gets it, especially those suffering from existing conditions like cancer, MS, diabetes or a stroke.

If you shop for long-term care, be sure to look at more than one product. Review the benefits and premiums carefully. Consult with your lawyer, financial advisers and family, and be sure to get a consumer guide available from the Health Insurance Association of America, the state department of insurance or the AARP (see the resource list in "Nursing Homes," later in this chapter).

When it comes to planning for long-term care, experts agree: People of all ages should draw up a legal document known as a durable power of attorney, naming another person as a proxy. The proxy can then make financial decisions in case you're unable to make them for yourself. The usual lawyer's fee is $75 to $125.

A similar document, a durable power of attorney for health, empowers someone else to make medical decisions for the incapacitated person, and can also include the person's wishes about which medical procedures should be taken and which avoided. It has more flexibility than a living will.

Resources

The National Academy of Elder Law Attorneys (602-881-4005) will send you a free brochure on questions to ask when selecting an elder-law attorney. Send a large self-addressed stamped envelope to 655 North Alvernon Way, Suite 108, Tucson, AZ 85711.

On Your Own

Most elderly adults would prefer to live on their own as long as possible, and there is a growing number of local agencies to help them do just that

One elderly Main Line couple who didn't want to move to a nursing home managed at home with the help of three shifts of health aides looking after the bedridden wife and the husband, who had Alzheimer's. A private-care manager monitored the arrangement for the couple's adult children, who lived miles away. (Needless to say, it was expensive, costing as much as a nursing-home stay.) But maybe your parent doesn't need skilled nursing help. Most elderly people just need help with the activities of daily living—walking, bathing, grooming, dressing, eating, getting in and out of bed.

The Area Agencies on Aging offer free services, but—this is beginning to sound familiar—waiting lists are long. The Philadelphia Corporation for the Aging's In-Home Care Program serves about 3,000 people, and sometimes has a waiting list half that long. The city's Community Care Option Program diverts people from nursing-home care by patching together supports at home, but it, too, is overwhelmed by demand. The program has 600 slots and a waiting list nearly as long. "The funds are insufficient, and don't begin to meet the need and demand out there," says Emily Amerman, the program's director of care management.

One pioneering idea in home care is Friends Life Care at Home. Similar in concept to continuing-care retirement homes but more affordable, it guarantees a continuum of long-term care at home for people who wish to live independently as long as possible. For an entrance fee of $5,600-$18,400 and monthly fees of $222-$237, members receive a broad range of health and homemaker services for the rest of their lives. The plan pays 70 percent of the cost of a stay at one of 18 local nursing homes, if such a stay is needed. At this point the service area includes Northeast and Northwest Philadelphia, eastern Montgomery and lower Bucks counties, the Main Line and most of Delaware County (628-8964).

Resources

Bayada Nurses
546-5000

A private home-care agency founded in 1975, with 18 area offices serving Philadelphia, lower Montgomery and Delaware counties and southern New Jersey. A staff of RNs, LPNs, aides, homemakers and live-in companions provides services 24 hours a day, at fixed hourly or daily rates.

Share the Care Respite Program
487-1750

Run by Intercommunity Action, Inc., provides health aides in East Falls, Germantown, Roxborough, Andorra and Manayunk. Hourly rates are $8 to $10, with a minimum two-hour weekday and three-hour weekend usage level.

Episcopal Community Services
351-1400

Provides free RN-supervised home-care services, including Meals on Wheels, to SSI recipients and lower-income individuals in Philadelphia. Some health-aide services are available on a sliding fee scale for those ineligible for the free services.

Jewish Family and Children Service
545-3290; 609-662-8611 IN NEW JERSEY

Has worked with Philadelphia and suburban elderly since 1953. All home care is provided in coordination with a social worker, on a sliding fee scale, from two to 20 hours a week, with occasional overnight service. In the Cherry Hill area, JFS provides homemakers through the Carl Auerbach Friends of JFS.

Neighborhood Home Health Service
755-6464

A private Medicare-certified agency with 15 years' experience providing primary-care RNs who work mainly with Medicare referrals.

Philadelphia Geriatric Center
456-2900

Health and social services for Jewish elderly and their families. Recreational and religious activities. Also, full-care nursing home.

The Ralston-Penn Center
662-2746

Medical, nursing and social assistance for the elderly. Focus on improving the quality of life of seniors. The various programs include a post-stroke nursing consultation program and a geriatric psychiatry program.

Supportive Older Women's Network (SOWN)
477-6000

Organizes community self-help groups that help older women cope with health issues, social issues and widowhood.

Surrey Services for Seniors
647-6404

Volunteers and a small paid staff provide home care and chore services, on a sliding fee scale, to elderly people on the Main Line between Bryn Mawr and Malvern. Formerly known as the Surrey Club, it also sponsors social programs for the elderly.

....

Senior Outreach Services
642-2688

A nonprofit agency providing home care in the western suburbs. Rates are generally $8 to $10 an hour.

....

The Visiting Nurse Association of Greater Philadelphia
473-7600

One of the oldest nonprofit home health-care agencies in the nation, dating to 1886. The Medicare-certified agency provides health professionals and homemaker services in Philadelphia and the surrounding counties. It also offers services to uninsured and underinsured patients.

Nursing Homes
Making the most of the least-favorite choice

Most people shrink at the idea of a nursing home. Who hasn't heard horror stories about the high cost, the institutional callousness, at times the outright patient abuse? But not all nursing homes are *60 Minutes* fodder. In many cases, a nursing home may be the best solution.

"When someone requires institutionalization, there is no alternative," says Avalie Saperstein, of the Philadelphia Geriatric Center. "Families should not be beating themselves up to put together these fragmented plans to avoid nursing homes."

Today's nursing-home population is much different from what it was even a decade ago, when such homes were a residential choice for elderly folks with no other place to live. Now the homes are much "sicker" places—the patients are older, more frail. Dementia is common, since almost half of all people 80 or older suffer from some form of memory loss or confusion. Some families use nursing homes as a temporary solution, so more homes have begun to offer "respite care" of brief duration—a boon to family caregivers who want to go on vacation.

Nursing-home care is not cheap; on the average it costs $75 a day, or $27,500 a year, according to the American Health Care Association, the nursing-home industry's lobby. At Bryn Mawr Terrace Convalescent Center, one of the area's most opulent nursing homes, a suite with weekly beautician visits and limousine service for restaurant outings can cost as much as $65,000 a year.

If you have money, you'll probably have few problems getting into a nursing home, but if you're a Medicaid patient, it will be much more difficult—especially in Philadelphia proper, where 3,000 to 4,000 elderly people are usually on waiting lists for nursing-home beds. It's now illegal, but some participating homes may still try to get away with admitting private-pay patients ahead of Medicaid ones. In that case, getting in the door may be the hardest part. Once you're in, federal law now says the nursing home can't evict you for depleting your savings as long as it accepts Medicaid—and most do.

If your relative needs a nursing home, be prepared to spend as much time looking for one as the situation allows. Several organizations publish detailed brochures on nursing-home selection. A good rule of thumb is to select four or five facilities that meet your needs, then visit each, taking time to talk to the staff and to residents and their families.

Make at least one visit—several are better—to your preferred choice. Ask questions about care for your parent's specific condition. Look at the state licensing inspector's latest report, which should be on file at the home. Learn what costs are considered "extras," not covered in the daily rate for room, board and services. Finally, don't pick a nursing home without checking with the ombudsman at your Area Agency on Aging. Every AAA maintains such an overseer to monitor local nursing homes and boardinghouses and resolve consumer complaints. These watchdogs can also help you if problems arise later.

In response to complaints about nursing homes, Congress enacted sweeping reforms in 1987 aimed at making nursing homes more responsive to residents' needs. The legislation, which is being phased in, applies to facilities that participate in Medicare and Medicaid.

Nursing homes must now complete a comprehensive assessment of every resident upon admission and annually thereafter. Then a "plan of care" is developed with a patient and his or her family. This individualized outline spells out daily routines and also sets goals for resolving a resident's medical and nonmedical problems. Whenever a patient's condition changes, the plan of care is supposed to be amended.

In a separate reform, patients in nursing homes and hospitals—or their families, by proxy—are now also entitled to refuse treatment in critical medical situations. Those decisions used to be made by medical directors. Now every nursing home is required to disclose its philosophy on lifesaving measures at admission time. This issue can be particularly significant in a nursing home run by a religious organization.

Reforms have also been adopted aimed at improving the quality of the nurse's aides—the low-paid people who dress, feed, bathe and toilet nursing-home patients. Aides must now complete 75 hours of training and be certified. To address complaints of patient abuse by aides, states maintain registries of abuse findings so that nursing homes can check prospective employees.

Perhaps the most dramatic change involves the use of physical and chemical restraints. At one time, at least 40 percent of a typical nursing home's patients were kept in restraints—strapped into chairs or tranquilized, for example. Now the law says restraints can't be imposed for discipline or the nursing home's convenience; a doctor must cite medical reasons for using them.

Keep in mind that chemical restraints are invisible, and families should be aware that some nursing homes may administer psychotropic drugs. If you're concerned, ask to see statistics on the nursing home's use of these drugs and discuss the facility's philosophy with the medical director.

Resources

In the Philadelphia area, there are more than 200 nursing homes. Here is a list of agencies that can help narrow the choices and provide referral services.

Nursing Homes in Philadelphia: A Directory and Consumer Guide provides a description of the homes in Philadelphia and general information on choosing one. It costs $20 (including shipping and handling), but is provided free to low-income citizens. Send a check payable to Northwest Interfaith Movement to: Long-term Care Connection, Northwest Interfaith Movement, 6757 Greene Street, Philadelphia, PA 19119 (843-5600).

A second edition of the comprehensive guide to the four-county suburban Philadelphia area is also available ($20) : *Nursing Homes in Suburban Philadelphia: A Directory and Consumer Guide.* Call 783-5067, or write to Family Information Service, Box 574, Valley Forge, PA 19481.

The National Citizens' Coalition for Nursing Home Reform, 1224 M Street NW, Suite 301, Washington, DC 20005 (202-393-2018), offers clear, helpful information on reforms and patient rights.

Health Insurance Association of America, P.O. Box 41455, Washington, DC, 20018, helps prepare for the financial costs of nursing-home care by offering a list of long-term care policies that keep up with inflation.

Most hospitals will provide home services for patients with less than six months to live. For more information on these services, contact the following groups:

Children's Hospice International, 700 South Princess, L.L., Alexandria, VA 22314, 800-242-4453

Hospice Education Institute, 190 Westbrook Road, Essex, CT 06426, 800-331-1620

National Hospice Organization, 1901 North Moore Street, Suite 901, Alexandria, VA 22209, 800-658-8898

When You Can't Be There
Hiring a manager

Many of us must deal with our parents from a distance, and that's spurred development of a new industry: private geriatric care management. Think of it as hiring a consultant. Geriatric care managers, usually former social workers or nurses, will assess a person's condition, then arrange for and oversee care. Such managers are well versed in what's available in home meal delivery, nursing and personal-care services, adult day-care and long-term care.

For instance, Marsha York Solmssen and Marion Thompson of Intervention Associates in Wayne helped one disoriented elderly woman continue living in her Chester County farmhouse after they set up a house-sharing arrangement and scheduled regular outings to an adult day-care center. (But first they saw that the house was cleaned up—it was a firetrap, full of papers and piles of twigs the woman had collected on nature walks.)

Geriatric care management is so new that you won't find it listed in the Yellow Pages. But referrals are available free from the National Association of Private Geriatric Care Managers, based in Tucson (602-881-8008), or for $2 from Children of Aging Parents in Levittown, a nonprofit information center and support group for caregivers (945-6900).

If you feel you need guidance in selecting a care manager, Aging Network Services of Bethesda, Maryland, can help. They evaluate your case, then call on a network of 250 social workers nationwide, matching them with families for an initial fee of $295 (301-657-4329).

A good care manager may recommend a geriatric assessment—a comprehensive physical workup, offered by many hospitals, that can include exams by neurologists, psychologists or psychiatrists, and specialists in geriatric medicine. It can pinpoint, for example, whether a person has dementia or just a nutrition problem.

Private care management doesn't come cheap. Most geriatric managers charge from $50 to $150 an hour. (Family members typically pay for the services themselves.) But they may be able to give a client more personalized attention than care managers at public agencies like the AAAs. There are also care managers who work for insurers—but they might have a vested interest in keeping costs low or in limiting your choice of services.

Be forewarned: Geriatric care management is an unregulated industry, so it's important to shop carefully. Says Betty Mullen, the director of the American Association of Retired Persons International Activities, "I was in Florida a couple of years ago at a long-term care conference, and I was told that a bunch of MBAs, recent graduates, had hung up shingles as care managers—without knowing anything about the whole area of geriatrics and where to go for help."

The National Association of Private Geriatric Care Managers has established voluntary standards for the profession, but consumers should check a care manager's background, experience and references. A good full-time care manager should handle no more than 50 to 75 clients, the AARP says.

Resources

There are other private-care managers in the area, but the Greater Philadelphia Association of Private Geriatric Care Managers is the only professional organization. The following belong to the association:

Columbus Life Management, Inc.
2000 VALLEY FORGE TOWERS, KING OF PRUSSIA, PA
19406; 1-800-229-5116

Clients undergo complete physical, emotional and social evaluations to help them identify the appropriate home health care or nursing-home options. Trained experts act as professional, objective advocates and liaisons in dealing with long-term care needs. They also monitor and manage client services.

Comprehensive Health and Human Services Inc./Eldercare
8329 HIGH SCHOOL ROAD, ELKINS PARK, PA 19117; 635-6849

Contact: Sheila R. Bergman.

Comprehensive Health and Human Services Inc./Eldercare
435 EAST LANCASTER AVENUE, #211, WAYNE, PA 19087; 686-5579

Contact: Barbara R. Feinstein.

Elder-Service, Inc.
301 NORTH YORK ROAD, SUITE 105, WARMINSTER, PA 18974; 442-1800

Contact: Jennifer Castan.

Geriatric Planning Services
2 SOUTH ORANGE STREET, SUITE 201, MEDIA, PA 19063; 566-6686

Contact: Anneta Kraus.

Intervention Associates
P.O. BOX 572, WAYNE, PA 19087; 254-9001

Marsha Solmssen, Marion Thompson.

Retirement and Transition, Inc.
1049 LANCASTER AVENUE, P.O. BOX 451, BRYN MAWR, PA 19010; 527-4578

Contact: Caroline V. Holton, Helena A. Stewart.

The Patient Advocates
CEDARBROOK HILL APTS., A-404, 8460 LIMEKILN, WYNCOTE, PA 19095; 884-4229

Contact: Toby L. Mazer, MPH.

Supportive Care Services, Inc.
507 WEST 9TH STREET, WILMINGTON, DE 19801; 302-655-5518
Contact: Thomas J. Posatko.

AgeWise Family Services
1250 GLENBURNIE LANE, DRESHER, PA 19025; 659-2111
Contact: Susan P. Weiss, Roberta Rosenberg.

JoAnn M. Burke
100 WEST EVERGREEN AVENUE, PHILADELPHIA, PA 19118; 836-1280

Star Systems Consultation and Training, Inc.
MADISON HOUSE, SUITE D-122, 3900 CITY AVENUE, PHILADELPHIA, PA 19131; 477-2211
Contact: Janice Brown.

Pay Now, Stay Put
The Life-Care Option

Imagine spending your retirement years being coddled like a college kid. You'll never lift a mop or a snow shovel. You'll share meals with friends every night without bickering over how to split the bill. There will be art instructors, hairdressers, bank tellers and medical staff available right where you live. And most important, if and when the time comes that you need nursing-home care, you don't have to worry about the cost, the move or waiting lists.

This is life in the continuing-care retirement community—also known as a life-care community. (They're sometimes called retirement communities, although that can be misleading; some retirement communities offer housing only.) It's a relatively new concept in elder care that has caught on in the past two decades, growing from 380 communities nationwide in 1973 to more than 700 today; in the Philadelphia area, where such communities started, there are more than 40. A one-time entrance fee, along with monthly service fees, generally pays for your apartment, outpatient health care and your stay in the on-site nursing home, if and when you need that level of care.

These places demand fairly deep pockets. Studios for singles, the least expensive option, generally start at $30,500 at places like Rydal Park and Rosemont Presbyterian Village; prices climb to more than $200,000 for your own villa at the most exclusive communities, such as White Horse Village in Newtown Square. Most facilities have a clause providing a pro-rated refund if a resident decides to move, or dies, within a specified period of time.

These communities remain solvent for one simple reason: The management takes the calculated risk that not every resident will require the expensive nursing-home care they offer. And of those who do, some may not require it for years, allowing management to invest the sizable entrance fee in the meantime.

Many of these communities have waiting lists. If you're not ready to move out of the house, it is possible to get your name in ahead of time. Planning ahead is essential, because the application procedure itself could take several months; admission is based largely on ability to pay and on current health, so a physical is usually required, as is information from your doctor. Then there are admissions committee meetings, interviews and visits to the facility, all of which should be taken care of before the applicant's health deteriorates beyond the point of acceptance. "We turn a lot of people down—I'd say 30 to 50 percent of our applicants," says Joan Sterrett, marketing director at Martins Run, in Media. "They wait too long. They're not approved."

While life-care communities look into your finances, you should be looking into theirs. From the late '70s to the mid '80s, a flurry of news stories reported on several such places that went bankrupt or incurred financial problems due to fraud and/or mismanagement. It is of some comfort to note that no Pennsylvania life-care community has shut down for financial reasons. Three have sought protection under federal bankruptcy laws, however, but through reorganization plans they have stayed open, and no residents were forced to go elsewhere.

About 15 percent of the nation's 700 homes are currently accredited by the Continuing Care Accreditation Commission, an organization formed in 1985. (To obtain a list of facilities in this area, see below.) The accreditation process is costly and time-consuming. And new communities must be 90 percent occupied for a year before the commission will consider their applications.

Resources

The Pennsylvania Insurance Department has free brochures and a *Directory of Licensed Continuing-Care Communities*. For the brochures, send a business-size envelope with your request to the Insurance Department Press Office, 1326 Strawberry Square, Harrisburg, PA 17120. For the directory, send a $5 check with your request to the same address.

The Continuing Care Accreditation Commission also has free brochures, including an accredited facilities list and an explanation of the accreditation process. Write to the CCAC, Suite 500, 901 E Street NW, Washington, DC 20004-2037; or call 202-783-7286.

The American Association of Homes for the Aging, the above commission's parent organization, offers the *Continuing-Care Retirement Community—A Guide Book for Consumers* for $4. Send a check and your request to AAHA Publications to the above address. Other good sources include: American Health Care Association, 1201 L Street NW, Washington, DC 20005, 202-842-4444; and the National

Consumers League, 815 15th Street NW, Suite 928, Washington, DC 20005, 202-639-8140.

Adult Daycare Centers
Relief for you, recreation for them

It's 10:30 on a Thursday morning, and a few elderly women are sitting on sofas in a big, cheery room, tending to needlework projects. At a table, another group plays Trivial Pursuit, fielding questions like "Who was the 'It Girl'?" One woman sits hunched over all by herself, moaning and crooning to a stuffed animal.

Just a typical day at Adult Day Care of Chester County, in West Chester, one of 45 such centers in Southeastern Pennsylvania.

Adult day-care is one of the bright spots in elder care. Just 20 years ago, only 12 such centers were operating in the whole country; now there are 2,200. They offer older people a structured, stimulating way to spend the day, and provide respite to caregivers who work or just want time off to see a movie or run errands.

At Adult Day Care of Chester County, the 30 to 35 clients participate in daily activities, and can also take showers and naps at the center. A hot lunch is delivered by nearby Chester County Hospital. A nurse is on hand all day. A local beautician visits three mornings a week.

Pat Shull, owner of the center and head of the Pennsylvania Adult Day Care Association, says almost half of those in adult day-care have Alzheimer's or some other dementia. But even those who seem most confused benefit in noticeable ways. For instance, one client insisted on bringing in a cake for her 50th wedding anniversary, even though her husband had died a year and a half earlier. The staff announced that she was remembering a special day and wanted to share. "She didn't say anything," says Shull, "but her face was so radiant, we didn't need to turn the lights on."

Though services and hours vary from center to center, most charge about $30 a day for a noon meal and snacks, personal care, social services, supervision by a physician and/or registered nurse and aides, recreational programs, physical therapy and counseling. The centers usually operate Monday through Friday during working hours. Fees are not covered by Medicare or Medicaid in Pennsylvania, but New Jersey Medicaid pays for "medical" day-care (a registered nurse on staff).

Resources

Coalition of Advocates for the Rights of the Infirm Elderly, 1315 Walnut Street, Philadelphia, PA 19107.

Pennsylvania Adult Day Care Association, P.O. Box 934, Exton, PA 19341; 431-9699.

New Jersey Adult Day Care Association, P.O. Box 584, Bloomfield, NJ 07003; 609-261-7003.

See hospital listings in Chapter 12 for specific programs.

Hotlines and help lines

Senior Helpline
765-9040

Funded by the Philadelphia Corporation for the Aging; provides information and referrals for Philadelphians over 60 and help on getting services and benefits.

CARIE-Line
545-4437

Offers legal, financial, social and health information; operated by the Coalition of Advocates for the Rights of the Infirm Elderly.

Association of Elderly Caregivers
609-235-0125

An informal network of men and women involved in the full-time care of elderly family members.

Publications

The American Association of Retired Persons publishes several free pamphlets on elder care (601 E Street NW, Washington, DC 20049):

Miles Away and Still Caring (D-12748). A guide for relatives who live far away from an elderly loved one.

Care Management: Arranging for Longterm Care (D-13803). A guide to services available in the home.

A Handbook About Care in the Home (D-955). A guide to at-home services.

Making Wise Decisions About Long-term Care (D-12435). Brochure describing services and financing.

Home Away From Home (D-12446). Information on boarding homes.

Nursing-Home Life: A Guide for Residents and Families (D-13063). How to select a nursing home and adjust to life in it.

Before You Buy: A Guide to Long-Term Care Insurance (D-12893).

Long-Term Care: A Dollar and Sense Guide, 1331 H Street NW, Suite 500, Washington, DC 20005. A guide to selecting insurance. Also describes alternatives to nursing-home placement.

Directory of Retirement Facilities. More than 22,000 facilities across the country are listed. Published by HCIA Inc. Priced at $249 for electronic-file formats. Contact Martina Kellner (1-800-568-3282).

The Pennsylvania Department of Aging publishes A Manual for Family Caregivers of Older Pennsylvanians. Good information on services available in Pennsylvania and tips for coping with caregiving. Available from Area Agencies on Aging or by writing to the Pennsylvania Department of Aging, 231 State Street, Harrisburg, PA 17101-1195.

A Shoppers' Guide to Long-Term Care Insurance, 120 West 12th Street, Suite 1100, Kansas City, MO 64105. A pamphlet that includes a checklist for comparing specific policies.

8

For Your Information

The Road Back

A survey of rehabilitation services from substance abuse to physical therapy

I n the world of health care, hospitals fall into two broad categories. General hospitals, as implied, treat a wide range of illnesses. Specialty hospitals, on the other hand, deal with very specific needs. In this section we focus on places geared toward some kind of rehabilitation. The first group concentrates on physical problems—recovery from an injury or debilitating illness, like a stroke. The second group is concerned with recovery from alcohol or drug abuse, which is sometimes treated in a psychiatric hospital under a dual diagnosis. Substance-abuse treatment has burgeoned into a booming business, fraught with operators who will refer you to places where they get kickbacks. In other instances, insurance companies steer people into psychiatric institutions when that level of care may not be necessary. Check out any referral carefully and discuss with your personal physician if it's the appropriate place for you.

Many general hospitals also have rehabilitation services. See the listings in Chapter 12.

Physical Rehabilitation

Bryn Mawr Rehabilitation Hospital

🛏 🎿 🍴 ⚖ 🚭 🎓 🐎

414 PAOLI PIKE, MALVERN: 251-5400. DOCTORS ON ACTIVE STAFF: 12; NUMBER OF BEDS: 131; ACCREDITATION: JCAHO WITH COMMENDATION, CARF.

Specialized treatment programs: brain injury, stroke (including young stroke), neurological disorders, spinal cord injury, MS, orthopedics, arthritis, Guillain-Barre.
Clinical services: physical, occupational and speech therapy; aquatic, equestrian, horticultural therapy; therapeutic recreation, psychology services.

Outpatient health and wellness programs: adapted driver education, vocational rehab, amputee clinic, occupational rehab medicine. Outpatient services are also offered at Bryn Mawr Rehab, Inc. in Lionville and Devon Manor. Bryn Mawr Rehab is a member of the Main Line Health System.

Chestnut Hill Rehabilitation Hospital

8601 STENTON AVENUE, WYNDMOOR; 233-6200. DOCTORS ON ACTIVE STAFF: SIX (*83% board-certified*). NUMBER OF BEDS: 88. SPECIAL GOURMET MENU: $10 PER MEAL. ACCREDITATION: JCAHO, CARF.

Specialized treatment programs: comprehensive rehabilitation for strokes, arthritis, orthopedic injury, amputation, cancer; skilled nursing services.
Medical rehabilitation services (inpatient and outpatient): physical medicine, internal medicine, rehabilitation nursing, physical and occupational therapy, therapeutic recreation, speech-language pathology, psychology and social work.
Outpatient health and wellness programs: wheelchair clinic, prosthetic and orthotic clinic, Arthritis Information and Management Club, Stroke Club, 55-Plus and Fit.

Chestnut Hill Rehabilitation Hospital, a service of Chestnut Hill Hospital HealthCare, offers comprehensive inpatient and outpatient medical rehabilitation for adults of all ages.

Magee Rehabilitation Hospital

SIX FRANKLIN PLAZA, PHILADELPHIA; 587-3000. DOCTORS ON ACTIVE STAFF: NINE (*100% board-certified*); NUMBER OF BEDS: 96; ACCREDITATION: JCAHO, CARF.

Specialized treatment programs: vision clinic; continence program; day hospital and community re-entry for brain injury survivors; pressure-sore program; amputee day hospital and clinic.
Physical rehab services: spinal cord injury, brain injury, stroke, geriatrics, amputation, pain management, orthopedics, occupational health, work hardening.
Outpatient health and wellness programs: Back School.

Magee's Brain Injury Rehab Program was the first in the country to be board-certified. Also serves as a federally designated regional Spinal Cord Injury Center of the Delaware Valley.

MossRehab Hospital

1200 West Tabor Road, Philadelphia; 456-9900, 800-CALL-MOSS. Doctors on active staff: 79 (*79% board-certified*); number of beds: 152; 1.25 RNs per bed; accreditation: JCAHO, CARF.

Specialized treatment programs: Drucker Brain Injury Center, MossRehab Stroke Center, Regional Amputee Center, orthopedic rehabilitation, Kardon Center for Pediatric Rehabilitation, Regional Spina Bifida Center for Adults, Einstein-Moss Arthritis Center, Einstein-Moss Joint Replacement Center, Moss-Einstein Limbs with Restricted Motion Program.

Physical rehab services: physical, occupational and speech therapy; therapeutic recreation; psychological services; electrodiagnostic center; gait and motion analysis laboratory; motor-control analysis laboratory; prosthetics and orthotics service; day hospital.

Outpatient health and wellness programs: fitness and exercise programs for people with physical disabilities, recreational programs, Driving School, Back School.

MossRehab, a division of Albert Einstein Medical Center, is the region's largest provider of medical rehab services and has outpatient centers in Olney, Northeast Philadelphia and Jenkintown.

Mount Sinai Hospital

4th and Reed streets., Philadelphia; 339-3456. Doctors on active staff: 45 (*91% board-certified*); number of beds: 220; one RN per 2.2 beds; accreditation: JCAHO, CAP.

Physical rehab services: Inpatient program serving patients recovering from stroke, head injury, amputation, arthritis, spinal cord injuries, chronic pain, neurologic illness and orthopedic problems. Also offers outpatient program in separate facility and a day hospital program. All patients have access to EASY STREET ENVIRONMENTS®, a therapy environment simulating a city street.

Skilled Nursing Facility: 50-bed unit for patients who no longer require acute hospital care but need services such as wound care, colostomy care, insulin injection and I.V. therapy.

Mt. Sinai, part of Graduate Health System, also offers free health lectures for the community.

Other Rehab Services

The Cancer Rehabilitation Center

8080 OLD YORK ROAD, ELKINS PARK; 782-8760

Staff composed of physical therapists, an occupational therapist, social worker and psychologist. Accreditation: American Physical Therapy Association, Pennsylvania Physical Therapy Association. A unique outpatient facility established to provide physical therapy, conditioning and strengthening programs to treat cancer patients physically and emotionally. Specialized treatment programs: pain management, strengthening and endurance training, services for post-operative stiffness and shoulder problems, lymph-edema management, medically supervised weight reduction, home exercise, aerobics, functional assessments for disability determinations, counseling, psychological evaluation, return-to-work programs.

The Philadelphia Center for Aquatic Rehabilitation

3600 GRANT AVENUE, PHILADELPHIA; 677-0400

Staff composed of five physical therapists, ten physical therapy assistants and aides, two exercise specialists. Aquatic physical therapy services: most-advanced techniques used for outpatient services for patients recovering from work, orthopedic and sports-related injuries, utilizing 165-foot, 83-degree pool, 35-foot, 94-degree pool and an oversize 105-degree whirlpool.

Land-therapy services: outpatient services utilizing equipment for strengthening and conditioning. Activities of daily living and back and neck care are emphasized.

Work Conditioning Center: outpatient treatment utilizing fully equipped conditioning center to aid in quick return to work with less risk of re-injury; emphasizing job skills.

Remed Recovery Care Centers

CORPORATE OFFICE, 625 RIDGE PIKE, BUILDING C, CONSHOHOCKEN; 834-1300

Staff composed of five doctors and 47 specialists; number of beds: 74; accreditation: CARF. Provides post-acute, community-based rehabilitation to people with brain injuries and other neurological impairments.

Specialized treatment programs: Behavioral Programs in Malvern and Valley Forge offer therapy in a safe, structured environment; Community Re-Entry Services supervise apartment living, teaching skills for daily living; Community Apartment Living Programs are a less-structured support for apartment living in Malvern and Philadelphia; Living Community in Malvern provides long-term rehab with supportive therapy; Community Services Network in Bryn Mawr has day treatment and outpatient services; Program for Adults With Autism; Speech Pathology Consultants, Inc. (affiliated company); all programs incorporate substance-abuse treatment when needed. ReMed is Pennsylvania's largest provider of post-acute brain injury rehab.

Substance Abuse

Hospitals

Eagleville Hospital

100 EAGLEVILLE ROAD, EAGLEVILLE; 539-6000, 800-255-2019 (*out-of-state*). DOCTORS ON ACTIVE STAFF: 15 (*82% board-certified*); NUMBER OF BEDS: 159; 51 RNS; 72 PROFESSIONAL CLINICAL STAFF; ACCREDITATION: JCAHO, PDH, PODAP; PERFORMS DETOX; ACCEPTS BLUE CROSS, MEDICAID, MEDICARE AND OTHER INSURANCE.

Specialized treatment programs for adults 18 and over: Program for Employed Persons, a short-term intensive program for men and women; medically supervised detox; men's inpatient rehab program (focused on the special issues confronting chemically addicted men); women's inpatient rehab program (a multidisciplinary approach for chemically addicted women); Continuum, a partial hospitalization program.

A pioneer in the field of combined drug and alcohol treatment, Eagleville is the only hospital in Pennsylvania licensed exclusively for drug and alcohol rehabilitation. It has provided substance-abuse treatment for more than 27 years and is nationally recognized for quality care.

Hampton Hospital
See Chapter 23.

Mount Sinai Hospital
See listing under Rehabilitation.

Other services

Abraxas Foundation, Inc.
ADMINISTRATIVE OFFICES, 162 WEST CHELTEN AVENUE, PHILADELPHIA; 849-2551

Treatment programs for court-referred dependent and delinquent youth, ages 12-18. Provides residential and non-residential community-based programs for adolescents and their families in Philadelphia and throughout Pennsylvania.

Achievement Through Counseling and Treatment (ACT)
5820 OLD YORK ROAD; 276-8400 AND 1745 NORTH FOURTH STREET; 236-0100

Outpatient services for drug and alcohol dependency and aftercare include medical and psychiatric evaluation, individual, group and family therapy. Special-needs programs include Parole and Probation, Homeless Shelter and HIV Disease/AIDS.

Client support services also available at both locations. ACT is part of the nonprofit, nonsectarian Jewish Employment and Vocational Service.

Advantage Recovery Network
ADMINISTRATIVE OFFICES AT 1314 CHESTNUT STREET, TREATMENT SITES IN CENTER CITY, NORTHEAST PHILADELPHIA AND SWARTHMORE; 24-HOUR NUMBER: 800-220-4801.

A six-week intensive outpatient program for chemical dependency. Patients receive treatment while living and working in the community. This lets a social-support network help with the recovery process and reduces the stigma of addiction treatment. Flexible schedule features both day and evening sessions. Patients also attend 12-step fellowship meetings. Family therapy involves relatives and significant others of addicted people in the treatment process. All major insurance accepted.

Alcohol and Mental Health Associates
1200 WALNUT STREET, 2ND FLOOR, PHILADELPHIA; 545-8078

Provides methadone treatment for heroin addicts as well as outpatient drug and alcohol counseling.

Bowling Green Brandywine
495 NEWARK ROAD, KENNETT SQUARE; 268-3588, 800-662-2438

Medical director on staff 24 hours; number of beds: 60; detox services in acute cases; accepts most insurance plans. Provides intensive outpatient programs for those who need help in overcoming a substance-abuse problem without hospitalization. After-Work Recovery allows patients to live at home and continue to work while getting support and treatment. All entering patients receive medical, social and psychological assessment.

Bridge Therapeutic Center
8400 PINE ROAD; 342-5000

Residential drug and alcohol treatment facilities with schooling for teenagers ages 14-19. Bridge Family and Youth offers outpatient drug and alcohol facilities for adults as well as teenagers, at 1912 Welsh Road.

The Charter Fairmount Institute
See Chapter 23.

Congreso
704 W. GIRARD AVENUE; 625-0550, 229-4040 (PREVENTION INTERVENTION FOR YOUTHS AT 640 WEST LUZERNE)

Offers outpatient drug and alcohol facilities and provides counseling on prevention for Hispanic inner-city adolescents.

The Consortium

4025 CHESTNUT STREET, PHILADELPHIA; 596-8011, 596-8083. OUTPATIENT DRUG AND ALCOHOL FACILITIES AT THREE AREA LOCATIONS: 451 UNIVERSITY AVENUE, 596-8000; 6408 WOODLAND AVENUE, 727-4420; 4219 CHESTER AVENUE, 596-8175 (FOR COCAINE BABIES).

University Avenue location also has a methadone clinic for heroin addicts.

Cora Services

733 SUSQUEHANNA ROAD, PHILADELPHIA; 342-2660

Outpatient drug and alcohol facilities as well as counseling and referral.

Diagnostic and Rehabilitation Center

229 ARCH STREET, PHILADELPHIA; 625-8063

Has outpatient drug and alcohol as well as residential treatment facilities. Provides emergency care and detox services. Separate programs for men and women, including an inpatient program for women and their children.

Gaudenzia House

39 EAST SCHOOL HOUSE LANE; 849-7200

Eleven area locations, each providing services to the chemically dependent:

Gaudenzia Broad Street, 3025-29 North Broad Street; 223-9460. Long-term residential treatment for men and women with a dual diagnosis of substance abuse and mental illness.

Focus House, 701 North Broad Street; 477-0063. Long-term residential treatment for dual diagnosed men.

Joy of Living, 1509 Cecil B. Moore Avenue; 765-2026. Long-term residential treatment for homeless men and women with a dual diagnosis.

New Beginnings, 1300 Spring Garden Street; 440-9669. Long-term residential treatment for homeless men and women with dual diagnosis.

New Image, 1300 Tulpehocken Street; 924-6322. Long-term residential treatment program for homeless, addicted, pregnant women and mothers with up to two of their children.

People With Hope, 1834 West Tioga Street; 228-0644. Long-term residential treatment for addicted men and women who are diagnosed HIV-positive or with AIDS.

Progress House, 607 East Church Lane, Apt-6; 848-0280. Community residential rehabilitation serving dual-diagnosed men and women.

Gaudenzia Outreach-Adult Outpatient, 1415 North Broad Street; 235-5200. Intensive treatment for addicted adults and after-care services for residential completions, and Juvenile Outpatient, intensive treatment for adolescents who are at risk and court-adjudicated youth.

Centro Primavera, 2755 North 5th Street; 423-6766. Prevention/education for children at high-risk.

West Chester Campus-Gaudenzia House West Chester, 1030 South Concord Road, West Chester; 329-6969. Long-term residential treatment for chemically addicted men and women.

Kindred House, 1030 South Concord Road, West Chester; 399-3382. Long-term residential treatment for addicted pregnant women and mothers with up to two of their children, also children's drug and alcohol prevention component.

Horizon House, Inc.
120 SOUTH 30TH STREET; 386-3838
Provides outpatient drug and alcohol treatment facilities, case management and residential facilities, and acts as a homeless shelter.

Livengrin Foundation
4833 HULMEVILLE ROAD, BENSALEM; 638-5200, 800-245-4746. ACCREDITATION: JCAHO, ODAP. COVERED BY US HEALTHCARE, INDEPENDENCE BLUE CROSS AND OTHER MAJOR INSURANCE COMPANIES.

In- and outpatient evaluation and assessment and residential family/codependency program.

Inpatient: detox, rehab, relapse program, gay men and lesbian program (in- and outpatient), continuing care.

Outpatient: day and evening intensive programs, ambulatory detox, adolescent counseling (ages 12-18), individual counseling, group therapy, family counseling, intervention. Outpatient offices in Bensalem (638-5262), Fort Washington (540-2490), Doylestown (340-1765), Reading (370-1300) and Allentown (264-5521). Industrial services: drug-free workplace consulting management training, referral network, educational services. Community services: speakers' bureau, 12-step meetings, DUI services. Livengrin is a not-for-profit chemical dependency treatment center with more than a quarter-century of experience.

Malvern Institute
940 KING ROAD, MALVERN: 647-0330, 800-486-0017. DOCTORS ON ACTIVE STAFF: TWO; NUMBER OF BEDS: 36; ACCREDITATION: JCAHO; DETOX AVAILABLE; ACCEPTS INDEPENDENCE BLUE CROSS, SOME HMOS, MOST COMMERCIAL INSURANCE CARRIERS.

Specialized treatment programs: drug and alcohol rehab, dual diagnosis, free evaluation, inpatient rehab, family services, 12-step recovery groups.

Outpatient health and wellness programs: free evaluation and referral services, relapse prevention, continuing care, intervention (for those reluctant to get help). A comprehensive addiction treatment facility, Malvern has been providing inpatient and intensive outpatient services for more than 40 years.

Northeast Treatment Center
2205 BRIDGE STREET; 289-2100

Has outpatient drug and alcohol and residential treatment facilities.

North Philadelphia Health Systems
8TH AND GIRARD AVENUES; 787-2000

Has outpatient drug and alcohol and residential treatment facilities, and a methadone clinic for heroin addicts. Provides counseling on prevention and performs detox.

Penn Recovery Systems
MUTCH BUILDING NO. 4, 39TH AND MARKET STS.; 386-4280 (24-HOUR PHONE SERVICE). BRANCHES IN MEDIA, FORT WASHINGTON, PHILADELPHIA AND POTTSTOWN. DOCTORS ON ACTIVE STAFF: SEVEN; ACCREDITATION: JCAHO; DETOX AVAILABLE; ACCEPTS INDEPENDENCE BLUE CROSS, HMO/PA AND OTHER INSURANCE ON A FLEXIBLE BASIS.

A private health-care organization providing direct and supportive in- and outpatient services. Specializes in chronic drug and alcohol abuse. Stresses 12-step program groups such as AA, NA and CA. Admission to outpatient program is based on the following criteria: regular substance abuse for less than six months; frequency of abuse no more than twice weekly; minimal impairment of occupational and social functioning; absence of significant psychosocial stress; presence of positive social support system; willingness and ability to attend 12-step program meetings such as AA, NA and CA.

ReEnter
3331 POWELTON AVENUE (MALE FACILITY), 4003 BALTIMORE AVENUE (FEMALE FACILITY), ALL CALLS ACCEPTED AT 222-2770. ONE PHYSICIAN ALWAYS ON STAFF; 14 BEDS (MALE), 11 BEDS (FEMALE); NO DETOX; ACCEPTS MOST DRUG AND ALCOHOL POLICY; NO EMERGENCY ROOM.

A therapeutic inpatient recovery-room home for males between the ages of 18 and 60 and females age 21 and over struggling with substance abuse. Patients must be ambulatory and substance-free for a minimum of five to seven days prior to admission. Average stay: three to 12 months.

Clinical services: history and physical examination, diagnostic and psychiatric evaluation, relapse prevention program, individual and group psychotherapy, family education and group therapy program, random drug screens.

Rehab After Work

FOUR LOCATIONS: CENTER CITY, NORTHEAST PHILADELPHIA, KING OF PRUSSIA AND AIRPORT/ISLAND AVENUE, 800-238-HELP (24-HOUR HELP ALSO AVAILABLE). FULLY LICENSED AND JCAHO ACCREDITED. A PROGRAM OF FITZGERALD MERCY HOSPITAL.

Rehab After Work is a nationally recognized outpatient drug and alcohol rehabilitation program that provides services for adults, adolescents and their families. Day and evening therapy sessions allow individuals to receive treatment while continuing to lead independent lives. Sessions are combined with family support meetings and integration into AA and NA. Fully covered by most insurers. Proven effective by independent research conducted by the University of Pennsylvania's Addiction Research Center.

Other services include: addiction awareness program for DUI offenders and persons tested positive for drug use, aftercare groups (ongoing support for individuals in recovery), family counseling, adolescent treatment, and evaluations conducted by addiction counselors and/or psychiatrist.

Treatment Research Center

3900 CHESTNUT STREET; 222-3200 OR 243-9959

Active medical and clinical staff of 40. The center provides comprehensive outpatient treatment for those with alcohol, cocaine and other drug dependencies who qualify for research studies. The patient receives a thorough emotional and medical evaluation followed by state-of-the-art substance-abuse treatment involving the latest medications and psychosocial interventions. Typically this includes six months of outpatient individual therapy and the option of group and/or family therapy.

Valley Forge Medical Center and Hospital

1033 WEST GERMANTOWN PIKE, NORRISTOWN; 539-8500. MULTIDISCIPLINARY STAFF OF PHYSICIANS, PSYCHIATRISTS, NURSES AND COUNSELORS; NUMBER OF BEDS: 70; ACCEPTS ALL MAJOR INSURANCE AND SOME MEDICAL ASSISTANCE.

Specializes in the treatment of drug addiction, alcoholism, compulsive gambling and accompanying medical and psychiatric conditions. Provides medical detox and intensive inpatient therapy in addition to outpatient counseling for continued care. Special programs include psychological testing, individual and group therapy, biofeedback and stress management, exercise physiology, education lectures and self-help meetings.

Woodside Hall Addiction Treatment Program

BELMONT CENTER FOR COMPREHENSIVE TREATMENT, 4200 MONUMENT ROAD; 581-3757. STAFF INCLUDES: TWO PSYCHIATRISTS, THREE PSYCHOLOGISTS, 12 PSYCHOTHERAPISTS, THREE NURSES, FOUR DRUG/ALCOHOL COUNSELORS, TWO SOCIAL WORKERS; NUMBER OF BEDS: 20; DETOX AVAILABLE; ACCESS TO EMERGENCY FACILITIES AT ALBERT EINSTEIN MEDICAL CENTER; ACCREDITATION: JCAHO, ODAP; ACCEPTS MOST INSURANCES.

Specialized treatment programs: inpatient, outpatient and day treatment for alcoholism, chemical dependency and pathological gambling. Services for adolescents, adults, older adults, deaf patients and dual diagnosis; provides treatment for individuals, families and couples. Programs encourage and sometimes require attendance of AA, CA, NA, and GA meetings. The CAREER (R) day program offers treatment for alcohol or drug addiction with minimal disruption to a patient's work routine. Programs for business and industry are also offered to help identify troubled employees. Woodside Hall Addictions Treatment Center is a part of the Albert Einstein Healthcare Network.

CHAPTER 27

We've Got Your Number

A potpourri of services geared toward a particular audience

Special Programs

Annual Physicals

The Executive Health and Wellness Center
TWO LOGAN SQUARE, SUITE 1800, PHILADELPHIA, PA
19103; 299-3800

Aimed at the busy executive, this center provides fast and personally designed annual physicals, including all the latest testing equipment under one roof. A total workup covers: detailed personal history and physical exam, the complete spectrum of laboratory tests, X-rays, glaucoma screening, gynecologic exams, cardiovascular stress test, flexible sigmoidoscopy and a fitness/nutrition assessment. Treatments with a variety of specialists also provided.

Brain Waves

The Mastery Program
700 SOUTH HENDERSON ROAD, SUITE 302A, KING OF
PRUSSIA, PA 19406; 337-4550

A medically directed, seven-week outpatient treatment program for depression, anxiety, stress-related medical disorders, attention deficit disorders, post-traumatic stress disorders and some substance abuse cases. Treatment involves a combination of cognitive behavior psychotherapy and brain-wave biofeedback. Patients are hooked up to a computer that monitors electrical activity of the brain and are taught how to change their patterns without drugs. The Mastery Program claims an 80 percent success rate.

Brain/Body Connection

International Behavioral Medical Center (IMBC)
300 WEST BASIN ROAD (ROUTE 141), NEW CASTLE, DE
19720; 302-328-2262

This outpatient hospital practices the theories of behavioral medicine as its primary treatment modality. Its interdisciplinary approach to disease brings together a broad range of disciplines—things like imagery, biofeedback, massage therapy, stress reduction, exercise, medical psychotherapy and more—to deal with illnesses related to daily living. IMBC considers its strengths to be in heart disease, chronic pain and muscle disorders, gastrointestinal and addiction problems, allergies, sexual dysfunction, PMS and pharmacotherapy disorders. All major insurance is accepted.

Eating Disorders

The Renfrew Center
75 SPRING LANE; PHILADELPHIA, PA 19128; 1-800-REN-FREW OR 1-800-334-8415

The country's first residential center exclusively for the treatment of women with eating disorders. Programs last seven to nine weeks, and there is an emphasis on the active participation of women in their own treatment. A new intensive outpatient program is based on the same philosophy, and structured around 12 hours of group therapy each week along with designated meal times.

Women's Recovery Center
110 NORTH ESSEX AVENUE, NARBERTH, PA 19072; 664-5858

Specializing in the treatment of anorexia, bulimia, binging, compulsive overeating and other eating disorders that occur in conjunction with a drug or alcohol problem or as a result of post-traumatic stress due to sexual, physical or emotional abuse. Also available: an evening intensive outpatient program as well as individual, group, family and nutrition counseling. Educational programs, individual and intensive therapy, day treatment and residential programs are also available for survivors of abuse and women struggling with dissociate, depression and anxiety disorders.

Learning Problems

Vision Development Center
8117 OLD YORK ROAD, ELKINS PARK, PA 19117; 885-8900

Many children diagnosed as having learning difficulties may, in fact, be suffering from a vision disability. Visual disorders stem from an improper interplay of signals between the eye and the brain. While they cannot be corrected by glasses, they can be detected by special tests and corrected with specific visual exercises. Optometrist Arthur S. Seiderman, O.D., M.A., F.A.A.O., F.C.O.V.D., co-author of *20/20 Is Not Enough*, evaluates and treats patients having trouble in school with an optometric visual and perceptual therapy program he's developed.

Headaches

Comprehensive Headache Center at the Germantown Hospital
ONE PENN BOULEVARD, PHILADELPHIA, 19144; 951-8926

Some 45 million people suffer from recurring headaches, and while there is no cure, doctors can control the pain and related symptoms in up to 90 percent of them. The

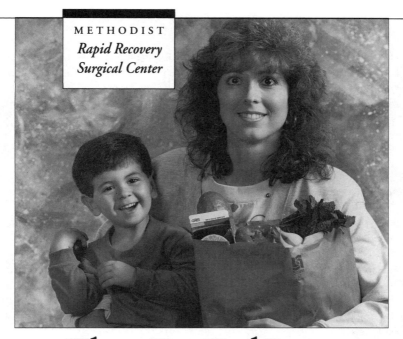

Headache Center is a research and treatment facility dedicated solely to the headache sufferer. Patients are evaluated medically by a neurologist, then seen and tested by a psychologist or psychiatrist. Treatment includes medication, behavior modification, biofeedback, diet changes, psychological and physical therapies.

Heart Healthy

Benjamin Franklin Health Clinic
PUBLIC LEDGER BUILDING, 6TH AND CHESTNUT STREETS, PHILADELPHIA, PA, 19106; 925-4300

The Benjamin Franklin Clinic concentrates on programs in the following areas: The Cardio Health Initiative is based on the research of Dr. Dean Ornish, who has found that coronary artery disease can be stopped and reversed by rigorous lifestyle changes. Participants learn about fitness, yoga, stress reduction, nutrition and the causes of coronary heart disease, and participate in group counseling. The Weight Management and Metabolism Center is a medically supervised, personally oriented nutrition program that emphasizes a well-balanced diet with real food. Senior Shape-Up and Get Fit is an exercise and weight-management fitness program. Sessions meet four hours a week for eight weeks and are led by an exercise specialist and/or dietician.

Sick Kids

Under the Weather
602 SOUTH BETHLEHEM PIKE, AMBLER, PA, 19002; 643-9460

This state-licensed daycare facility provides a haven for sick children between the ages of six weeks and 12 years who are unable to attend their school or regular day-care center due to illness. The center is specially designed to reduce the spread of illness. Medical care provided by nurses and pediatricians from Ambler Pediatrics. Children are supervised full-time, and the center is filled with books, games and activities. Open Monday-Friday, 8 a.m.-5:30 p.m.

Workplace Stress

Corporate Crisis Intervention Network (CCIN)
THE WOODS, SUITE 719, 987 OLD EAGLE SCHOOL ROAD, WAYNE, PA, 19087; 1-800-221-6776

David Reed, formerly of the Marriage Council, is executive director of this organization, which does strategic management of traumatic stress in the workplace. Included in its evaluation services is the design and implementation of a crisis intervention program to be used when something causes a major emotional upset at work. Its psychological trauma experts are on 24-hour alert and can be accessed by a toll-free hotline in case of a critical incident of violence or physical endangerment.

Support Groups

These listings include many of the organized self-help and support groups in the Delaware Valley. In addition, most local hospitals have regularly scheduled support groups too—check the hospital listings, Chapter 12. Meeting times and dates tend to change, so for current information, it's a good idea to check first. The National Self-Help Clearinghouse number is 212-642-2944.

Autism

Philadelphia Center for Autistic Children (CAC)
878-3400

Groups for parents and friends. In New Jersey, call (609) 877-4443.

Post-Abortion Counseling

Amnion Crisis Pregnancy Center
525-1557

One-on-one counseling for women experiencing post-abortion stress.

AIDS

Philadelphia AIDS Task Force
545-8686

Various special groups meet throughout the area for those diagnosed with AIDS, or testing HIV-positive. These include men, women, children, couples and families. Also check independent hospital listings.

AIDS Psychotherapy
567-2260

Dr. Mary Cochran conducts sessions, by appointment, in Center City for both men and women. Fees are on a sliding scale.

Alcoholism

Al Anon
222-5244

For the relatives and friends of alcoholics. Over 175 regular meeting places in the Delaware Valley. Call for locations.

Ala-Teen
222-5244

For teens with a drinking problem.

Alcoholics Anonymous
574-6900

The world's most successful program for people who want to stop drinking. More than 1,500 ongoing meeting places in the Delaware Valley. Call for information.

Alzheimer's

Alzheimer's Association of Greater Philadelphia

568-6430 (INSIDE PHILADELPHIA); 1-800-559-0404 (PENNSYLVANIA, OUTSIDE PHILADELPHIA AREA); 609-346-8883 (NEW JERSEY)

Provides information, emotional support and referrals. Operates Wanderer's Alert Program. For $25, a person's identifying data is added to a computerized registry of Alzheimer's sufferers. The association will notify a network of police agencies and hospitals when a victim is reported missing.

Alzheimer's Disease and Related Disorders Association

1-800-621-0370

Alzheimer's Disease Clearing House

1-800-367-5115

Sponsored by the Pennsylvania Council on Aging. For caregivers or others interested in support groups, care and information.

ALS

National ALS Association

277-3508

The Philadelphia branch operates support groups in Philadelphia, New Jersey and Delaware. Call for specific locations.

Anorexia/Bulimia

Anorexia/Bulimia Association of Philadelphia

662-1906

For people with eating disorders. Separate groups for parents and friends.

Arthritis

The Arthritis Foundation

665-9200

Various meeting places scattered through the Delaware Valley for those suffering from any form of arthritis. Family and friends invited.

Bereavement

Abington Memorial Hospital

1200 OLD YORK RD., ABINGTON; 576-2700

Compassionate Friends

952-6777

For parents who have lost a child. Several meeting places. Call for locations.

Delaware County Memorial Hospital

501 N. LANSDOWNE AVE., DREXEL HILL; 284-8550

Elkins Park Library
CHURCH ROAD NEAR OLD YORK ROAD., ELKINS PARK;
635-0176
The library has a group that is geared specifically for adults who have lost a parent.

Fox Chase Cancer Center
7701 BURHOLME AVE; CHILDREN'S GROUP: 728-2668;
ADULTS: 728-3014

Mercy Catholic
MISERICORDIA DIVISION, 5301 CEDAR AVE.,
PHILADELPHIA; 748-9440

Montgomery Cancer Center
1330 POWELL ST., SUITE 507, NORRISTOWN; 270-2711

Unite
For parents who've lost a baby during pregnancy or shortly after birth. Program is available at most area hospitals; check Chapter 12.

Widow and Widowers Counseling and Referral Service
624-8190
For people who have lost a partner. Also check hospitals, Chapter 12.

Breast-Feeding

La Leche League
666-0359
An international organization offering breast-feeding information and support for mothers. Call for information about meeting times and locations.

Cancer

American Cancer Society
665-2900 IN PHILADELPHIA AND MONTGOMERY COUN-
TIES; 717-553-6144 FOR PENNSYLVANIA LISTINGS; OR
908-297-8000 FOR NEW JERSEY
The society sponsors a great variety of support groups for cancer patients, families, and caregivers at many locations.

Philadelphia Candlelighters
884-0413
For the families of children diagnosed with cancer. Meetings held at members' homes.

Cardiac

Cardiac Support Group
576-2204
For those who have had angina, a heart attack, open-heart surgery or any cardiac disease. Families and friends invited.

Zipper Club
887-6644

For those who have had any sort of heart problem (heart attack, angioplasty, open-heart surgery, etc.) Support groups are run in conjunction with 38 area hospitals. Family and friends are invited.

Caregivers

CAPS (Children of Aging Parents)
945-6900

Sponsors support groups for middle-aged children and caregivers dealing with elderly parents or relatives. Meetings deal with medical, legal, and financial matters.

Disabled Issues

Coalition of Active Disabled of Chester County
436-6502

Advocacy, referral, and support services.

Depression

The National Depressive and Manic Depressive Association
566-3334

An organization run by and for individuals with these emotional disorders. Emphasis is on support and advocacy. Family members, friends, and health-care workers are invited.

Diabetes

American Diabetes Association
828-5003; 908-469-7979 IN NEW JERSEY

The association has a complete listing of the various support groups for those suffering from juvenile or adult-onset diabetes. Family and friends are welcome. Also check area hospitals, Chapter 12.

Epilepsy

Epilepsy Foundation of Southeastern Pennsylvania and New Jersey
667-7478; 609-858-5900 IN NEW JERSEY

Sponsors self-help groups, guest speakers, and informative lectures for epilepsy patients, as well as family and friends.

Delaware Valley Parents of Children with Epilepsy
789-2142

For the parents of epileptic children. Education and support.

Fibromyalgia

Fibromyalgia Support Group
782-1241

Groups geared to sufferers of this muscular disease. Families and friends invited.

Guillain-Barre Syndrome

Guillain-Barre Syndrome Foundation International
667-0131

The foundation helps those with this disorder by focusing on education, support, and research. Family and friends are invited to meetings.

Huntington's Disease

Huntington's Disease Society of America
569-0536

The society has a complete listing of groups for those suffering from the disease, their family, and friends. Also check specific hospital listings, Chapter 12.

Laryngectomee

Support groups are available to people who've had their larynxes removed:

Calvary Baptist Church
MARSHALL AND HAWS STS., NORRISTOWN; 337-4677

Delaware County Memorial Hospital
501 N. LANSDOWNE AVE., DREXEL HILL; 259-7021

Fox Chase Cancer Center
7701 BURHOLME AVE.; 728-2668

Lung Disease

American Lung Association
735-2200

A nonprofit organization offering support and information for those with various kinds of lung diseases. Meeting places at area hospitals.

Lupus

Lupus Foundation
743-7171 IN PHILADELPHIA; 649-9202, FOR MORE DELAWARE VALLEY LOCATIONS

Sponsors various groups for sufferers, family, and friends. Also check area hospitals.

Mental Illness

Families Unite
321-9840

Run by Ed and Kate LeBlanc for families of the chronically mentally ill.

Project SHARE
735-2465

Managed by former mental patients. Provides support, information, referral, and technical assistance to 20,000 patients nationwide.

Multiple Sclerosis

National Multiple Sclerosis Society
71-2400

Greater Delaware Valley Chapter runs meetings for sufferers, families, and friends. Also check specific hospital listings, Chapter 12.

Narcotics

Narcotics Anonymous
934-3944

For those ready to confront a narcotic addiction. Meets at over 50 area hospitals.

Organ Transplants

National Heart Assist and Transplant Fund
527-5056

Offers advice, support groups, alternative payment opportunities and public education for those needing a heart, heart/lung, or lung transplant.

Obsessive-Compulsive Behavior

Obsessive-Compulsive Support Group
842-4010

A group designed to help people dealing with this condition is held at the MCP.

Ostomy

Philadelphia Ostomy Association
483-1818

Refers to various area support groups dealing with specific ostomies.

Parkinson's Disease

Parkinson's Disease Association of America
893-2000

Has a thorough listing of support groups. Also check area hospitals, Chapter 12.

Spinal Cord Injury

Support groups sponsored through various hospitals. Check Chapter 12.

Stroke

Support groups for people recovering from strokes, as well as their families and friends are held at various hospitals. Check Chapter 12.

Survivors of Suicide

Survivor Support Group of the Delaware Valley
586-5171
Various programs for those who have attempted suicide, their family, and friends.

Tourette's Syndrome

Tourette's Syndrome Support Group
853-3798 OR 337-0159
Meetings alternate between Bryn Mawr and Lankenau hospitals.

Hot Numbers

These are some of the more widely used national 800 numbers. Try them if you are looking for information, referrals, counseling or technical assistance.

Aging
MEDICARE TELEPHONE HOTLINE, 1-800-638-6833
NATIONAL COUNCIL ON AGING, 1-800-424-9046

AIDS
NATIONAL AIDS HOTLINE, 1-800-342-2437
NATIONAL AIDS INFORMATION CLEARINGHOUSE, 1-800-458-5231

Alzheimer's
ALZHEIMER'S DISEASE AND RELATED DISORDERS ASSOCIATION, 1-800-272-3900

Arthritis
ARTHRITIS FOUNDATION INFORMATION LINE, 1-800-283-7800

Alcoholism and Drug Dependence
NATIONAL COUNCIL ON ALCOHOLISM AND DRUG DEPENDENCE, INC., 1-800-NCA-CALL

Cancer
AMERICAN CANCER SOCIETY CANCER RESPONSE LINE, 1-800-ACS-2345
AMERICAN INSTITUTE FOR CANCER RESEARCH, 1-800-843-8114
AMC CANCER INFORMATION, 1-800-525-3777
CANCER INFORMATION SERVICE, 1-800-4-CANCER

Children
AMERICAN SIDS INSTITUTE, 1-800-232-SIDS
NATIONAL CHILD ABUSE HOTLINE, 1-800-422-4453
NATIONAL RESOURCE CENTER ON CHILD ABUSE AND
NEGLECT, 1-800-2-ASK-AHA

Care for the Dying
CHOICE IN DYING, 1-800-989-WILL
COMPASSION IN DYING, 206-624-2775
HEMLOCK SOCIETY USA, 1-800-247-7421
NATIONAL HOSPICE ORGANIZATION, 1-800-658-8898

Cystic Fibrosis
CYSTIC FIBROSIS FOUNDATION, 1-800-344-4823

Diabetes
AMERICAN DIABETES ASSOCIATION, 1-800-ADA-DISC

Down's Syndrome
NATIONAL DOWN'S SYNDROME CONGRESS, 1-800-232-6372

Hearing Problems
DEAFNESS RESEARCH FOUNDATION, 1-800-535-3323
EAR FOUNDATION, 1-800-545-4327
HEARING HELPLINE, 1-800-327-9355
NATIONAL HEARING AID HELPLINE, 1-800-521-5247

Lead Poisoning
1-800-LEADFYI

Liver and Kidney
AMERICAN LIVER FOUNDATION, 1-800-622-9010
NATIONAL KIDNEY FOUNDATION, 1-800-622-9010

Lung Illness
ASTHMA AND ALLERGY FOUNDATION OF AMERICA, 1-800-7-ASTHMA
ALLERGY INFORMATION REFERRAL LINE, 1-800-822-ASMA

Lupus
AMERICAN LUPUS SOCIETY, 1-800-331-1802
LUPUS FOUNDATION OF AMERICA, 1-800-558-0121

Marijuana Therapy
ALLIANCE FOR CANNABIS THERAPEUTICS, 202-483-8595

Mental Illness
NATIONAL FOUNDATION FOR DEPRESSIVE ILLNESS, 1-800-248-4344
NATIONAL MENTAL HEALTH ASSOCIATION, 1-800-969-6642
PANIC DISORDER, 1-800-64-PANIC

Multiple Sclerosis
NATIONAL MULTIPLE SCLEROSIS SOCIETY, 1-800-944-4151

Miscellaneous Diseases
AMYOTROPHIC LATERAL SCLEROSIS ASSOCIATION, 1-800-782-4747
ANOREXIA/BULIMIA: RENFREW CENTER, 1-800-334-8415
BALANCE DISORDERS ASSOCIATION, 1-800-782-4747
HUNTINGTON'S DISEASE SOCIETY OF AMERICA, 1-800-345-4372
THE VESTIBULAR DISORDERS ASSOCIATION, 1-800-837-8428

Sexual Problems
IMPOTENCE INFORMATION CENTER, 1-800-843-4315
STD HOTLINE, 1-800-227-8922

Sickle-Cell Anemia
NATIONAL ASSOCIATION FOR SICKLE-CELL DISEASE, 1-800-421-8453

Stroke
COURAGE STROKE NETWORK, 1-800-553-6321
NATIONAL STROKE ASSOCIATION, 1-800-367-1990

Vision Problems
NATIONAL CENTER FOR SIGHT, 1-800-221-3004

Women
INTERNATIONAL CHILDBIRTH EDUCATION ASSOCIATION, 1-800-624-4934
PMS ACCESS, 1-800-222-4767
WOMEN'S INTERNATIONAL PHARMACY, 1-800-279-5708

Local Organizations

Ambulance Services
ACTION AMBULANCE CO., 725-1880
BRIDESBURG CIVIC ASSOCIATION COMMUNITY AMBULANCE, 288-8545
BURHOLME FIRST AID CORPS, 745-1550
HEALTHTECH-SOUTH JERSEY DIVISION, 609-365-1911

Lindenwold Transportation, Inc., 609-784-8583
Metropolitan Ambulance, Inc., 609-661-8176
Northeast First Aid Corps, 624-7024
Northwest Community Ambulance Corps, 537-2120
Olney Community Ambulance, 549-4848
Rhawnhurst Bustleton Ambulance Association, 698-9111
Wissahickon Community Ambulance Association, 482-6400
Wissonoming First Aid Corps, 332-1509
Wynne-Brook Community Ambulance Association, 473-4043

Diseases and Disorders
Action AIDS, 981-0088
Alzheimer's Association, 568-6430
American Cancer Society, 665-2900
American Diabetes Association, 828-5003
Arthritis Foundation, 665-9200
Asthma and Allergy Foundation, 610-630-8050
Center for the Advancement of Cancer Therapy, 642-4810
City of Hope, 731-9000
Community AIDS Hotline, 985-2437
Crohn's and Colitis Foundation, 396-9100
Cystic Fibrosis Research Foundation, 587-2800
Delaware Valley Transplant, 1-800-543-6391
Easter Seals Society, 879-1000
Elm LifeLine (cancer counseling and support programs), 609-654-4044
Epilepsy Foundation of Philadelphia, 667-7478
Guillain-Barre Syndrome Foundation International, 667-0131
Heart Association, 735-3865
Hemophilia Foundation, 885-6500
Juvenile Diabetes, 567-4307
Lupus Foundation of Delaware Valley, 649-7171
Lupus Foundation of Philadelphia, 743-7171
Multiple Sclerosis Telephone Support, 271-2400
National Multiple Sclerosis Society, 271-2400
National Kidney Foundation, Delaware Valley Chapter, 923-8611
Operation VENUS (venereal disease), 567-6969
Ostomy Association of Philadelphia, 483-1818
Overeaters Anonymous, 848-3191
Pennsylvania Tourette's Syndrome Association, 1-800-446-6356
Parkinson's Disease Center, 545-8406
Philadelphia Community Health Alternatives (VD screening and treatment), 545-8686

PHILADELPHIA HELP GROUP (HERPES), 763-2247
REYE'S SYNDROME FOUNDATION, 677-1730
SCLERODERMA FEDERATION OF THE DELAWARE VALLEY,
609-678-6707
SICKLE-CELL ANEMIA, VOLUNTEERS IN AID OF, 877-3485
SPINA BIFIDA ASSOCIATION, 676-8950
UNITED CEREBRAL PALSY, 242-4200
ZIPPER CLUB (CARDIAC SURGERY AND HEART INFORMA-
TION), 887-6644

Drug and Alcohol

ALCOHOLICS ANONYMOUS, 574-6900
AL-ANON, 222-5244; 609-547-0855
AL-ASSIST, 592-4241
CODAAP (COORDINATION OFFICE FOR DRUG AND
ALCOHOL ABUSE PROGRAM), 627-5490
FAMILY CENTER (PREGNANT ADDICTS), 955-8577
GREATER PHILADELPHIA HEALTH ACTION, 288-9200
JEWISH EMPLOYMENT AND VOCATIONAL SERVICES
(ACT), 236-0100
JEWISH EMPLOYMENT AND CHILDREN'S AGENCY, 698-
9950
NARCOTICS ANONYMOUS, 496-2826
OFFICE OF SUBSTANCE ABUSE, SCHOOL DISTRICT OF
PHILA., 875-3975
TEEN CHALLENGE CENTER, 849-2054
WOMEN IN TRANSITION, 564-5301

Hospice Programs

ALBERT EINSTEIN MEDICAL CENTER HOSPICE, 456-7155
BRYN MAWR HOSPITAL HOSPICE PROGRAM, 526-3265
HOLY REDEEMER HOSPICE, 671-9200
HOSPICE OF PENNSYLVANIA HOSPITAL, 829-5335
HOSPICE OF PRESBYTERIAN MEDICAL CENTER, 662-8996
HOSPICE OF THE UNIVERSITY OF PENNSYLVANIA
HOSPITAL, 662-3927
LANKENAU HOSPITAL HOSPICE PROGRAM, 645-2022
WISSAHICKON HOSPICE, 247-0277

Suicide

CONTACT, 879-4402; 609-667-3000
SUICIDE AND CRISIS INTERVENTION CENTER, 686-4420
SURVIVORS OF SUICIDE, 545-2242

Visual Impairment

ASSOCIATED SERVICES FOR THE BLIND, 627-0600
BLINDNESS AND VISUAL SERVICES, 560-5700
BLIND RELIEF FUND OF PHILADELPHIA, 222-7613
FEDERATION OF THE BLIND OF PENNSYLVANIA, 988-0888

FIGHT FOR SIGHT OF GREATER PHILADELPHIA (CHILDREN'S EYE CLINIC), 928-3240
LIBRARY FOR THE BLIND AND VISUALLY HANDICAPPED, 925-3213
LIONS EYE BANK OF DELAWARE VALLEY, 627-0700
PENNSYLVANIA COUNCIL FOR THE BLIND, 238-1410

Women's Services
SEE PAGE 219 FOR SPECIFIC LISTINGS.

Professional Profile Section

❧ As an additional source to our readers, the following health professionals have elected to list their services. ❧ These listings are paid advertisements and the information they contain has been furnished by the doctors and other medical practitioners. Philadelphia Magazine's Guide To Good Health is not responsible for the credentials, affiliations, associations or other claims provided and does not endorse or recommend any medical professionals on the basis of their advertisement in this space. The listings appear in alphabetical order by specialty and name.❧

ACUPUNCTURE

ACUPUNCTURE HEALTH CARE, CATHY LYN GOLDSTEIN, REG. ACU., QING-YAO SHI, REG. ACU., REG. HERBOLOGIST

Female Imbalances, Allergies
1700 Sansom St., Philadelphia, PA 19103; (215)988-9898 *and* 14 Market Place, Logan Square, New Hope, PA 18938; (215)862-2663.
Chinese and Japanese training. Using traditional Eastern medicine, acupuncture and herbology to balance and bring health. Menopause, PMS, asthma, migraines, injuries, pain, arthritis, GI, fatigue. Foreign language spoken: Chinese.

C.M.D. ACUPUNCTURE CENTER AND HERBS STORE, CHENGHUI ZHU, L.A., C.A.

Herbology
1644 Bridge St., Philadelphia, PA 19124; (215)744-8260.
25 years experience of acupuncture. Chinese medicine and herbology. Specializing in relieving pain, quitting smoking, losing weight and controlling diseases, depression, stress. Foreign language spoken: Chinese.

PATRICK J. LARICCIA, M.D.

Hypnosis, Biofeedback
Presbyterian Medical Center of Philadelphia, 51 N. 39th St., Suite 340, Philadelphia, PA 19104; (215)662-8988.
Vice President Acupuncture Society of Pennsylvania. Board-certified in internal medicine. Major hospital and university affiliations. Post-graduate training in mind-body techniques of hypnosis and biofeedback.

MARLTON PAIN CONTROL AND ACUPUNCTURE CENTER. WAN B. LO, M.S., D.O., PH.D.

Evesham Commons, Suite 301, 525 Rt. 73 S., Marlton, NJ 08053; (609)596-1005.
Board-certified. Specializing in traditional Chinese art of acupuncture. 23 years experience in treating arthritis, rheumatism, allergies, tendinitis, stress, smoking, weight,

chronic pain, etc. Foreign language spoken: Chinese.

RONG-BAO LU, M.D.

Acupuncture and Pain Control
1218 Walnut St., Room 901, Philadelphia, PA 19107; (215)546-7806.
Trained in China and USA. Free consultation. Arthritis, back/neck pain, headache, migraines, car accidents, sports injuries. Nervousness, insomnia, PMS, weight control, smoking, stress, allergies. Foreign language spoken: Chinese.

MARSHALL H. SAGER, D.O.

One Bala Plaza, Suite 133, Bala Cynwyd, PA 19004; (215)668-2400.
University-trained, Certified Medical Acupuncture Physician combining acupuncture, osteopathic manipulation, and Western medicine. Smoking, pain control, arthritis, backs, migraines, allergies, tendinitis, colitis, PMS, fatigue, stress.

ADDICTIONS

UNIVERSITY OF PENNSYLVANIA TREATMENT RESEARCH CENTER, EXECUTIVE DIRECTOR: JOSEPH VOLPICELLI, M.D., PH.D., PROGRAM DIRECTOR: PETER GARETI, PH.D., MEDICAL DIRECTOR: ROBERT WEINRIEB, M.D., CLINICAL COORDINATOR: EILEEN HOLUB-BEYER, M.H.R., C.A.C., RESEARCH COORDINATOR: DELINDA MERCER, M.S.

Alcohol and Cocaine Addiction
3900 Chestnut St., Philadelphia, PA 19104; (215)222-3200 ext. 158.
Comprehensive outpatient treatment is offered at no cost in exchange for research participation. State of the art services include individualized outpatient detoxification and therapy programs.

ALLERGY

SHERYL TALBOT, M.D.

822 Pine St., Suite 2A, Philadelphia, PA

19107; (215)922-5080.
Chief, Section of Allergy, Pennsylvania Hospital, specializing in all types of allergy, allergic and non-allergic asthma, and sinus problems in patients 12 or older.

ALLERGY/IMMUNOLOGY

MAIN LINE ALLERGY AND PULMONARY SPECIALISTS, LILLIAN P. KRAVIS, M.D., JEFFREY M. GREENE, M.D., P.C., RUTHVEN A. WODELL, M.D., SHARON K. SWEINBERG, M.D.
Pediatrics, Pulmonary
233 E. Lancaster Ave., Ardmore, PA 19003 *and* 491 Allendale Rd.; (610)642-1643.
Patient-friendly physicians all board-certified. Allergy/immunology; special interests: asthma, hay fever, food/drug hypersensitivities. Teaching and staff appointments; Children's Hospital Philadelphia, Bryn Mawr Hospital.

ALTERNATIVE MEDICINE

MYOFASCIAL RELEASE TREATMENT CENTER, JOHN F. BARNES, P.T.
Physical Therapy for Complex Chronic Pain and Dysfunction
10 S. Leopard Rd., Rts. 30 and 252, Suite One, Paoli, PA 19301; (800)FASCIAL, (610)644-0136.
Patients treated from around the world to resolve chronic pain using innovative, hands-on myofascial release. Specialty: back/neck pain, headaches, traumatic injuries. Whole-body approach to return you to pain-free, active lifestyle.

AQUATIC PHYSICAL THERAPY

THE PHILADELPHIA CENTER FOR AQUATIC REHABILITATION
3600 Grant Ave., Philadelphia, PA 19114; (215)677-0400.
33,000 square-foot aquatic therapy facility

specializing in orthopedic, sports, work-related injuries, aquatic, land therapy and work conditioning. Most insurances accepted, including Medicare and US Healthcare.

ARTHRITIS/RHEUMATISM

ARTHRITIS ASSOCIATES AND THE PHILADELPHIA ARTHRITIS INSTITUTE. PRESBYTERIAN MEDICAL CENTER
Arthritis and Rheumatism
39th and Market sts., Philadelphia, PA 19104; (215)662-9292.
Drs. Warren A. Katz, Fredrick B. Vivino and David A. Allan, experienced board-certified specialists in multidisciplinary approaches to all forms of arthritis, connective-tissue diseases, low-back problems, gout, fibrositis and occupational medicine.

PHILADELPHIA ARTHRITIS CONSULTANTS, BRUCE FREUNDLICH, M.D. FACR, LAWRENCE LEVENTHAL, M.D., FACP, FACR, KENDRA KAYE, M.D.
The Graduate Hospital, Suite 801, Pepper Pavilion, 1800 Lombard St., Philadelphia, PA 19146; (215)893-7565.
Comprehensive team of specialists (board-certified physicians, therapists) expert in diagnosis and individualized treatment of arthritis, osteoporosis, all forms of muscular, bone and joint pain.

BREAST SURGERY

ARNOLD M. BASKIES, M.D., F.A.C.S.
Surgical Oncology
1000 Salem Rd., Suite A, Willingboro, NJ 08046; (609)877-1737.
Specializing in the diagnosis and treatment of benign and malignant breast problems.

CARDIOLOGY

MARK D. BERGER, M.D., PENNSYLVANIA CARDIOLOGY ASSOCIATES, LTD.
Pennsylvania Hospital, 801 Spruce St.,

Philadelphia, PA 19107; (215)829-5064.
Cardiac catheterization, stress echocardiography; Clinical Assistant Professor of Medicine, University of Pennsylvania School of Medicine; Clinical Assistant Physician, Pennsylvania Hospital; Affiliated with Presbyterian Medical Center; board-certified in Internal Medicine Cardiovascular Diseases.

BRANDYWINE VALLEY CARDIOVASCULAR ASSOCIATES
3456 E. Lincoln Highway, Thorndale, PA 19372; (215)384-2211.
Cardiovascular disease, interventional cardiology, critical-care medicine, internal medicine. Arthur B. Hodess, M.D., FACC, Thomas S. Metkus, M.D., FACC, David J. Bernbaum, M.D., FACC, Alan D. Troy, M.D., FACC, Donald V. Ferrari, D.O., FACC

CERTIFIED MEDICAL SPECIALISTS, PHILIP BHARK, M.D., ARTHUR MELTZER, M.D., LESLIE POOR, M.D., ROGER WEINER, M.D., SAMUEL RUBY, M.D.
Taylor Hospital Medical Bldg., Donald P. Jones Bldg., 1 Bartol Ave., Suite 210, Ridley Park, PA 19078; (610)521-0150 *and* Crozer-Chester Medical Center, 1 Medical Center Blvd., Ambulatory Care Pavillion, Suite 534, Upland, PA 19013; (610)490-1744.
A progressive multi-specialty group practice committed to patient wellness in the disciplines of cardiology, infectious disease, internal medicine, family medicine, endocrinology and ophthalmology: A quality health-care provider located in Delaware County, PA. Other specialties in practice: Internal Medicine: Edward Cikowski, D.O., Mark Zibelman, M.D.; Family Medicine: Ronald D'Orazio, D.O., Wayne Garraway, D.O., John Fanning, D.O.; Infectious Disease: Jeffrey Darnall, M.D.; Endocrinology: Liselle Douyon, M.D., Ophthalmology: Marguerite Billbrough, M.D.

NICHOLAS L. DEPACE, M.D., F.A.C.C., DAVID ELBAUM, D.O., DANIEL CONSTANTINESCU, M.D.,

**PH.D., F.A.C.C.,
EDGAR SMITH, M.D.**
Internal Medicine
2422 S. Broad St., Philadelphia, PA 19145;
(215)755-5449.
Board-certified, five locations in Philadel-
phia and New Jersey, Director of the Heart
Repair Program at the Philadelphia Heart
Institute at Presbyterian Medical Center.

**JOSEPH R. DESANTOLA, M.D.,
PENNSYLVANIA CARDIOLOGY
ASSOCIATES, LTD.**
Pennsylvania Hospital, 801 Spruce St.,
Philadelphia, PA 19107; (215)829-5064.
Cardiac catheterization, interventional car-
diology, transesophageal ochocardiography.
Staff Physician, Pennsylvania Hospital;
Clinical Assistant Professor of Medicine,
University of Pennsylvania School of
Medicine; affiliated with Presbyterian
Hospital; board-certified Internal Medicine
Cardiovascular Diseases.

**WILLIAM S. FRANKL, M.D.,
HERBERT A. FISCHER, M.D.,
JOHN G. IVANOFF, M.D.**
Medical College of Pennsylvania and
Medical College Hospitals, Main Clinical
Campus, 3300 Henry Ave., Philadelphia, PA
19129; (215)842-7520.
A full-service cardiovascular practice in the
Delaware Valley's regional health system-
Medical College Hospitals, where Dr. Frankl
is Director, Regional Cardiovascular
Programs.

**MICHAEL S. FELDMAN, M.D.,
F.A.C.C.**
Cardiovascular Diseases
Philadelphia Heart Institute, Presbyterian
Medical Center, 51 N. 39th St., Philadelphia,
PA 19104; (215)222-7000.
Board-certified and University-affiliated,
specialist in diagnoses and treatment of
coronary artery disease, hypertension, ar-
rhythmias, high cholesterol and heart failure.

GREATER PHILADELPHIA CARDIOLOGY ASSOCIATES, INC., LOUIS R. LEO, M.D., GAETANO J. CAPONE, M.D.

439 Lankenau Medical Bldg. West, 100 Lancaster Ave., Wynnewood, PA 19096; (610)658-0489 *and* Suite 207, Physicians' Office Bldg., 2701 Holme Ave., Philadelphia, PA 19152; (215)335-7700.
Primary and interventional cardiology practice specializing in, but not limited to, echocardiography, cardiac catheterization, angioplasty, atherectomy and coronary stents. Hospital affiliations: Lankenau, Hahnemann, Nazareth, Montgomery.

GROSSMAN & HARKINS, M.D., P.A., MARVIN GROSSMAN, M.D., MICHAEL J. HARKINS, M.D.

Cardiovascular Disease
409 Route 70 E., Cherry Hill, NJ 08034; (609)428-5857.
Board-certified cardiologists providing in-patient and out-patient cardiovascular services at Our Lady of Lourdes Medical Center and New Jersey Heart Institute. Cardiac catheterization, balloon angioplasty, atherectomy, coronary stents, stress radionuclide and echocardiography, color-flow and doppler echocardiography. Diagnosis and treatment of angina, hypertension, high cholesterol and heart failure.

JEFFERSON CARDIOVASCULAR ASSOCIATES, SHELDON GOLDBERG, M.D., DIRECTOR

Department of Medicine, Thomas Jefferson University, 824-26 Walnut St., Philadelphia, PA 19107; (215)955-6672.
Board-certified faculty cardiologists provide programs including clinical cardiology, risk-factor reduction, cardiac catheterization, angioplasty, arrhythmia management/electrophysiology, echocardiography and stress testing.

MICHAEL KIRSCHBAUM, D.O.

Cardiovascular Medicine
G.S.B. Bldg., Suite 400, City and Belmont aves., Bala Cynwyd, PA; (610)667-8558.
Board-certified, Deborah trained, Fellow

American College of Cardiology, textbooks published, nationally known, highest quality support staff. Consultation, stress testing, treatment of all cardiovascular problems. Weekdays, evenings.

MAIN LINE CARDIOVASCULAR ASSOCIATES, LTD., M. DIBATTISTE, M.D., F.A.C.C., PAUL M. COADY, M.D., F.A.C.C., TIMOTHY A. SHAPIRO, M.D., F.A.C.C.

Primary and Interventional Cardiology
Suite 430 Lankenau Medical Bldg. West, 100 Lancaster Ave., Wynnewood, PA 19096; (215)649-8599.
A unique, patient-oriented practice with extensive cardiac diagnostic/therapeutic skills. Caring treatment of chest pain, valve problems, arrhythmias, arterial blockages, etc. Available day and night.

NORTHEAST CARDIOLOGY CONSULTANTS, INC.

2701 Holme Ave., #105, Philadelphia, PA 19152; (215)335-4944.
Personalized diagnostic and therapeutic cardiology services in a community/university setting. Specializing in critical-care internal medicine. Richard W. Vassallo, M.D., FACC, Cheryl L. Leddy, M.D., FACC, Stuart Snyder, M.D., FACC, Deepak K. Parashara, M.D.

PHILADELPHIA CARDIOLOGY ASSOCIATES, BERNARD L. SEGAL, M.D., AMI E. ISKANDRIAN, M.D., MARIELL JESSUP, M.D., MARK W. PREMINGER, M.D., MARC A. TECCE, M.D.

Presbyterian Medical Center, Philadelphia Heart Institute, Suite 2A, 39th and Market sts., Philadelphia, PA 19104; (215)662-5050 *and* Nazareth Physician's Office, 2701 Holme Ave., Suite 203, Philadelphia, PA 19152; (215)332-5050.
Heart Failure, Electrophysiology
University-affiliated and board-certified specialists in the diagnosis and treatment of angina, hypertension, high cholesterol, heart failure, abnormal heart rhythm, catheterization and angioplasty.

**DAVID S. POLL, M.D.,
PENNSYLVANIA CARDIOLOGY
ASSOCIATES, LTD.**
Pennsylvania Hospital, 801 Spruce St.,
Philadelphia, PA 19107; (215)829-5064.
Director, Electrophysiology Laboratories,
Pennsylvania Hospital; Clinical Assistant
Professor of Medicine, University of Penn-
sylvania School of Medicine, affiliation with
Presbyterian Hospital; Board-certified in
Internal Medicine, Cardiovascular Diseases,
Clinical Electrophysiology.

**P.M. PROCACCI, M.D., F.A.C.C.,
MARK F. VICTOR, M.D., F.A.C.C.,
DANIEL J. MCCORMICK, D.O.,
F.A.C.C., VERONICA A. COVALESKY,
M.D., F.A.C.C., DEAN G. KARALIS,
M.D., F.A.C.C., STANLEY SPITZER,
M.D., F.A.C.C., TED M. PARRIS, M.D.,
F.A.C.C., GARO S. GARIBIAN, M.D.,
F.A.C.C., KEVIN G. ROBINSON,
M.D., F.A.C.C., DANIEL MASON,**

**M.D., F.A.C.C., JAMES U. CARDELIA,
M.D., F.A.C.C.**
1703 S. Broad St., Suite 300, Philadelphia,
PA 19148; (215)463-5333.
We at Cardiology Consultants of Philadelphia are a group of physicians dedicated
to providing the highest quality, most up-to-
date, and comprehensive cardiac care in the
Philadelphia area.

**GREGG J. REIS, M.D.,
PENNSYLVANIA CARDIOLOGY
ASSOCIATES, LTD.**
Pennsylvania Hospital, 801 Spruce St., Phil-
adelphia, PA 19107; (215)829-5064.
Interventional cardiology, cardiac catheter-
ization, atherectomy, coronary stents. Staff
Physician, Pennsylvania Hospital; Clinical
Assistant Professor, University of Pennsyl-
vania School of Medicine; affiliated with
Presbyterian Hospital; cardiology fellowship
Harvard Medical School; Board-certified in
Internal Medicine Cardiovascular Diseases.

**W.M.K. ASSOCIATES, LTD.,
MORTON S. MANDELL, M.D.,
DONALD L. KAHN, M.D.,
JAMES F. MCDONALD, JR., D.O.,
ANDREW B. WOLDOW, M.D.,
STEVEN H. GOLDSTEIN, D.O.**
Klein Professional Office Bldg., Suite 401,
5401 Old York Rd., Philadelphia, PA 19141;
(215)329-0633 *and* 2308 E. Allegheny Ave.,
Philadelphia, PA 19134; (215)634-5400.
A full-service adult cardiology practice
including echocardiogram, cardiac cath-
eterization, angioplasty, and atherectomy
procedures.

**HARVEY L. WAXMAN, M.D.,
WILLIAM J. UNTEREKER, M.D.
HEART INSTITUTE OF SOUTHERN
NEW JERSEY**
Cooper Hospital/University Medical Center,
3 Cooper Plaza, Suite 311, Camden, NJ
08103; (609)342-2604.
Cardiology consultation by 12 faculty cardiologists, cardiac catheterization, new-device
angioplasty, arrhythmia management
including EPS and radio frequency ablation,
transesophageal and routine echocardiography and thallium stress testing.

**JACOB ZATUCHNI, M.D.,
PENNSYLVANIA CARDIOLOGY
ASSOCIATES, LTD.**
Pennsylvania Hospital, 801 Spruce St.,
Philadelphia, PA 19107; (215)829-5064.
Heart failure, electrocardiography. Senior
Diagnostician Director Clinical Services
Section on Cardiovascular Diseases, Penn-
sylvania Hospital; Clinical Professor of
Medicine, University of Pennsylvania School
of Medicine; affiliated with Presbyterian
Medical Center; Emeritus Professor of
Medicine, Temple University School of
Medicine; board-certified in Internal
Medicine Cardiovascular Diseases.

CARDIOTHORACIC SURGERY

**WILLIAM G. HENDREN, M.D.,
F.A.C.S., CHIEF, DIVISION OF
CARDIOTHORACIC SURGERY**
The Graduate Hospital, 1800 Lombard St.,

Suite 1100, Philadelphia, PA 19146;
(215)893-4442.
Full-service adult cardiac surgery, utilizing
state-of-the-art techniques, including valve
repair and complex revascularization. Large
experience in high-risk problems.

**MAIN LINE CARDIOTHORACIC
SURGEONS, P.C. SCOTT M.
GOLDMAN, M.D., F.A.C.S., FRANCIS
P. SUTTER, D.O., F.A.C.S.**
Lankenau Medical Bldg., East, Suite 558, 100
Lancaster Ave., Wynnewood, PA 19096;
(610)896-9255.
Board-certified. State of the art techniques
include heart valve repair vs. replacement,
surgery without blood supply interruption
to the heart, blood conservation preventing
transfusions.

STEVEN J. WEISS, M.D.
Albert Einstein Medical Center, Hackenberg
Bldg., Third Floor, Philadelphia, PA 19141;
(215)324-5508.
State-of-the-art cardiothoracic surgical
team. Special expertise in warm heart
surgery, valve repair instead of replacement,
high-risk and reoperative bypass surgery
using a microscope.

CARDIOTHORACIC SURGERY

**CTS CARDIAC & THORACIC
SURGEONS PC**
Cardiothoracic Surgery
Hahnemann University Hospital, Broad and
Vine sts., M.S. 111, Philadelphia, PA 19102-
1192; (215)762-7802.
Drs. Brockman, Strong, Grunewald, Kuretu,
Morris and Alpern. A full-service adult prac-
tice providing all aspects of thoracic, cardiac
and open-heart surgery, including trans-
plantation.

CARDIOVASCULAR DISEASES

**GRADUATE CARDIOLOGY
CONSULTANTS, INC.**
Graduate Hospital, One Graduate Plaza,
Suite 101, Philadelphia, PA 19146; (215)893-
2495.

Cardiac Center: Complete cardiac care, inpatient and outpatient, including catheterization, angioplasty, electrophysiology, echocardiography, holter monitoring, stress testing, plus cardiac surgery.

MAINLINE ARRHYTHMIA AND CARDIOLOGY, CONSULTANTS, P.C., PETER R. KOWEY, M.D., ROGER A. MARINCHAK, M.D., SETH J. RIALS, M.D., PH.D., ANDREW RUBIN, M.D.

Electrophysiology, Cardiac Rhythm Problems
Lankenau Medical Office Bldg. East, Suite 556, 100 Lancaster Ave., Wynnewood, PA 19096-3425; (610)649-6980.
Physicians are trained in treatment of all heart disorders with advanced training in rhythm disorders. Specializing in electrophysiology, pacemakers/internal defibrillators, catheterization, ablation, unexplained fainting.

CHILD ASSESSMENT/ TREATMENT

LESLIE RESCORLA, PH.D., BARBARA LORRY, PH.D., KATHERINE GORDON-CLARK, PH.D., FRANCES SUTHERLAND, PH.D, STEVEN UNDERWOOD, M.D., ANN GLUCK, PSY.D. AND STAFF

Tutoring and Speech & Language Services
Wyndon Ave. and Roberts Rd., Bryn Mawr, PA 19010; (610)527-5090.
Highly qualified specialists in psychological assessment, educational support, speech-language therapy and psychotherapy work together as a team and collaborate closely with parents and schools.

CHIROPRACTIC

JESS P. ARMINE, D.C.

2710 Township Line Rd., Upper Darby, PA 19082; (610)449-9716 and (800)254-PAIN.
Over 19 years medical and chiropractic experience. Diverse health-care background. Board-qualified chiropractic orthopedist. Specializing in painful and difficult cases. Daily appointments available. We care!

Foreign languages spoken: Russian, Greek.

DR. BRETT D. CARDONICK *IN CHESTNUT HILL*

7926 Germantown Ave., Philadelphia, PA 19118; (215)242-8632.
A doctor you can trust. "We are committed to a comprehensive approach that effectively and efficiently meets the needs of individuals, families and the community."

HARLEYSVILLE CHIROPRACTIC CENTER, DR. RONALD BUNT

354 Main St., Harleysville, PA 19438; (215)256-8616.
Board-certified auto injuries, work injuries, family health-care, nutritional counseling, soft-tissue rehabilitation. A conservative health-care since 1973. X-ray on premises. Most insurances accepted.

DAVID W. NADLER, D.C., C.C.S.P.

Back and Neck Specialist
3217 West Chester Pike, Suite A., Newtown Square, PA 19073; (215)353-3888.
Board-certified–National Board of Chiropractic Examiners. Advanced methods, nonsurgical and drug-free approach; gentle, safe adjustments; state-of-the-art therapy equipment.

O'KEEFE CHIROPRACTIC CENTER, MICHAEL J. O'KEEFE, D.C., DAVID L. JONES, D.C.

Sports Injuries
Cedarbrook Professional Bldg., Taunton Blvd., Medford, NJ 08055; (609)654-4299, (609)654-1972(fax).
Dr. Michael J. O'Keefe, an American Academy of Pain Management Diplomat, and Dr. David L. Jones specialize in pain treatment, including spinal disorders, headaches, neck and back, herniated discs sciatic and arm pain.

CLINICAL PSYCHOLOGY

THOMAS A. BARTLETT, M.A.

Individuals and Couples
Institute of Pennsylvania Hospital, Room

K325S, 111 N. 49th St., Philadelphia, PA 19139; (215)471-2080.
Sensible, respectful psychotherapy for stress, depression, anxiety and interpersonal difficulties. Licensed. Insurance accepted. Affordable, sliding fee scale. Evenings possible. Can arrange medication consultation, when indicated.

WILMA CAFFENTZIS, PH.D.
P.O. Box 309, R.D. 1, New Hope, PA 18938; (215)862-5161.
Individual, couple and group psychotherapy. Also supervision/therapy groups for psychotherapists; ongoing and newly forming; in-depth work on self development and case problems.

COLON/RECTAL SURGERY

DR. LOWELL D. MEYERSON
Proctology
7516 City Line Ave., Philadelphia, PA; (215)877-3639 *and* Medical College Hospital, Elkins Park Campus, 60 E. Township Line Rd., Elkins Park, PA (215)379-0444.
Board-certified. Emphasis on office procedures for hemorrhoid treatment and cancer screening of colon and rectum. Laser surgery.

DENTAL

EXTON DENTAL HEALTH GROUP, JONATHAN SCHARF, D.M.D., FAACD, ARTURA GARCIA, D.M.D.
The Commons at Lincoln Center, W. Lincoln Highway, Exton, PA 19341; (610)363-2300.
Dr. Scharf is an internationally recognized expert in the field of cosmetic dentistry. Advanced procedures. Blue Shield, Delta, insurance-participating doctors. Convenient hours. See ad on back page of Doctor Profile Section.

OSCAR GOREN, D.M.D., P.C., JOSE ZAYAS, D.M.D.
Family Cosmetic and Implant Dentistry
2412 Rhawn St., Philadelphia, PA 19152;

(215)332-5259.
Providing personal dental care in a safe, friendly environment. Convenient hours and location in Northeast Philadelphia. Intra-oral video technology utilized to assist diagnosis and communication.

K.W. LAUDENBACH, D.D.S., LTD.
220 S. 16th St., Suite 1100, Philadelphia, PA 19102; (215)985-4337.
Integrated fine dentistry for adults: oral diagnosis, periodontal prosthesis, dental implants, coordinated care of patients experiencing head/neck pain.

KENT LANE MUELLER, D.D.S.
Implant and Cosmetic Dentistry
The Abington Professional Courtyard, 1858 Guernsey Ave., Abington, PA 19001; (215)885-1515.
Dr. Kent Mueller provides personal care in the delivery of: implant surgical placement and prosthetic restoration, crown and bridge reconstructive dentistry. Cosmetic smile enhancement and preventive and general care.

EDWIN S. ROSENBERG, B.D.S, H. DIP. DENT., D.M.D., JOSEPH E. GIAN-GRASSO, D.M.D., FARSHID SANAVI, D.M.D.
Periodontics and Dental Implants
Suite 1408-1500 Locust St., Philadelphia, PA 19102-4314; (215)732-4450 *and* Suite 300-7601 Castor Ave., Philadelphia, PA 19152-4026; (215)722-4290.
Board-certified and board-eligible specialists delivering state-of-the-art treatment in a caring and highly professional manner. We want to make you Smile! Foreign languages spoken: Italian, Farsi.

DERMATOLOGY

ARTHUR K. BALIN, M.D., PH.D., F.A.C.P.
2129 Providence Ave., Chester, PA 19013; (610)876-0200.
Skin cancer and aging-skin specialist. Cosmetic skin surgery, liposuction, lipoinjec-

Thomas Jefferson University

THE JEFFERSON FACULTY PRACTICE PLAN

Quality, Experience, Compassion

Continuing Jefferson's Tradition of Excellence Into the 21st Century

► Anesthesiology/
Pain Management ...955-7300

► Dermatology...........955-6680

► Family Medicine 955-7190

► Medicine:
Cardiology 955-6672

Endocrinology/
Metabolic Diseases..955-1925

   Diabetes 928-3400

Gastroenterology/
Hepatology (Digestive
Diseases) 955-7546

Hematology (Cardeza
Foundation)............955-8417

Infectious Diseases ..955-7785

Internal Medicine ...955-6180

Medical Genetics 955-6955

Neoplastic Diseases
(Cancer)..................955-8874

Nephrology
(Renal)....................955-6550

Environmental Medicine
and Toxicology........955-2471

Osteoporosis
Center 578-3433

Pulmonary Medicine/
Asthma 955-5161

Rheumatology.........955-8430

► Neurology...............955-6692

► Neurosurgery 955-7621

► Obstetrics and
Gynecology.............955-5000

► Orthopaedic
Surgery 955-6688
Sports Medicine......955-2001

► Otolaryngology-Head and
Neck Surgery 955-6760

► Pediatrics 955-6520

► Psychiatry and
Human Behavior 955-6912

► Radiation Oncology and
Nuclear Medicine ...955-6702

► Radiology...............955-7112
Ultrasound..............955-8531

► Rehabilitation
Medicine................955-1202

► Surgery 955-6925

► Urology..................955-6963

*Jefferson Medical College
Thomas Jefferson University*

tion. Board-certified in dermatology, dermatopathology, internal medicine, geriatric medicine, and Mohs micrographic surgery and cutaneous oncology.

DAVE B. OLIM, M.D.

1244 Fort Washington Ave., Fort Washington, PA 19034; (215)643-6868.
Board-certified dermatologist with 30 years experience specializing in general dermatology and skin surgery. Evening and Saturday hours. Most insurance plans accepted.

GREGORY A. PISTONE, M.D.

Cosmetic Dermatology
1318 Ritner St., Philadelphia, PA; (215)336-1300 *and* Meetinghouse Square, Greentree and Church rds., Marlton, NJ; (609)596-7725.
An experienced board-certified dermatologist with a gentle touch, Dr. Pistone specializes in natural-hair transplantation, sclerotherapy of varicose and spider veins, earlobe repair and skin renewal utilizing skin peels, Retin-A/glycolic acid and collagen.

LORETTA PRATT, M.D.

2129 Providence Ave., Chester, PA 19013; (610)876-0200.
Specializing in treatment of women's skin problems, acne, aging skin. Individual complexion evaluation. Sclerotherapy, liposuction, lipoinjection, chemical peels, and collagen injections are performed in the office.

ENDOCRINOLOGY

JEFFERSON ENDOCRINOLOGY AND METABOLIC DISEASES, BARRY J. GOLDSTEIN, M.D., PH.D., DIRECTOR

Department of Medicine, Thomas Jefferson University, Walnut Towers, 211 S. 9th St., Suite 601, Philadelphia, PA 19107; (215)955-1925.
Board-certified faculty specializing in managing all endocrine (hormonal) and metabolic diseases. Diabetes care coordinated with the Joslin Center staff.

FAMILY MEDICINE

VINCENT E. BALDINO, D.O., P.C.

1701 Ritner St., Philadelphia, PA 19145 *and* 5737 Chester Ave., Philadelphia, PA 19143; (215)336-2145.
Specializing in family/general medicine—all ages accepted. Please call for appointment–evening hours available Monday through Thursday.

CERTIFIED MEDICAL SPECIALISTS, RONALD D'ORAZIO, D.O., JOHN FANNING, D.O., WAYNE GARRAWAY, D.O.

Taylor Hospital Medical Bldg., 8 Morton Ave., Suite 206, Ridley Park, PA 19078; (610)521-0150 *and* Morton Medical Bldg., 1803 Franklin Ave., Morton, PA 19070; (610)543-0100.
A progressive multi-specialty group practice committed to patient wellness in the disciplines of cardiology, infectious disease, internal medicine, family medicine, endocrinology and ophthalmology: a quality health-care provider located in Delaware County, PA.
Other specialties in practice: Cardiology: Philip Bhark, M.D., Arthur Meltzer, M.D., Leslie Poor, M.D., Samuel Ruby, M.D., Roger Weiner, M.D.; Infectious Disease: Jeffrey Darnall, M.D.; Internal Medicine: Edward Cikowski, D.O., Mark Zibelman, M.D.; Endocrinology: Liselle Douyon, M.D.; Ophthalmology: Marguerite Billbrough, M.D.

NORRISTOWN FAMILY PRACTICE, P.C., JOSEPH M. DI MINO, D.O., JOHN J. ZARO, D.O., PH.D., JOSEPH A. CALAMIA, D.O., KEVIN R. MELNICK, D.O.

1437 DeKalb St., Suite 201, Norristown, PA 19401; (610)272-5341.
Board-certified family practice/geriatrics. Convenient hours evening/weekends. On-site X-ray, lab, phys. therapy, special studies (EKG, Holters). Affiliated with local hospitals/nursing homes. Oldest family practice in Montgomery County.

RICHARD M. PAPA, D.O.

1101 Snyder Ave., Philadelphia, PA 19148; (215)463-0330 *and* 257 N. 52nd St., Philadelphia, PA 19139; (215)474-3400. Board-certified in general practice and pain management.

GASTROENTEROLOGY

GRADUATE HOSPITAL GASTROENTEROLOGY ASSOC., P.C.

19th and Lombard sts., Suite 100, Philadelphia, PA 19146; (215)893-2532. Julius Deren, M.D., Steven Greenfield, M.D., Jeffrey Retig, M.D., Donald Castell, M.D., George Ahtaridis, M.D., S. Philip Bralow, M.D., Anthony Infantolino, M.D., David Katzka, M.D.

ANTHONY J. DIMARINO, JR., M.D., STEPHEN S. FROST, M.D., HOWARD S. KROOP, M.D., JORGE A. PRIETO, M.D., MITCHELL I. CONN, M.D., ROBERT M. COHEN, M.D.

Presbyterian Medical Center, 51 N. 39th St., Philadelphia, PA 19104; (215)662-8900. Board-certified physicians proficient in all advanced outpatient endoscopic and laser treatments of gastro-intestinal disorders involving the esophagus, stomach, pancreas, liver, gallbladder, small intestine and colon.

L. EHRLICH, M.D., S. NACK, M.D., AND D. MILLER, M.D.

2303 N. Broad St., Colmar, PA 18915; (215)997-9377 *and* 8815 Germantown Ave., Philadelphia, PA 19118; (215)247-4604. Experts at the diagnosis and treatment of diseases of the gastrointestinal tract, liver, bile ducts and pancreas. Experience at endoscopic procedures including colonoscopy, endoscopy, etc.

UNIVERSITY OF PENNSYLVANIA MEDICAL CENTER, DIVISION OF GASTROENTEROLOGY

3rd Floor Dulles, 3400 Spruce St., Philadelphia, PA 19104; (215)349-8222. Comprehensive treatment and diagnosis of digestive tract and liver disease. Sub-specialties include: inflammatory bowel disease, liver disease, motility disorders. Physicians certified in advanced endoscopic procedures.

JEFFERSON DIGESTIVE DISEASE SERVICE, MARK A. ZERN, M.D., DIRECTOR

Hepatology
Department of Medicine, Division of Gastroenterology and Hepatology, Thomas Jefferson University, 132 S. 10th St., Suite 480, Philadelphia, PA 19107; (215)955-7546. Board-certified specialists in the treatment of gastrointestinal and liver diseases. State-of-the-art endoscopy procedure unit and outpatient office in one convenient location.

WARREN WERBITT, M.D., JANE FRIEHLING, D.O., NEIL COHEN, M.D.

1939 Route 70 E., Suite 250, Cherry Hill, NJ 08003; (609)429-4433 *and* Ganttown Professional Plaza, Ganttown Rd., Sewell, NJ 08080; (609)582-8787.
Board-certified. University affiliations. Complete comprehensive care. Specializing in all diseases of digestive system and liver. All endoscopic procedures performed. Most insurances accepted. Evening hours.

GENERAL SURGERY

DAVID ROSE, M.D.

Laparoscopic Surgery
101 Bryn Mawr Ave., Suite 201, Bryn Mawr, PA 19010; (610)520-0700.
Dr. Rose specializes in laparoscopic surgery. Call (610)520-0700 for appointments.

GENERAL/PERIPHERAL VASCULAR

VALLEY FORGE SURGICAL ASSOCIATES, LTD., WASFY F. FAHMY, M.D., FACS, DEBORAH M. ROSA, M.D.

General Thoracic and Endoscopic
750 S. Main St., Suite 300, Phoenixville, PA 19460; (610)935-7772.
Board-certified and diplomate in general surgery. Chest and abdominal surgery, endoscopic hernia repair.

HAIR REPLACEMENT

KEYSTONE HAIR REPLACEMENT CENTER, "THE HAIR BUILDERS," BARBARA WILSON, OWNER, STACEY SCOTT, GENERAL MANAGER
Full Cranial Prosthesis and Wigs
1544 Bristol Pike, Bensalem, PA 19020; (215)245-5556.
We make a difference! This family business specializes in all phases of hair replacement. Male/female hair additions made and serviced on premises. Complimentary consultations available.

STYL-RAMA, MICHAEL LABRIOLA
150 Allendale Rd., Bldg. 3R, King of Prussia, PA 19406.
Specializing in chemotherapy and alopecia prosthesis. Integration for thinning hair, weaving and extentions. Scalp treatments and tricoanalysis. Hairpieces and wigs for women, men and children. Private rooms, free consultation.

HAND SURGERY

ELLIOT L. AMES, DO
Hand Surgery and Microsurgery
1878 Route 70 E., Suite 5, Cherry Hill, NJ 08003; (609)751-6464.
Practice encompasses all aspects of hand surgery, including acute trauma to the hand and upper extremity, cervical spine, industrial injuries, repetitive injuries, motor vehicle accidents.

MAIN LINE HAND SURGERY P.C., STEPHEN L. CASH, M.D.
Suite 253, Lankenau Hospital, Wynnewood, PA 19096; (610)642-8823 *and* 3740 West Chester Pike, Newtown Square, PA 19073; (610)356-9358.
Certified by American Board Orthopaedic Surgery with Added Qualification Surgery of the Hand, active member of American Academy of Orthopedic Surgery, American Society for Surgery of the Hand and American Society for Reconstructive Microsurgery. Practice devoted exclusively to treatment of disorders of the hand and upper extremity. Including fractures and joint injuries, arthritis, congenital deformities, nerve-compression syndromes and injuries of tendon, nerves, ligaments. Latest techniques of microsurgery, arthroscopy and endoscopic carpal tunnel release employed. Clinical Assistant Professor of Orthopedic Surgery, Thomas Jefferson University; Chief Hand Surgeon, Lankenau Hospital. Medical Director of Outpatient Hand Clinic, Magee Rehabilitation Hospital.

JAY POMERANCE, M.D.
Hand and Mircrosurgical Specialist
5501 Old York Rd., WCB Bldg., 4th Floor, Philadelphia, PA 19141; (215)456-7900.
Fellowship trained, university affiliated, board eligible. Specializes in traumatic upper-extremity injuries (hand, wrist and elbow), work-related hand problems, arthritis, congenital hand problems and microvascular surgery.

THE HAND AND SHOULDER INSTITUTE, RICHARD J. MANDEL, M.D., DONALD F. LEATHERWOOD II, M.D.
6404 Roosevelt Blvd., Philadelphia, PA 19149; (215)744-HAND.
Board-certified orthopedic surgeons; Assistant Clinical Professors of Orthopaedic Surgery, University of Pennsylvania. Comprehensive diagnosis, rehabilitation and surgery of upper-extremity disorders. Arthritis, sports and overuse injuries and nerve problems are areas of special expertise.

HEALTH INFORMATION

TEL-MED–THE HEALTH INFORMATION SYSTEM
Pennsylvania Hospital, 800 Spruce St., Philadelphia, PA 19107-6192; (215)829-5500.
Tel-Med is a free community service provided by Pennsylvania Hospital that contains more than 360 taped messages on a variety of health topics.

HEMATOLOGY

H. JAMES DAY, M.D.
Hematology/Oncology

2701 Blair Mill Rd., Suite 16, Willow Grove, PA 19090; (215)443-8625.
Board-certified university professor. Specialties: benign and malignant hematological disorders, geriatric hemotology and oncology, thrombosis, hemostasis, hemochromatosis and chronic fatigue syndrome.

HOLISTIC MEDICINE

ACUPUNCTURE ALLIANCE
Physical Medicine and Acupuncture
1320 Race St., Second Floor Suite, Philadelphia, PA 19107; (215)567-3088.
We care for each patient individually, combining nutrition, exercise, biofeedback, hypnosis, bodywork and conventional medicine with Eastern Medicine. Foreign languages spoken: French, Spanish, Portuguese.

**NEW LIFE CENTERS, P.
JAYALAKSHMI, M.D., K.R.
SAMPATHACHER, M.D., JOHN**

BRIGHTON, M.D.
Ayurveda, Residential Panchakasma
6366 Sherwood Rd., Philadelphia, PA 19151; (215)473-4226 *and* 330 Breezewood, Lehighton, PA 18235; (215)473-7453.
New Life Center has been in existence for 15 years. Services include chelation, colonic, allergy control, stress reduction, treatment for candidiasis, chronic fatigue and all chronic diseases.

STEVEN C. HALBERT, M.D.
1442 Ashbourne Rd., Wyncote, PA 19095; (215)886-7842.
A unique medical practice that combines both traditional and alternative healing methods, including nutrition, vitamins, herbs, homeopathy and acupuncture.

IMPLANTOLOGY

RICHARD S. TOBEY, JR., D.M.D., M.S.

Prosthodontics, Periodontics
1601 Walnut St., Medical Arts Bldg., Suite 822, Philadelphia, PA 19102; (215)557-7979. For the highest level of care in a warm, personal environment, Dr. Tobey's practice specializes in implantology, dental reconstruction, periodontics and cosmetic dentistry. Foreign languages spoken: French, Polish.

INDUSTRIAL REHABILITATION

PENNSYLVANIA BACK TO WORK INSTITUTE, THEOPHILA SEMANOFF, M.D.
Physical and Rehabilitation Medicine, Physiatry
87 Steamwhistle Dr., Ivyland, PA 18974; (215)322-4577.
Specializing in rehabilitation of injuries limiting return to work status: Imes, physical therapy, functional capacity evaluations, work hardening. Affiliated with Doylestown Hospital. Located in Bucks County. Foreign language spoken: Spanish.

INFECTIOUS DISEASE

MATTHEW E. LEVISON, M.D., DONALD KAYE, M.D., OKSANA KORZENIOWSKI, M.D., CAROLINE JOHNSON, M.D., ALLAN TUNKEL, M.D.
Medical College of Pennsylvania and Medical College Hospitals, Main Clinical Campus, 3300 Henry Ave., Philadelphia, PA 19129; (215)842-6975.
Internationally recognized infectious disease specialists available for consultation services, which include Lyme Disease Center, Travel Health Center (immunizations, health conditions abroad) and HIV Clinic.

JEROME SANTORO, M.D., F.A.C.P. MARK INGERMAN, M.D., F.A.C.P. LAWRENCE L. LIVORNESE JR., M.D.
Travel Health
Lankenau Medical Bldg. E., Suite 467, Wynnewood, PA 19096; (215)896-0210.
Three-member group practice of board-certified infectious disease specialists with special interest in travel health, immunization, Lyme disease and diseases caused by infectious agents.

RUSSELL J. STUMACHER, M.D., HENRY S. FRAIMOW, M.D.
Infectious Diseases
Infectious Diseases Unit, Graduate Hospital, Pepper Pavillion, Suite 504, Philadelphia, PA 19146; (215)893-2415.
Diagnosis, treatment and prevention of adult infectious diseases: travel-related infections; Lyme disease; HIV; vaccinations; STS's; antibiotic infusion therapy; chronic fatigue syndrome.

JOAN C. WALLER, M.D., MARGARET TREXLER HESSEN, M.D., F.A.C.P.
Internal Medicine
5101 Township Line Rd., Drexel Hill, PA 19026; (610)446-5550 *and* 875 County Line Rd., Bryn Mawr, PA 19010; (610)527-9490.
Infectious disease, travel medicine, internal medicine. Board-certified. Infectious disease consultation; travel immunizations, internal medicine.

INFERTILITY

STEPHEN L. CORSON, M.D., FRANCES R. BATZER, M.D., BENJAMIN GOCIAL, M.D., MAUREEN KELLY, M.D., JACQUELINE N. GUTMANN, M.D.
815 Locust St., Philadelphia, PA 19107; (215)922-2206 *and* Suburban: 5217 Militia Hill Rd., Plymouth Meeting, PA 19462; (610)834-1230.
Philadelphia Fertility Institute. Care from puberty through menopause, focused on infertility, endocrinology, menopause, IVF and reproductive surgery.

MICHAEL E. TOAFF, M.D.
Gynecology/Reproductive Medicine
1201 County Line Rd., Bryn Mawr, PA 19010; (610)525-9999.
Bryn Mawr Hospital, board-certified, university-affiliated. All aspects of infertility, microsurgery, tubal surgery, operative laparoscopy, hysteroscopy, myomectomy, ovulation induction. Intratubal insemina-

Thomas Jefferson University

DEPARTMENT OF SURGERY

1025 Walnut Street, Philadelphia, PA 19107

Francis E. Rosato, MD, Chairman

For more than a century and a half, Jefferson surgeons have been setting standards for surgical care in this country through landmark advances in research, diagnosis and treatment.

► **Division of Cardiothoracic Surgery**................**955-5654**

Richard N. Edie, MD
John D. Mannion, MD
Thomas L. Carter, MD

► **Division of Colorectal Surgery**................**955-5869**

Robert D. Fry, MD
Gerald J. Marks, MD
Jan Rakinic, MD
John P. Bannon, MD

► **Division of General Surgery**................**955-6925**

Francis E. Rosato, MD
Donna J. Barbot, MD
James E. Colberg, MD
Murray J. Cohen, MD
Herbert E. Cohn, MD
Diane R. Gillum, MD
John C. Kairys, MD
Pauline K. Park, MD
Reuven Rabinovici, MD
Jerome J. Vernick, MD

► **Division of Pediatric Surgery**................**955-7635**

Philip J. Wolfson, MD
E. Stanton Adkins, III, MD
Aviva Katz, MD
John Noseworthy, MD

► **Division of Transplant Surgery**................**955-4888**

Michael J. Moritz, MD
John S. Radomski, MD
Vincent T. Armenti, MD, PhD

► **Division of Trauma**................**955-2600**

Jerome J. Vernick, MD
Murray J. Cohen, MD
Reuven Rabinovici, MD

► **Division of Vascular Surgery**................**955-4912**

R. Anthony Carabasi, MD
Samuel C. Aldridge, MD

Board-certified surgeons.

tion: a lower cost GIFT alternative.

MAIN LINE FERTILITY AND REPRODUCTIVE MEDICINE, WILLIAM H. PFEFFER, M.D., MICHAEL J. GLASSNER, M.D., LINDA M. CHAFFKIN, M.D.
Infertility
1 Lankenau Medical Bldg. E., Suite 563, 100 Lancaster Ave., Wynnewood, PA 19096; (610)649-0500 *and* Paoli Pointe, Suite 100, 11 Industrial Blvd., Paoli, PA 19301; (610)993-8200.
Specializing in infertility and gynecologic care in a personalized, informed and warm atmosphere. Advanced laparoscopic/hysteroscopic and microscopic surgery, insemination, IVF and GIFT. Many insurance plans accepted.

INTERNAL MEDICINE

ROMEO S. ABELLA, M.D.
Nephrology
915 E. Cayuga St., Philadelphia, PA 19124; (215)743-2250.
Practice limited to internal medicine and kidney disease including dialysis, personalized care the old-fashioned way with understanding and compassion.

JOHN JENKS, M.D.
Nutrition/Obesity Treatment
Benjamin Franklin Clinic, Public Ledger Bldg., 6th and Chestnut sts., Suite 104, Philadelphia, PA 19106; (215)925-4300.
The Benjamin Franklin Clinic specializes in the diagnosis and treatment of various metabolic and nutritional problems including cholesterol and lipid disorders, obesity, thyroid disease and early diabetes. Focus of the clinic is to prevent progression of disease.

GENE BETH BISHOP, M.D.
Internal Medicine, Women's Health
Suite 220, Medical Office Bldg., Presbyterian Medical Center, 51 N. 39th St., Philadelphia, PA 19104; (215)662-8870.
General adult internal medicine with special interest in women's health. Comprehensive care, attentive listening, "on time" office in a caring environment.

DRY MOUTH CENTER AND SJOGREN'S SYNDROME CENTER
Dry Mouth Disorders
Presbyterian Medical Center, 39th *and* Market sts., Philadelphia, PA 19104; (215)662-9292.
Frederick B. Vivino, M.D., is Director of this center dedicated to diagnosing and managing Sjogren's syndrome and other dry-mouth conditions, using innovative and traditional techniques.

PINE MEDICAL ASSOCIATES OF PENNSYLVANIA HOSPITAL, ROSALIND KAPLAN, M.D., FRANCI KRAMAN, M.D., JENNIFER NIZEN, M.D., KATALIN ROTH, M.D., JULIE UFFNER, M.D.
Women's Health
191 Presidential Blvd., Suite W-1, Bala Cynwyd, PA 19004; (610)667-1034.
Board-certified specialists in internal and geriatric medicine specializing in the treatment of adults and adolescents with an emphasis on preventive care and women's health.

JEFFERSON INTERNAL MEDICINE ASSOCIATES, GENO J. MERLI, M.D., DIRECTOR
Department of Medicine, Thomas Jefferson University, Walnut Towers, 211 S. 9th St., Suite 300, Philadelphia, PA 19107; (215)955-6180.
Board-certified physicians providing patient-focused primary-care adult medicine; offering personalized care with the advantages of a major medical center.

MEDICAL AND DIAGNOSTIC CENTER, RICHARD KONES, M.D., PH.D.
1525 Locust St., Philadelphia, PA 19102-3732; (215)545-4444.
Allergy, lung, heart, metabolic, blood, hormone and nutritional analysis; infections, fatigue and general medical ailments are treated. A refreshingly sophisticated, thorough, caring and personalized approach.

Scientific, comprehensive yet personal treatment of the entire patient.

**BRADLEY W. FENTON, M.D.,
STEVEN A. SILBER, M.D.**
Presbyterian Medical Center, 39th and Market sts., Suite 260, Medical Office Bldg., Philadelphia, PA 19104; (215)662-8347.
Board-certified internists providing health promotion and prevention, primary care and consultations for complex or perplexing internal medicine problems with a caring, individualized approach.

**ANDREW R. SCHWARTZ, M.D.,
JOHN KIRBY, M.D.**
Infectious Diseases
6 E. Miami Ave., Cherry Hill, NJ 08034; (609)428-1800.
We care for the whole person! Specialty care in internal medicine and infectious diseases in the office and in the hospital. We provide special understanding for the mature adult.

EUGENE E. VOGIN, M.D., PH.D.
Geriatrics
2682 Welsh Rd., Philadelphia, PA 19152; (215)464-7689.
Adult medicine, minor procedures, X-rays, physical therapy. Staffed at three hospitals. Hours by appointment. Friendly staff. Conveniently located between I-95 and Roosevelt Blvd. All insurance plans accepted.

MAMMOGRAPHY

DIAGNOSTIC BREAST CENTER
Mammography and Breast Ultrasound
101 Bryn Mawr Ave., Suite 201, Bryn Mawr, PA 19010; (610)520-0900.
The Diagnostic Breast Center, located in Bryn Mawr, PA, was developed to provide women with mammogram and ultrasound examinations in a private, personal atmosphere, utilizing the most modern approach to the diagnosis of breast diseases.

MEDICAL GENETICS

JEFFERSON MEDICAL GENETICS
Perinatal Genetics

1100 Walnut St., Philadelphia, PA 19107; (215)955-6955.
Jefferson's medical genetics program provides comprehensive diagnostic management and counseling services for inherited diseases and birth defects, including prenatal diagnosis and genetic testing.

NEPHROLOGY

**CLINICAL NEPHROLOGY
ASSOCIATES, LTD., JOSEPH H.
BREZIN, M.D., ARTHUR R. OLSHAN,
M.D., PH.D., LARRY E. KREVOLIN,
D.O., M. BLANCHE LTM, M.D.,
MARIA MENDEZ, M.D., ANNA
DUBYANSKITE, M.D.**
Clinical Nephrology
205 N. Broad St., Suite 600, Philadelphia, PA 19107; (215)762-8053.
All kidney problems, high blood pressure, kidney failure, stones, infections, dialysis, transplantation. Board-certified. On staff–Hahnemann University, St. Agnes Medical Center, Episcopal Hospitals. All insurances accepted. Foreign language spoken: Spanish.

**JEFFERSON RENAL ASSOCIATES,
JAMES F. BURKE JR., M.D.,
DIRECTOR**
Division of Nephrology, Thomas Jefferson University, 111 S. 11th St., Suite 7320, Philadelphia, PA 19107; (215)955-6550.
Board-certified physicians treat all kidney problems; high blood pressure; kidney failure, stones, infections, dialysis and transplantation.

NEUROLOGY

**DEPARTMENT OF NEUROLOGY,
THOMAS JEFFERSON UNIVERSITY,
ROBERT J. SCHWARTZMAN, M.D.,
CHAIRMAN, FRED D. LUBLIN, M.D.,
PATRICIO F. REYES, M.D.,
ROBERT L. KNOBLER, M.D., PH.D.,
RODNEY D. BELL, M.D.,
LEOPOLD J. STRELETZ, M.D.,
RICHARD A. CHAMBERS, M.D.,
TERRY D. HEIMAN-PATTERSON,**

**M.D., MICHAEL E. SHY, M.D.,
ALBERT J. TAHMOUSH, M.D.,
FRANCA CAMBI, M.D.**
Benjamin Franklin House, 9th and Chestnut
sts., Suite 420, Philadelphia, PA 19107;
(215)955-6692.
Distinctive, personalized attention given to
all phases of neurological treatment by a staff
of board-certified and caring physicians. By
appointment only.

**MEDICAL COLLEGE OF PENNSYL-
VANIA, SLEEP DISORDERS CENTER**
Neurology and Sleep Disorders
3200 Henry Ave., Sleep Disorders Center,
Philadelphia, PA 19129; (215)842-4250.
Thorough, cost-effective sleep disorders
diagnosis and treatment by board-certified
specialists, Drs. June M. Fry and Rochelle
Goldberg, in accredited sleep disorders cen-
ter.

**NEUROLOGY ASSOCIATES, DRS. M.
MOSTER, J. BURKE, M. ZALEWSKA,
M. FAYNBERG, N. VOLPE, G.
HOROWITZ, S. SILLIMAN, M.
MCGLAMERY**
Neuro-ophthalmology
5401 Old York Rd., Klein Bldg., Suite 300,
Philadelphia, PA 19141; (215)456-7290.
Board-certified physicians providing care in
neurology including neuro-ophthalmology,
neuromuscular, stroke, behavioral, epilepsy
and pain. Neurodiagnostics: EEG, EMG,
EPs, brain mapping and oculomotor-ENG.

NEUROSURGERY

**LEONARD A. BRUNO, M.D.,
GENE SALKIND, M.D.,
MURRAY D. ROBINSON, M.D.**
1601 Walnut St., Suite 908, Philadelphia, PA
19102; (215)843-8908.
Practice of neurosurgery, cranial, spinal, and
peripheral nerve operations, including
microsurgical and stereotactic techniques.
Hours by appointment (215)843-8908.

**THE SPINECENTER, MAURICE
ROMY, M.D., BOARD-CERTIFIED
NEUROSURGEON, MEDICAL**

DIRECTOR
1911 Arch St., Philadelphia, PA 19103;
(215)665-8300, (800)950-PAIN.
An outpatient diagnostic and treatment center specializing in spine, disc and pain management. Accredited by the American
Academy of Pain Management. Foreign languages spoken: Spanish, Italian, French.

OB/GYN

**DRS. BOLTON, VAUGHN & RONNER,
INC.**
700 Spruce St., Suite B-01, Philadelphia, PA
19106; (215)829-7400.
Four-physician practice, Pennsylvania
Hospital. All board-certified. Offices in Bala
Cynwyd and Haddonfield, NJ. Comprehensive obstetric/gynecologic services,
menopausal care, gynecologic surgery, operative laparoscopy.

**JUNIATA WOMEN'S HEALTH,
CAROLYN SHAW, M.D.**
Juniata Medical Arts Bldg., 1216 E. Hunting
Park Ave., Philadelphia, PA 19124;
(215)553-8080.
Comprehensive obstetric and gynecologic
care including menopausal care and gyneco-
logic surgery. Most insurances accepted.

**VANGUARD OB/GYN ASSOCIATES,
P.C., SAUL JECK, D.O.**
Graduate Health Systems - City Ave.
Hospital, Rowland Hall, 4190 City Ave.,
Suite 411, Philadelphia, PA 19131; (215)871-
1144.
Comprehensive gynecologic care including
menopausal care and gynecologic surgery.
Most insurances accepted.

**JOHN B. FRANKLIN, M.D.,
ASSOCIATES, GANDHI NELSON,
M.D., ADELE O'NEILL, CNM, CINDY
CULLEN, CNM, JUDY POLITZER,
CNM, CAROL VEDDOR, CNM,
ELIZABETH HARMON, RNC**
2119 N. 63rd St., Philadelphia, PA 19151;
(215)878-7870.
Comprehensive obstetric and gynecologic
care including menopausal care and gyneco-

logic surgery. Four nurse midwives available. Most insurances accepted.

WOMEN'S HEALTH OF ROXBOROUGH, NEIL E. SLOANE, M.D., PHILIP J. HORN, JR., M.D., PATRICIA A. LOKEY, M.D., W. SOYINI POWELL, M.D., MARY ANN HORN, MSN, RNC

Roxborough Memorial Hospital, 5735 Ridge Ave., Suite 104, Philadelphia, PA 19128; (215)483-7701 and Andorra Shopping Center, Ridge Ave. and Cathedral Rd., Philadelphia, PA 19128; (215)482-7979. Comprehensive obstetric and gynecologic care, including menopausal care and gynecologic surgery. Most insurances accepted.

VANGUARD OB/GYN ASSOCIATES, P.C., NEIL E. SLOANE, M.D., PHILIP J. HORN, JR., M.D., PATRICIA A. LOKEY, M.D., W. SOYINI POWELL, M.D., MARY ANN HORN, MSN, RNC

Carlton House, 1819 JFK Blvd., Suite 210, Philadelphia, PA 19103; (215)564-2545 and Graduate Health Systems - City Ave. Hospital, Rowland Hall, 4190 City Ave., Suite 315, Philadelphia, PA 19128; (215)871-1970 and Germantown Hospital & Medical Center, One Penn Blvd., Suite 100, Philadelphia, PA 19144; (215)848-5500. Comprehensive obstetric and gynecologic care including menopausal care and gynecologic surgery. Most insurances accepted.

MONTGOMERY OB/GYN ASSOCIATES, VALERIE RILEY, M.D., GRACE ADOLFO, M.D.

Montgomery Hospital, 1330 Powell St., Suite 507, Norristown, PA 19401; (215)279-9003. Comprehensive obstetric and gynecologic care including menopausal care and gynecologic surgery. Most insurances accepted.

ABINGTON PERINATAL ASSOCIATES, PC, LINDA K. DUNN,

M.D., FRANK J. CRAPARO, M.D., RICHARD A. LATTA, M.D., STEPHEN J. SMITH, M.D.
Maternal-Fetal Medicine and Genetics
Abington Memorial Hospital, 1200 Old York Rd., Suite 111R, Abington, PA 19001; (215)572-5270.
Consultation and management services for women with complicated pregnancies and serious maternal illnesses. Comprehensive ultrasound services, prenatal diagnostic procedures (CVS, amnio, PUBS) and genetic counseling are offered. Foreign language spoken: Spanish.

BI-COUNTY OB/GYN ASSOCIATION. DR. LESTER A. RUPPERSBERGER, D.O., F.A.C. O.O.G., DR. NEIL D. BLUEBOND, D.O., F.A.C.O.O.G.
404 Middletown Blvd., Suite 305, Langhorne, PA 19047; (215)750-6611.
Drs. L. Ruppersberger and N. Bluebond are both board-certified Obstetricians and Gynecologists. They engage in a progressive practice in the lower Bucks County area, which provides total women's health care.

NEIL P. CAMPBELL, M.D., F.A.C.O.G.
Urogynecology (Female Urinary Incontinence)
The Courtyard at Oxford Valley, Suite 100, 300 Middletown Blvd., Langhorne, PA 19047; (215)547-2670.
Advanced laser laparoscopy; advanced hysteroscopy and endometrial ablation.

DELLA BADIA & PODOLSKY, PC
Offices in Blackwood, NJ, Center City and South Philadelphia; (215)271-8000.
Drs. Carl Della Badia, Michael Podolsky, Lisa Turri and Martin Zeluck specialize in the practice of OB/GYN with expertise in laser and all laparoscopic surgery, including laparoscopic hysterectomy and endometrial ablation.

THE GRADUATE HOSPITAL DEPARTMENT OF GYNECOLOGY, THOMAS V. SEDLACEK, M.D., CHAIRMAN, FRANCIS L. HUTCHINS, **JR., M.D., VICE-CHAIRMAN, MICHAEL J. CAMPION, M.D., MITCHELL D. GREENBERG, M.D., VINCENT M. VACCARO, M.D., SHARON DERSTINE, C.R.N.P., SUSAN SPADT, C.R.N.P., M.S.N., RANDY HUTCHINS, P.A.-C.**
One Graduate Plaza, Suite 805, 1800 Lombard St., Philadelphia, PA 19146; (215)893-5477.
Expertise in general gynecology, gynecologic oncology and gynecologic surgery.

MANGAN RIVA GYNECOLOGIC ONCOLOGY, ASSOC. CHARLES E. MANGAN, M.D., RICHARD Z. BELCH, M.D., ROBERT L. GIUNTOLI, SR., M.D., TIMOTHY B. MCGUINNESS, D.O.
Two Independence Place, 233 S. 6th St., Philadelphia, PA 19106; (215)627-8500.
Emphasis on pelvic cancer, difficult gynecologic surgical procedures, abnormal pap smears needing coloscopy, prevention and research. High-risk patients (i.e.: family cancer syndrome) encouraged. Foreign languages spoken: Spanish, Polish, Italian, Vietnamese, Chinese and Korean (upon request).

DAVID IDDENDEN MEDICAL PRACTICE
Infertility and Reproductive Endocrinology
1328 Ritner St., Philadelphia, PA 19148; (215)336-2896.
Warm and friendly practice specializing in gynecology, infertility and reproductive endocrinology. Personalized attention is a priority in our practice; we employ caring, supportive individuals who are constantly working to make your experience with us a pleasant and rewarding one. Our staff is assisted by a full-time nurse practitioner. Our practice offers state-of-the-science laparoscopic services. We are a close affiliate of Thomas Jefferson University Hospital.

LINDA C. WILSON, M.D., DONALD F. WILSON, M.D., CHRISTINE W. LYONS, M.D., CAROL COLDREN, M.D.
Brandywine Professional Bldg., 213

Reeceville Rd., Suite 17, Coatesville, PA 19320; (215)383-9400.
Board-certified gynecologists specializing in the management of pregnancy and complete gynecologic care, including surgery, infertility, operative laparoscopy and hysteroscopy.

WOMAN TO WOMAN CARE, P.C., ROBYN R. JONES, M.D., F.A.C.O.G., LYNDA T. THOMAS, M.D., F.A.C.O.G.
40 West Evergreen Ave., Suite 101-102, Philadelphia, PA 19118; (215)242-4442.
We provide personalized care with an emphasis on education. This allows each of our patients to share in the decision-making process regarding their obstetric and gynecologic well-being.

NATHAN J. ZUCKERMAN, M.D., F.A.C.O.G.
1205 Langhorne-Newtown Rd., Suite 311, Langhorne, PA 19047; (215)752-8039.
General obstetrics and gynecology with interest in modern gynecological procedures, i.e., advanced laparoscopy (LAVH, removal of fibroids, endometriosis) and advanced hysteroscopy (endometrial ablation and resection of fibroids).

OCCUPATIONAL MEDICINE

CENTRAMED, HAROLD F. SHUSTER, M.D., JOHN R. DUDA, M.D., RICHARD J. MANDEL, M.D., DONALD F. LEATHERWOOD II, M.D.
Orthopedics
630 Fairview Rd., Suite 100, Swarthmore, PA 19081; (215)690-1050.
Industrial medicine specialists serving the Delaware Valley for over 10 years. Full range of services including ortho, general medicine. P.T., O.T. Injury prevention and employment screening.

CENTRAMED. RICHARD J. MANDEL, M.D., JOHN R. DUDA, M.D.,

DONALD F. LEATHERWOOD II, M.D., HAROLD F. SHUSTER, M.D.

6404 Roosevelt Blvd., Philadelphia, PA 19149 *and* 2 Penn Blvd., Philadelphia, PA 19144 *and* 625 Chester Rd., Swarthmore, PA 19081; (800)249-CMED.

Aggressive, quality medical treatment for work-related injuries; injury prevention and post-offer screenings; managed care programs for work-related injuries; case management. Independent medical evaluations. Interpretation available on request.

INDUSTRIAL HEALTHCARE CENTER. DENNIS J. BONNER, M.D., RITA A. MARIOTTI, M.D.

1854 New Rodgers Rd., Route 413, Levittown, PA 19056; (215)750-6426.

Specializing in occupational/industrial medicine; treatment of work-related injuries. D.O.T. physicals, executive health screens, substance-abuse testing, physical therapy, x-ray, work hardening, IMEs, lab, etc. Foreign languages spoken: Spanish, Italian.

JEFFERSON OCCUPATIONAL AND ENVIRONMENTAL MEDICINE PROGRAM, LANCE SIMPSON, PH.D., DIRECTOR

Environmental Medicine

Department of Medicine, Thomas Jefferson University, 111 S. 11th St., Suite 4240, Philadelphia, PA 19107; (215)955-2471.

Board-certified physicians provide diagnosis and treatment for individuals exposed to hazardous chemicals, as well as preventive medical surveillance for entire workplace populations.

PHILADELPHIA ARTHRITIS INSTITUTE, ARTHRITIS ASSOCIATES, PRESBYTERIAN MEDICAL CENTER

Arthritis and Rheumatism

39th and Market sts., Philadelphia, PA 19104; (215)662-9292.

Drs. Warren A. Katz, Fredrick B. Vivino, David A. Allan, experienced board-certified specialists in multidisciplinary approaches to all forms of arthritis, connective tissue diseases, lower back problems, rheumatic occu-

pational medicine, gout and fibrositis.

BARRY M. KOTLER, M.D., F.A.C.D.E.M.

6320 Stenton Ave., Philadelphia, PA 19138; (215)224-7775.

I have been in practice for 33 years. I see patients who have occupational problems and I do evaluations on-site and in my office. A full physical-therapy department on site of office. I am a Senior Aviation Medical Examiner as well as a medical review officer.

ONCOLOGY

FOX CHASE CANCER CENTER, ROBERT C. YOUNG, M.D., F.A.C.P., PRESIDENT, BURTON I. EISENBERG, M.D., F.A.C.S., CHAIRMAN, SURGICAL ONCOLOGY, PAUL F. ENGSTROM, M.D., F.A.C.P., SENIOR VICE PRESIDENT, POPULATION SCIENCE, GERARD E. HANKS, M.D., F.A.C.R., CHAIRMAN, RADIATION ONCOLOGY, ROBERT F. OZOLS, M.D., PH.D., VICE PRESIDENT, MEDICAL SCIENCE

7701 Burholme Ave., Philadelphia, PA 19111; (215)728-2570.

Fox Chase Cancer Center is one of 27 National Cancer Institute-designated comprehensive cancer centers in the nation. The Center's activities include basic and clinical research; prevention, detection and treatment of cancer; and community outreach programs.

ONCOLOGY/HEMATOLOGY

I. BRODSKY ASSOCIATES, I. BRODSKY, M.D., S. BENHAM KAHN, M.D., JAMES F. CONROY, D.O., PAMELA CRILLEY, D.O., DAVID TOPOLSKY, M.D., MICHAEL J. STYLER, M.D.

Broad and Vine sts. Philadelphia, PA 19102; (215)762-7735.

All physicians are certified in hematology/oncology. They are dedicated to state-of-the-art management of hematologic malignancies and solid tumors, including bone-marrow transplants.

OPHTHALMOLOGY

KARP- GOLDMAN EYE ASSOCIATES, P.C.; LOUIS A. KARP, M.D., F.A.C.S.; STEPHEN M. GOLDMAN, M.D.
Suite 100, Garfield Duncan Bldg., 700 Spruce St., Philadelphia, PA 19106; (215)829-5311.
A general ophthalmology practice affiliated with Pennsylvania Hospital. Special interests: cataract and implant surgery, glaucoma management including laser and surgery, refractive surgery and contact-lens care.

ACCUVISION ASSOCIATES, RALPH S. SANDO, M.D., CHARLES G. STEINMETZ, III, M.D., BENJAMIN H. BLOOM, M.D., PRATIMA R. TOLAT, M.D.
Cataract, Glaucoma and Refractive Surgery
913 Walnut St., Philadelphia, PA 19107; (215)627-1515 *and* 100 Church Rd., Ardmore, PA 19003; (610)649-7616.
Wills Eye Hospital staff ophthalmologists in modern offices, with free parking adjacent and caring staff, offer latest and full range of eye services. Most HMO's and insurances accepted. Foreign languages spoken: Spanish, French, Italian, German, Hindi.

IGNATIUS S. HNELESKI, JR., M.D., RAYMOND R. JONES, M.D., RICHARD B. KENT, M.D.
Eye Surgery
845 West Chester Pike, West Chester, PA 19382; (610)692-8100.
Board-certified ophthalmic surgeons. Fellowship-trained retina and oculoplastic specialists. Small-incision cataract surgery. In-office laser and radial keratotomy.

DANIEL MERRICK KANE, M.D., F.A.C.S.
Wills Eye Hospital, 9th and Walnut sts. Philadelphia, PA 19107; (215)352-1166, (215)352-4457, (215)688-2733.
Excimer laser refractive surgery for near-

sightedness and astigmatism. Surgical correction of cataract with implant, second opinion, especially for implant difficulties.

MICHAEL L. KAY, M.D., JANINE G. TABAS, M.D.
Cataract/Implant/Refractive Surgery
130 S. 9th St., Philadelphia, PA 19107; (215)925-6402 *and* 102 Bala Ave., Bala Cynwyd, PA; (215)667-6760.
Specializing in outpatient no-stitch cataract implant surgery and radial keratotomy. Caring office, most insurance accepted. Named by *Philadelphia Magazine* in "Top Doctors" issue.

FREDERIC B. KREMER, M.D.
Offices in Philadelphia, Radnor, Pottstown, Hatboro; 1-800-432-EYES.
Specialists in eye surgery. Refractive surgery to eliminate glasses and contact lenses. Cataract surgery; no needles or sutures with lens implantation. Glaucoma surgery. Transportation available.

RETINA AND DIABETIC EYE SPECIALISTS, LEONARD H. GINSBURG, M.D., C.D.E., MICHAEL COLUCCIELLO, M.D.
Mercy Haverford Hospital, Retina and Diabetic Eye Institute, Havertown, PA (off Route 476), Crozer-Chester Medical Center, Abington Memorial Hospital, Fitzgerald Mercy Hospital; (610)449-0400.
Board-certified retina specialists concentrating in treatment of diabetic retinopathy, age-related macular degeneration and retinal detachments. Outpatient laser surgery and retinal microsurgery utilizing superior technology. Convenient location and personalized treatment.

NAIDOFF ALTMAN EYE HEALTH ASSOCIATES
1100 Walnut St., Suite 603, Philadelphia, PA 19107; (215)922-2455.
Drs. Michael A. Naidoff and Adam J. Altman. Board-certified ophthalmologists specializing in cataract and corneal surgery including radial keratotomy. Consultations

and second opinions are available. Our offices are located in Center City and Philadelphia. Listed in *Philadelphia Magazine's* "Top Doctors" issue, 1991.

IRVING M. RABER, M.D.

Suite 158, Lankenau MOB E., Wynnewood, PA 19096; (610)649-7000.
Practice limited to cornea, anterior segment and refractive surgery, and external eye disease. Offices located at Lankenau and Wills Eye Hospitals and Marlton, NJ.

JERRY A. SHIELDS, M.D.

Ocular Oncology
Wills Eye Hospital, 900 Walnut St., Philadelphia, PA 19107; (215)928-3105.
World-renowned eye specialist in the field of eye cancer and ocular tumors. Written authoritative textbooks on intraocular tumors and orbital tumors.

SURGICAL EYE CARE LTD.
STEVEN B. SIEPSER, M.D.,
ANDREA H. FRIEDBERG, M.D.

Eye Surgery
91 Chestnut Rd., Paoli, PA 19301; (215)296-3333.
Excimer laser and refractive surgery. Practice limited to anterior segment surgery.
Corrections of nearsightedness and astigmatism using composite refractive techniques along with anterior segment reconstructive surgery for injured/damaged eyes and problems with previous surgery. Laser and surgical treatment of glaucoma, corneal transplantation, adjustment of astigmatism, intraocular lens exchanges, and reconstructive techniques to obtain good vision without glasses.

SOLL EYE ASSOCIATES

5001 Frankford Ave., Philadelphia, PA 19124; (215)288-5000.
Internationally recognized eye physicians providing medical and surgical care for: cataracts, glaucoma, retina problems, pediatric eye care, eye plastic surgery, low vision and laser therapy.

GEORGE L. SPAETH, M.D.,

L. JAY KATZ, M.D.,
ANNETTE K. TEREBUH, M.D.

900 Walnut St., Philadelphia PA, 19107; (215)928-3197.
Specializing in the diagnosis and management of patients with glaucoma and associated conditions, including cataracts.

ORTHOPEDIC SURGERY

ABINGTON ORTHOPEDIC SPECIALISTS, PC.

Spine Care, Sports Medicine
1327 Old York Rd., Abington, PA 19001; (215)885-1112.
Eight physicians specializing in spine sports, reconstructive, industrial and rehabilitation medicine, physical therapy, work hardening. New 34,000 sq. ft. Regional Orthopedic Center opens August 1994.

DAVID J. ADAMS, M.D.

27 S. Bryn Mawr Ave., Bryn Mawr, PA 19010; (610)525-1261.
Temple graduate with 20 years experience in total joint-replacement surgery and general orthopedic care. Special expertise in spinal surgery. Team physician for Villanova University.

HAHNEMANN ORTHOPAEDIC ASSOCIATES, P.C., ARNOLD T. BERMAN, M.D.

Joint Replacements & Adult Reconstruction
221 N. Broad St., Philadelphia, PA, 19102; (800)762-8500.
Internationally known for total hip, knee replacements and other adult reconstructive orthopedic surgery for arthritis. Professor and Chairman, Department of Orthopaedic Surgery and Rehabilitation, Hahnemann University Hospital.

ROBERT E. BOOTH, JR., M.D.

Total Joint Replacement. Knee Revisions
Rothman Institute, 800 Spruce St., Philadelphia, PA 19107; (215)829-3458.
Practice specializes in problems of the knee and hip, with emphasis on surgical reconstruction of these areas. Foreign language spoken: French.

Thomas Jefferson University

DEPARTMENT OF PEDIATRICS

Robert L. Brent, MD, PhD, Chairman

Philadelphia families who want excellent general and specialty physician care for their children can find it at Jefferson.

▶ **Allergy & Clinical Immunology............955-6504**
Stephen J. McGeady, MD
Denise A. Di Primio-Kalman, DO
Herbert C. Mansmann Jr., MD

▶ **Child Neurology & Development 955-6940**
Leonard J. Graziani, MD
Peter R. Kollros, MD, PhD
Jeannette C. Mason, MD
Charles B. Brill, MD......955-2400

▶ **Child Psychiatry 955-6822**
Ruth P. Zager, MD

▶ **Gastroenterology & Nutrition.................955-7624**
Ian S. E. Gibbons, MD

▶ **General Pediatrics ..955-6755**
Allan R. DeJong, MD
Clara A. Callahan, MD
Ira H. Strassman, MD
Charles A. Pohl, MD

▶ **Metabolism & Endocrinology.........955-1648**
Judith L. Ross, MD
Gary Carpenter, MD 955-6822

▶ **Neonatology 955-6523**
Alan R. Spitzer, MD
Susan C. Adeniyi-Jones, MD
Michael J. Antunes, MD
Stephen Baumgart, MD
Hemant J. Desai, MD
Shobhana A. Desai, MD
Eric Gibson, MD
Jay S. Greenspan, MD
Michael S. Kornhauser, MD
Thomas E. Wiswell, MD
Barbara D. Ianni, DO....952-9997

▶ **Nephrology 955-6755**
Ruth P. Gottlieb, MD

▶ **Pediatric Cardiology...............955-7670**
Eshagh Eshaghpour, MD
Paul C. Anisman, MD
Bradley W. Robinson, MD

▶ **Pediatric Critical Care.............955-1533**
Louis J. Guernsey Jr., MD
Harry J. Sacks, MD
Rosa A. Vidal, MD

▶ **Pulmonology...........955-6504**
Louis H. Guernsey Jr., MD

These telephone numbers are for outpatient offices in the Clinical Office Building, 2nd Floor, 909 Walnut Street, Philadelphia, PA 19107. Please contact the desired specialty for information about satellite offices located at the Alfred I. duPont Institute, (Wilmington, DE) Allentown Hospital, Bryn Mawr Hospital, Crozer-Chester Medical Center (Upland, PA), Delaware County Memorial Hospital (Drexel Hill, PA) and Holy Redeemer Medical Center (Meadowbrook, PA). • *Board-certified physicians.*

NICHOLAS A. DI NUBILE, M.D.
Sports Medicine, Arthroscopic Surgery
Office in Havertown, PA; (610)789-0150.
Practice focus: Knee disorders (injuries,
rehabilitation, arthroscopy, surgery). Special
advisor, President's Council on Physical
Fitness and Sports. Orthopedist,
Pennsylvania Ballet. Faculty, Hospital of the
University of Pennsylvania.

WILLIAM D. EMPER, M.D.
27 S. Bryn Mawr Ave., Bryn Mawr, PA
19010, (215)527-1762.
Practice of general orthopedic surgery specializing in sports medicine, arthroscopic
surgery and joint replacement; surgery of the
knee and shoulder. Team physician for
Villanova University.

GARY NEIL GOLDSTEIN, M.D.
Plastic Surgery and Hand Surgery
600 Somerdale Rd., #215, Voorhees, NJ
08043; (609)795-8884.
Only combined board-certified orthopedic
and plastic surgeon in Philadelphia area.
Specializing in carpel tunnel, cosmetic
surgery and arthroscopic spine surgery.

RONALD B. GREENE, M.D.
Arthroscopic Surgery, Joint Reconstruction
Suite 2205 Medical Towers, 255 S. 17th St.,
Philadelphia, PA 19103; (215)735-6104.
Arthroscopic surgery, including percuta-
neous lumbar disk surgery and TMJ
arthroscopy; nerve compression syndromes,
including carpal tunnel syndrome, and joint
replacement and reconstruction.

**JEFFERSON ORTHOPAEDIC
ASSOCIATES, JEROME M. COTLER,
M.D., PAUL J. HECHT, M.D., B.
DAVID HORN, M.D., ERIC L. HUME,
M.D., PETER D. PIZZUTILLO, M.D.,
ALEXANDER R. VACCARO, M.D.,
KEITH L. WAPNER, M.D.**
Department of Orthopaedic Surgery,
Thomas Jefferson University, 850 Walnut
St., Philadelphia, PA 19107; (215)955-6688.
Board-certified specialists in spinal disorders,
hip and knee replacement, foot and ankle
surgery and pediatric orthopedic surgery.

**JOYCE AND CAUTILLI
PROFESSIONAL ASSOCIATION,
MICHAEL F. JOYCE, M.D., RICHARD
A. CAUTILLI, SR., M.D.,
JAMES V. MACKELL, JR., M.D.,
RICHARD A. CAUTILLI, JR., M.D.,
GEORGE P. CAUTILLI, M.D.**
Sports Medicine, Joint Replacement
7922 Bustleton Ave., Philadelphia, PA 19152;
(215)725-8500 *and* St. Mary Medical Office
Bldg., Suite #308, Langhorne, PA 19047;
(215)750-3625.
Experienced professionals utilize conserva-
tive management combined with specialized
treatment of joint, back, foot and hand
problems, sports-related injuries and frac-
tures.

MARY ANN KEENAN, M.D.
Neuromuscular Orthopedic Specialist
5501 Old York Rd., WCB Bldg., 4th Flr.,
Philadelphia, PA 19141; (215)456-7900.
Internationally recognized, university-affiliated, board-certified. Specializes in neuromuscular orthopedic problems with patients
with brain injury, stroke, post-polio syndrome, cerebral palsy and spinal cord injury.

**NORRISTOWN ORTHOPAEDIC
ASSOCIATES, INC. ARLO C.
ANDERSON, M.D., JAMES N. NUTT,
III, M.D., JOHN J. NEVULIS, M.D.,
EVAN S. KOVALSKY, M.D., JOSEPH
NOAH, M.D.**
1308 DeKalb St., Norristown, PA 19401;
(610)279-8686, (800)287-8685.
Our board-certified orthopedic surgeons
with fellowship training in total joint, hand
and spinal surgery and sports medicine have
been serving the Montgomery County community 24 hours a day for over 40 years.

**ORTHOPEDIC ASSOCIATES, P.C.,
MILTON A. WOHL, M.D.,
DAVID R. PASHMAN, M.D.,
ROBERT E. LIEBENBERG, M.D.,
VICTOR R. FRANKEL, M.D.,
JONATHAN BROMBERG, M.D.**
Klein Professional Office Bldg., 5401 Old
York Rd., Suite 200, Philadelphia, PA 19141;

(215)456-9400 *and* Warminster Medical Office Center, 205 Newtown Rd., Suite 103, Warminster, PA 18974; (215)672-3800 *and* Einstein Center One, 9880 Bustleton Ave., Suite 201-202, Philadelphia, PA 19115; (215)677-9140.

Specializing in total joint surgery, spine surgery, arthroscopic surgery and sports medicine, occupational injuries and arthritis, osteoporosis and geriatric orthopedics.

WILLIAM G. STEWART, JR., M.D.
27 S. Bryn Mawr Ave., Bryn Mawr, PA 19010; (610)527-1762.

Boston-trained general orthopedic surgeon with specialty interest in area of total joint replacement. Twenty-five years experience using the most modern technique and hospital facilities.

UNIVERSITY OF PENNSYLVANIA SHOULDER SERVICE
Reconstructive Surgery of the Shoulder

2 Silverstein Pavilion, 3400 Spruce St., Philadelphia, PA 19104; (215)349-8662.
The service includes four orthopedic surgeons specializing in the diagnosis and treatment of shoulder disorders, including rotator cuff injuries, unstable shoulders, arthroscopy and joint replacement.

STEVEN J. VALENTINO, D.O.
Orthopedic and Reconstructive Spine Surgery
Merion Bldg., 700 S. Henderson Rd., Suite 100, King of Prussia, PA 19406; (215)265-5795 *and* 2503 Lombard St., Philadelphia, PA 19146; (215)265-5795.

Board-certified orthopedic spine surgeon specializes in arthroscopic laser microdiscectomy and new reconstructive spine surgery techniques, as well as general orthopedics. He is associated with Graduate Hospital, Philadelphia and Suburban General Hospital, Norristown, and has offices in Philadelphia and King of Prussia, PA, as well as Cherry Hill and Blackwood, NJ.

OTOLARYNGOLOGY

DEPARTMENT OF OTOLARYNG-OLOGY-HEAD AND NECK SURGERY, WILLIAM M. KEANE, M.D., CHAIRMAN, LOUIS D. LOWRY, M.D., DIRAN O. MIKAELIAN, M.D., EDMUND A. PRIBITKIN, M.D., THOMAS O. WILLCOX, JR. M.D.

Thomas Jefferson University, 909 Walnut St., 3rd Floor, Philadelphia, PA 19107; (215)955-6760.
Board-certified faculty specializing in diagnosing and treating ear, nose and throat disorders, including head/neck cancer, sinus disease, hearing/balance disorders and snoring.

DANIEL A. NESI, M.D., ASSOCIATES
Allergy and Facial Plastic Surgery
800 West State St., Doylestown, PA 18901; (215)345-5494.
This practice offers comprehensive on-site evaluation with a certified laboratory for allergy testing and X-rays. We participate in most health-care plans. Foreign languages spoken: Italian, German.

WOLFSON AND MARLOWE ASSOCIATES, ROBERT J. WOLFSON, M.D., F.A.C.S., FRANK I. MARLOWE, M.D., F.A.C.S., STEVEN E. LADENHEIM, M.D., RAYMOND W. LESSER, M.D., SETH ZWILLENBERG, M.D., MATTHEW J. NAGORSKY, M.D., F.A.C.S., THOMAS E. BRANDEISKY, D.O.

1920 Chestnut St., Philadelphia, PA 19103; (215)561-2546 *and* Providence Medical Center, 415 S. Providence Rd., Media, PA 19063; (610)566-6117 *and* Hahnemann University Hospital, Broad and Vine sts., Philadelphia, PA 19102; (215)762-3700 *and* Medical College of Pennsylvania, 3300 Henry Ave., Philadelphia, PA 19129; (215)842-6565.
Ear, nose and throat, head and neck surgery, facial plastic and reconstructive surgery, related allergy, group practice providing comprehensive care using the latest techniques to diagnose and treat disease of the head and neck.

PAIN MANAGEMENT/ WELLNESS

BRANDYWINE VALLEY PAIN CONTROL CENTER
201 Reeceville Rd., Coatesville, PA 19320; (610)383-8489.
We perform comprehensive evaluation and management of chronic pain using state-of-the-art therapies, including: individual relaxation training, group therapy, pharmacologic means, nerve blocks, implantable pumps and spinal stimulators.

JEFFERSON PAIN CENTER, EVAN D. FRANK, M.D., PH.D., DIRECTOR
Department of Anesthesiology, Thomas Jefferson University, Benjamin Franklin House, T-150, 834 Chestnut St., Philadelphia, PA 19107; (215)955-7300.
Board-certified anesthesiologists skilled in interventional techniques provide specialized care for patients with chronic pain. Individually developed pain management programs, based on comprehensive medical evaluations.

HENRY SADEK, D.O., PETER LEIGHTON, D.C., JEFFREY COHEN, C.M.T., JACK RAQUET, R.A.
19 E. Lancaster Ave., Paoli, PA; (610)651-0840 *and* Presidential Apts., Suite D-123, Philadelphia, PA; (215)877-5600.
Specializing in pain management, chiropractic care, shiatsu therapeutic massage, biofeedback, psychological counseling, stress management, traditional acupuncture, nutrition, herbs, physical therapy- rehabilitation, exercise, hypnotherapy.

PEDIATRIC REHABILITATION MEDIC

MARK L. BATSHAW, M.D. (PHYSICIAN-IN-CHIEF), JOYCE E. MAUK, M.D., SUSAN E. LEVY, M.D., PEGGY S. EICHER, M.D., LINDA

MICHAUD, M.D., BALU ATHREYA, M.D., MARIANNE MERCUGLIANO, M.D.
3405 Civic Center Blvd., Philadelphia, PA 19104-4388; (215)895-3613.
Children's Seashore House is the nation's first hospital dedicated to helping children with physical and developmental disabilities and chronic illness achieve their full potential through excellence in patient care, research and training.

PEDIATRIC SURGERY

SCOTT P. BARTLETT, M.D.
Adult and Pediatric Plastic and Reconstructive Surgery
Hospital of the University of Pennsylvania, 10 Penn Tower, 3400 Spruce St., Philadelphia, PA 19104; (215)662-2096 *and* Children's Hospital of Philadelphia, 1st floor Wood Bldg., 34th St. and Civic Center Blvd., Philadelphia, PA 19104; (215)590-2208.
Aesthetic and reconstructive surgery of the face with emphasis on birth deformities, injuries, skin cancer and aging (facelift, eyelift, nasal surgery). Breast and general reconstructive surgery.

CHILDREN'S SURGICAL ASSOCIATES, LTD., WILLIAM P. POTSIC, M.D., STEVEN D. HANDLER, M.D., RALPH F. WETMORE, M.D., LAWRENCE W.C. TOM, M.D., MITCHELL B. AUSTIN, M.D.
Pediatric Otolaryngology
Richard Wood Bldg., Children's Hospital of Philadelphia, 34th St. and Civic Center Blvd., Philadelphia, PA 19104; (215)590-3440.
Pediatric surgical specialty care in ear, nose and throat disorders.

DENIS S. DRUMMOND, M.D., DIRECTOR, RICHARD S. DAVIDSON, M.D., JOHN P. DORMANS, M.D., JOHN R. GREGG, M.D., MALCOLM L. ECKER, M.D., BONG S. LEE, M.D.
Children's Hospital office; (215)590-1527 *and* King of Prussia office; (215)337-3232.

The Division of Orthopaedic Surgery provides diagnostic evaluation and treatment of all orthopedic conditions in children and adolescents, including spinal and foot deformities, sports injuries, tumors and chronic disorders. Office hours: Monday through Friday, 8:00 a.m.- 4:30 p.m.

JOHN W. DUCKETT, M.D., HOWARD M. SNYDER, III, M.D., STEPHEN A. ZDERIC, M.D., DOUGLAS A. CANNING, M.D.
Pediatric Urology
Richard D. Wood Ambulatory Care Center, Children's Hospital of Philadelphia, 34th St. and Civic Center Blvd., Philadelphia, PA 19104; (215)590-2754.
Complete pediatric urological care and evaluation, including all renal, bladder, and genital abnormalities. The D.O.V.E. (dysfunctional outpatient voiding education) Center provides comprehensive care for children with urinary incontinence.

DAVID W. LOW, M.D.
Adult and Pediatric Plastic and Reconstructive Surgery
Hospital of the University of Pennsylvania, 10 Penn Tower, 3400 Spruce St., Philadelphia, PA 19104; (215)662-2040 *and* Children's Hospital of Philadelphia, 1st floor Wood Bldg., 34th St. and Civic Center Blvd., Philadelphia, PA 19104; (215)590-2208.
General adult and pediatric plastic and reconstructive surgery practice, including microsurgery, laser surgery, hair transplantation, treatment of hemangiomas and vascular malformations, cleft lip and palate.

DON LAROSSA, M.D.
Adult and Pediatric Plastic and Reconstructive Surgery
Hospital of the University of Pennsylvania, 10 Penn Tower, 3400 Spruce St., Philadelphia, PA 19104; (215)662-2044 *and* Children's Hospital of Philadelphia, 1st floor Wood Bldg., 34th St.and Civic Center Blvd., Philadelphia, PA 19104; (215)590-2208.
Specializing in reconstructive and aesthetic surgery of the breast and face; cleft lip and palate surgery.

JAMES A. O'NEILL, JR., M.D., DIRECTOR, MARK A. HOFFMAN, M.D., HENRY T. LAU, M.D., LOUISE SCHNAUFER, M.D., PERRY W. STAFFORD, M.D., PAUL T. STOCKMANN, M.D., JOHN M. TEMPLETON, JR., M.D.
Children's Hospital of Philadelphia; (215)590-2730 *and* King of Prussia office; (215)337-3232.
A comprehensive service covering the surgical needs of children of all age groups with congenital malformations, endocrine disorders, vascular problems, tumors, injuries and various acquired conditions, including surgery and related endoscopy of the head and neck, thorax, abdomen and extremities.

MARSHALL T. PARTINGTON, M.D.
Adult and Pediatric Plastic and Reconstructive Surgery
Hospital of the University of Pennsylvania, 10 Penn Tower, 3400 Spruce St., Philadelphia, PA 19104; (215)662-7262 *and* Children's Hospital of Philadelphia, 1st floor Wood Bldg., 34th St. and Civic Center Blvd., Philadelphia, PA 19104; (215)590-2208.
General adult and pediatric plastic and reconstructive surgery, specializing in hand surgery, microsurgery and replantation.

LINTON A. WHITAKER, M.D.
Adult and Pediatric Plastic and Reconstructive Surgery
Hospital of the University of Pennsylvania, 10 Penn Tower, 3400 Spruce St., Philadelphia, PA 19104; (215)662-2048 *and* Children's Hospital of Philadelphia, 1st floor Wood Bldg., 34th St. and Civic Center Blvd., Philadelphia, PA 19104; (215)590-2208.
Plastic surgery, aesthetic and reconstructive surgery of the face with primary emphasis on aging face (face and eyelid lifts) and facial skeletal changes. Reconstructive craniofacial surgery, breast and abdominal surgery.

DAVID B. SCHAFFER, M.D., CHAIRMAN, JAMES A. KATOWITZ, M.D., GRAHAM E. QUINN, M.D., RICHARD W. HERTLE, M.D.
Pediatric Ophthalmology

Children's Hospital of Philadelphia, 34th St. and Civic Center Blvd., Philadelphia, PA 19104; (215)590-2389.
In addition to complete ophthalmological care for the full range of pediatric ophthalmological problems, the Division of Ophthalmology offers special testing not routinely available elsewhere. These include visual acuity testing for preverbal children, adult and pediatric visual fields, electroretinography, visual evoked responses, infrared oculography, ultrasonography and medical photography. In addition, there are complete oculoplastic and contact lens services.

EVELYN D. WITKIN, M.D., P.C.
Trauma and Reconstructive Surgery
643 2nd St. Pike, Southampton, PA 18966; (215)322-6683.
Practice limited to trauma fracture care, arthroscopic surgery, joint replacement, sports medicine and pediatric orthopedics! Note: X-rays on premises, and we accept most insurances.

PEDIATRICS

ROSEMARY CASEY, M.D., DIRECTOR
Children's Hospital of Philadelphia, Wood Ambulatory Center, 3rd floor, 34th St. and Civic Center Blvd., Philadelphia, PA 19104; (215)590-2178.
Unique private practice composed of five academically trained pediatricians from the University of Pennsylvania faculty. Focused on all aspects of children's health. 24-hour availability.

CHILDREN'S HEALTH CARE ASSOCIATES, INC.
Children's Hospital of Philadelphia, 34th St. and Civic Center Blvd., Philadelphia, PA 19104; (800)879-2467.
Listed in *Philadelphia Magazine*'s "Top Docs for Kids" as outstanding specialty pediatricians: allergy, cardiology, dermatology, diabetes, emergency, gastroenterology, genetics, hematology, metabolism, neonatology, nephrology, neurology, oncology, rehabilitation, general pediatrics.

CHILDREN'S PEDIATRIC CENTER, MARK SEY, M.D., F.A.A.P.

Adolescent Medicine

6608 Castor Ave., Philadelphia, PA 19149; (215)342-7711.

Board-certified pediatricians. Special interests in breast feeding and asthma management. Lots of unusual hours—very early (7 a.m.) and late (to 9 p.m.)—and we've been open for regular hours every Saturday and Sunday for the last 18 years!

COOPER PEDIATRIC ASSOCIATES, FRANK A. BRIGLIA, M.D., M.P.H., CHIEF, DEPARTMENT OF PEDIATRICS

Cooper Hospital/University Medical Center, Three Cooper Plaza, Suite 520, Camden, NJ 08103; (609)342-2546.

A multi-specialty group providing comprehensive pediatric services for all children of southern New Jersey and the Delaware Valley. For appointments or referrals please call (609)342-2546.

CAROLINE EGGERDING, M.D., CAITLIN PAPASTAMELOS, M.D.,

Developmental: Pulmonology

Voorhees Pediatric Facility, 1304 Laurel Oak Rd., Voorhees, NJ 08043; (609)846-3300.

Provide comprehensive medical care or consultation for medically fragile children with physical disabilities, pulmonary impairments and/or developmental problems.

EINSTEIN PEDIATRIC ASSOCIATES

Albert Einstein Medical Center, 5501 Old York Rd., Philadelphia, PA; (215)456-6595 *and* Einstein Center One, 9880 Bustleton Ave., Philadelphia, PA; (215)676-6060.

Professionals specializing in primary care of infants, children and adolescents, and various pediatric medical and surgical subspecialties: Adolescent medicine, allergy, behavioral pediatrics, cardiology, developmental pediatrics, specialized diagnostic imaging, endocrinology, gastroenterology, general surgery, general consultative pediatrics, genetics, hematology, infectious diseases, neonatology, neurology, ophthalmology, orthopedics, otorhinolaryngology and pul-

monology. Affiliated with Pediatric Surgical Subspecialties.

JEFFERSON ASSOCIATES IN NEONATOLOGY, ALAN SPITZER, M.D., DIRECTOR, JAY GREENSPAN, M.D., ASSOCIATE DIRECTOR, STEPHEN BAUMGART, M.D., DIRECTOR ECMO PROGRAM, SHOBHANA DESAI, M.D., DIRECTOR, NEONATAL FOLLOW-UP PROGRAM, ERIC GIBSON, M.D., DIRECTOR, INFANT APNEA PROGRAM

Newborn Medicine (Neonatology)

Thomas Jefferson University, Department of Pediatrics/College Bldg., 1025 Walnut St., Philadelphia, PA 19107; (215)955-6523.

Jefferson Associates in Neonatology offers complete comprehensive care services for the well and the critically ill newborn, with prenatal consultation for high-risk families.

THOMAS JEFFERSON UNIVERSITY CHILD & ADOLESCENT NEUROLOGY, PSYCHIATRY, AND GROWTH AND DEVELPOMENT, CHARLES B. BRILL, M.D., NEUROLOGY, GARY CARPENTER, M.D., ENDOCRINOLOGY, LEONARD J. GRAZIANI, M.D., NEUROLOGY, PETER KOLLROS, M.D., PH.D, NEUROLOGY, JEANNETTE C. MASON, M.D., DEVELOPMENTAL, RUTH P. ZAGER, M.D., PSYCHIATRY

Thomas Jefferson University, Department of Pediatrics, 909 Walnut St., Philadelphia, PA 19107; (215)955-6822/2400.

Specializing in problems including developmental and language disorders, cerebral palsy, seizures, genetic, endocrine and metabolic diseases, headaches, learning disabilities, and behavior and emotional disorders.

WILLIAM S. ZAVOD, M.D., FRANK H. KING, JR., M.D.

2400 Chestnut St., lobby level, Philadelphia, PA 19103; (215)567-PEDS and 100 Church Rd., Suite 300, Ardmore, PA 19003; (610)896-8582.

Closely-knit, two-person, academically oriented private practice, affiliated with Children's Hospital of Philadelphia, providing personalized care at prime Center City and suburban locations, 24-hour coverage.

PERIODONTICS

EMANUEL R. TRESS, DDS, PC
Implants
7848 Old York Rd., Suite 100, Elkins Park Professional Plaza, Elkins Park, PA 19117; (215)635-0465.
Board-certified periodontist, on several hospital staffs, specializing in preventive, nonsurgical and surgical periodontal care, as well as implants. State-of-the-art equipment and a caring, experienced staff. Foreign language spoken: Dutch.

PHARMACY

SHERBY PHARMACY AND MEDICAL EQUIPMENT INC.
Medical Equipment
Township Line and Burmont rds., Drexel Hill, PA 19026; (215)789-3400.
Offering the most innovative pharmacy practice in the Delaware Valley, including medication counseling; diabetes and asthma education; specialty compounded prescriptions and a complete line of home healthcare products. Free delivery and insurance billing.

PHYSICAL & REHAB MEDICINE

DENNIS J. BONNER, M.D., NANCY SHANAHAN, M.D.
Physiatry
St. Mary's Medical Bldg., Suite 304, Langhorne, PA 19047; (215)752-0200 *and* Rehab and Occupational Specialists, 1854 New Rodgers Rd. and Rt. 413, Levittown, PA 19056.
Specializing in PM&R. Treat functional disabilities, strokes, paralysis, amputations, burns, arthritis, osteoporosis, back pain. EMG studies, IMEs, CTS, sports medicine.

Workers compensation and auto injuries welcomed. Foreign language spoken: Spanish.

FRANCIS J. BONNER JR., M.D.
Physical Medicine and Rehabilitation
The Graduate Hospital, 1800 Lombard St., Philadelphia, PA 19146; (215)546-0440.
Specializing in diagnosis and rehabilitation management of back and neck pain, resulting from spinal arthritis, disc disorders and osteoporosis. Disability evaluation. Independent medical examination and electrodiagnostic evaluation.

JAMES F. BONNER, M.D., WILLIAM F. BONNER, M.D.
217 Kedron Ave., Folsom, PA 19033; (610)Rehab-75 *and* Offices at Oxford Crossings, 333 N. Oxford Valley Rd., Suite 102, Fairless Hills, PA 19030; (215)547-6611.
Auto/work injuries, chronic pain management, exercise rehabilitation, physical therapy, disability evaluation, trauma, neck and pain disorders, sports medicine, EMG, IMEs, peer review and case management.

EMMELINE P. ABELLA, M.D.
1648 Huntingdon Pike, Meadowbrook, PA 19046; (215)938-3620 *and* St. Mary's Hospital, Medical Office Bldg., Suite 108, Langhorn, PA 19047; (215)938-3620.
Evaluation and management of physical disabilities (strokes, amputations, arthritis, traumatic injuries, and the diagnosis of nerve and muscle diseases. Electromyography and nerve conduction studies.

PHYSICAL MEDICINE

REHABILITATION ASSOCIATES OF THE MAIN LINE PC
Neurology, Internal Medicine
414 Paoli Pike, PO Box 3007, Malvern, PA 19355-3300; (610)251-5450.
Evaluation and management of physical disabilities: head injuries, stroke, orthopedic conditions, amputation, arthritis, MS, spinal cord injuries, chronic pain, work-related injuries and EMG studies.

PHYSICAL THERAPY

MAIN LINE MEDICAL EXERCISE
Sports Medicine and Orthopedic Rehabilitation
Main Line Health and Fitness Bldg., 931 Haverford Rd., Bryn Mawr, PA 19010; (215)527-7870.
Main Line Medical Exercise is a dynamic and comprehensive physical-therapy facility featuring MedX testing and rehabilitative exercise equipment, proven to restore function and relieve pain from spinal injury.

PLASTIC SURGERY

COOPER PLASTIC SURGERY ASSOCIATES. ARTHUR S. BROWN, M.D., LENORA R. BAROT, M.D., MARTHA S. MATTHEWS, M.D.
Reconstructive Surgery
702 E. Main St., Moorestown, NJ 08057; (609)234-7073.
Full range of cosmetic and reconstructive surgery– breast surgery, liposuction, facial, hand, birth defects, microsurgery, maxillofacial, difficult wounds, post-traumatic reconstruction. Affiliated with Cooper Hospital.

RICHARD L. DOLSKY, M.D. COSMETIC SURGERY OF PHILADELPHIA
191 Presidential Blvd., Suite 105, Bala Cynwyd, PA 19004; (610)667-3341.
Specializing in facial surgery, rhinoplasty, liposuction and breast contouring. Dr. Dolsky is the only Philadelphia plastic surgeon certified by the American Boards of plastic surgery, otolaryngology and cosmetic surgery.

JAMES W. FOX, IV, M.D.
135 S. 18th St., Philadelphia, PA, 19103; (215)-563-8557.
Board-certified Plastic and Reconstructive Surgeon, Chief of Plastic Surgery Thomas Jefferson University Hospital, Professor of Plastic Surgery Jefferson Medical College. Specializes in cosmetic surgery, breast surgery, liposuction, and skin-cancer surgery.

ROBERT J. MIRABILE, M.D.
Plastic Surgery
1330 Powell St., Suite 402, Norristown, PA 19401; (215)272-8821.
Certified by the American Board of Plastic Surgery and the American Board of Surgery, Dr. Mirabile provides personalized attention to each patient. His practice highlights breast and cosmetic facial surgery. Other specialties include body contouring, liposuction and skin cancer surgery.

JOHN H. MOORE, JR., M.D.
Plastic and Reconstructive Surgery
135 S. 18th St. Philadelphia, PA 19103; (215)563-8557.
Plastic and reconstructive surgery, Thomas Jefferson University Hospital; specializing in cosmetic surgery, breast surgery, liposuction and skin cancer surgery. Certified, American Board of Plastic Surgery.

R. BARRETT NOONE, M.D., J. BRIEN MURPHY, M.D., RONALD A. LOHNER, M.D.
Reconstructive Surgery
888 Glenbrook Ave., Bryn Mawr, PA 19010; (215)527-4833.
This group specializes in all aspects of cosmetic, reconstructive and hand surgery.

CHARLES E. PAPPAS, M.D., F.A.C.S.
The Institute for Aesthetic Plastic Surgery, 467 Pennsylvania Ave., Suite 202, Fort Washington, PA 19034; (215)628-4300.
A board-certified plastic surgeon specializing in facial aesthetic and body contouring surgery. Director of the Institute for Aesthetic Plastic Surgery, a regional center for plastic surgery and a certified free-standing operating-room facility.

PLASTIC SURGERY SUITE, DR. MARCIA FITZPATRICK, DR. DAVID SAUNDERS
Liposuction and Facial Cosmetic Surgery
1001 West Chester Pike, routes 3 and 202, West Chester, PA 19382; (215)429-9000.
The Plastic Surgery Suite is an outpatient office and surgicenter for cosmetic surgery consultations and operations.

Penn Dental, postdoctoral periodontics/ prosthodontics; teaches/practices appearance enhancement dentistry; Amer. Acad. Esthetic Dentistry; C.L. Pincus Foundation Exec. Director; Leadership Devel. Institute, co-founder; Team Dentist Philadelphia 76ers.

PSYCHIATRY

ABINGTON STRESS MANAGEMENT CENTER, ERIC WHIKEHART, M.D., MEDICAL DIRECTOR
Preventive Medicine, Biofeedback
1245 Highland Ave., Suite 201, Abington, PA 19001; (215)886-2660.
ASMC's program includes a medical evaluation, relaxation and stress management training, and biofeedback instruction to help you overcome medical or psychological stress-related problems. Illnesses treated include headache, irritable bowel, hypertension and all anxiety disorders.

WILLIAM L. CLOVIS, M.D.
1930 Chestnut St., Philadelphia, PA 19103; (215)568-1380.
Listening for 30 years has taught me that there are very few rules in psychiatry. The problems may look the same, but each person is different. Board-certified. Individual psychotherapy, marriage and sexual counseling.

KATHERINE B. FRANTZ, M.D.
Psychoanalysis
4641 Roosevelt Blvd., Philadelphia, PA 19124; (215)831-4700.
General adult psychiatry with special interest in psychoanalysis and psychotherapy.

GORDON R. HODAS, M.D.
Family Psychiatry
8104 Germantown Ave., Philadelphia, PA 19118; (215)247-1707.
Experienced family psychiatrist, board-certified in both adult and child psychiatry, available to help families and/or couples explore and strengthen relationships.

THE HORSHAM CLINIC
722 E. Butler Pike, Ambler, PA 19002;

(215)643-7800, (800)643-7800.
Private psychiatric facility situated on 55 acres in a campus setting. Offering both inpatient and outpatient treatment and partial hospitalization programs for adults and adolescents.

DOROTHEA LEICHER, MED., LSW, BCD, NCPSYA
Psychiatry
Philadelphia Consultation Center, 313 S. 16th St., Philadelphia, PA 19102; (215)732-6283.
Specializing in reversing self-destructive behavior patterns: fear of success, depression, addictions to substances/relationships/behaviors, psychosomatic cond. Confidential, day/evening. Sliding fee. Foreign languages spoken: German, French.

SARA B. MILLER, M.D.
132 E. Beechtree Lane, Wayne, PA 19087; (610)964-0365.
Adult; marital; sexual dysfunction; eating disorders: anorexia and the overweight; premenstrual syndrome; and sleep problems.

EDWARD OPASS, M.D.
18 N. State St., Newtown, PA 18940; (215)579-9850.
Board-certified in psychiatry and specializing in intense individual psychotherapy, using medication where appropriate.

JAMES B. PIERCE III, M.D., SENIOR ATTENDING PSYCHIATRIST
The Institute of Pennsylvania Hospital, 111 N. 49th St., Philadelphia, PA 19139; (215)471-2462 *and* Main Line office; (610)527-4776 and fax (610)527-0846.
Psychoanalyst and board-certified psychiatrist. Individual, couple, family psychotherapy. Inpatient comprehensive treatment. Treatment of adolescents including hospitalization, coordinated with Mill Creek School. Depression, addictions, schizophrenia, anorexia/bulimia. Evaluation consultations. Referral for psychological testing.

SUSAN PORITSKY, M.D.
Psychotherapy/Psychopharmacology

800 Spruce St., Pennsylvania Hospital, Philadelphia, PA 19107; (215)471-2413 *and* Institute of Pennsylvania Hospital, 111 N. 49th St., Philadelphia, PA 19139.
Adult and adolescent psychiatry, specializing in treatment of anxiety, depression, troubled relationships, women's health. Faculty, University of Pennsylvania. Evening hours available.

DR. RICHARD SCHWARTZMAN
Drug-Free Therapy: An Alternative to Medication
2530 Pine St., Philadelphia, PA 19103; (215)732-2288.
This drug-free therapy is a treatment for the majority of emotional disorders, including schizophrenia, anxiety and depression. Through the controlled release of withheld and repressed emotions–such as sadness, fear and anger–natural functioning can be restored. Childhood traumas are cleared away. The treatment does not employ hypnosis. Twenty years of experience has proven this therapy to be effective and safe. Board-certified by The American Board of Psychiatry and Neurology.

PSYCHOLOGY

AGORAPHOBIA AND ANXIETY TREATMENT CENTER
Anxiety Disorders
112 Bala Ave., Bala Cynwyd, PA 19004; (610)667-6490.
Internationally recognized program for research and treatment of anxiety disorders including: agoraphobia, social anxiety, obsessive-compulsive and panic disorders, and P.T.S.D. for adults and children.

ALTERNATIVE CHOICES, CINDY N. ARIEL, PH.D., ROBERT A. NASEEF, PH.D.
514 S. 4th St., Philadelphia, PA 19147; (215)592-1333.
General practice. Brief and long-term psychotherapy. Specialties include: women's issues, men's issues, relationship conflicts, grief, special-needs families, stepfamilies,

HIV+ individuals and families, alternative lifestyles.

ROBERT J. BERCHICK, PH.D.
Cognitive Therapy
433 E. Street Rd., Warminster, PA 18974; (215) 674-9445.
Specialist in depression, relationship difficulties and various anxiety disorders. Formerly served as Clinical Director for Dr. Beck's Center for Cognitive Therapy/University of Pennsylvania.

STEVEN R. COHEN, PH.D.
8549 Bustleton Ave., Philadelphia, PA 19152; (215)745-7707.
Providing comprehensive psychological services since 1970 for adults, adolescents and children. Individual, marriage-family therapy are offered to treat a wide range of psychological–relationship problems.

DR. MARION RUDIN FRANK & ASSOCIATES; PROFESSIONAL PSYCHOLOGY SERVICES
Therapy/Counseling/Assessment
One Rittenhouse Square, Suite 701, 18th and Walnut sts., Philadelphia, PA 19103; (215)567-1306.
Confidential psychotherapy for individuals and couples. Specializing in relationship issues, depression, anxiety, grief work, sexuality, women's issues, family and work concerns. Also employee assistance programs and consultation for companies.

THERON C. MALE, PH.D. AND MARYANN MAGEE, PH.D.
Hypnosis, Marriage and Relationship Enhancement
Westtown Professional Center, Suite D2, 1515 West Chester Pike, West Chester, PA 19382; (215)692-2092.
Past-life regression therapy, an exciting and effective adjunct in psychotherapy, is used to alleviate the emotional, physical and/or spiritual pain associated with depression, anxiety, phobias, psychosomatic disorders and relationship problems. (Studied with Brian Weiss, M.D., author of "Through Time Into Healing.")

MICHELE M. MARSH, PH.D.

Family Therapy
827 W. Lancaster Ave., Bryn Mawr, PA
19010; (610)526-9515.
Family, couple and individual therapy.
Specialties: emotional/behavioral problems
of children and adolescents; relationship
conflicts; separation, divorce, remarriage.
Treatment for anxiety, depression, trauma,
sexual abuse.

PROFESSIONAL CLINICAL FORUM

130 Benson Manor, Jenkintown, PA 19046;
1-800-PSYCH-12.
Specializing in non-drug treatments of
depression and related disorders, provided
by professionals with over 25 years experience each. Serving Philadelphia,
Montgomery, Bucks, Chester, Delaware
counties, South Jersey, Lehigh Valley.

RITTENHOUSE COUNSELING ASSOCIATES. ROBERT J. CHAIKIN, PH.D., DIRECTOR

Counseling and Rehabilitation
Suite 101, 2201 Chestnut St., Philadelphia,
PA 19103; (215)557-9007.
Licensed psychologists experienced in psychotherapy (anxiety, depression, pain management, phobias); and counseling (addictions, career, marital, relationship, individual, family and group). Comprehensive psychological testing. Insurance accepted.

SYWULAK PSYCHOLOGICAL ASSOCIATES P.C., ANDREA E. SYWULAK, PH.D.

Child/Marriage/Family Psychology
928 Jaymor Rd., Suite B120, Southampton,
PA 18966; (215)355-8812.
Comprehensive, quality psychological services for adults, children, parents, couples,
and families. Specializing in the treatment of
young children, parent-child difficulties and
family communication problems.

PULMONARY DISEASE

JEFFERSON PULMONARY ASSOCIATES AND THE JEFFERSON ASTHMA CENTER, JAMES E. FISH,

M.D., DIRECTOR, JONATHAN E. GOTTLIEB, M.D., HAROLD L. ISRAEL, M.D., GREGORY C. KANE, M.D., HERBERT PATRICK, M.D., STEPHEN P. PETERS, M.D., PAUL SIEGEL, M.D., SANDRA WEIBEL, M.D.

Department of Medicine, Division of
Pulmonary Medicine and Critical Care,
Thomas Jefferson University, 111 S. 11th St.,
Suite 4240, Philadelphia, PA 19107;
(215)955-5161.
Board-certified physicians specializing in
diseases of the chest with special programs in
asthma, emphysema, bronchitis, cough, lung
cancer and occupational lung disease.

JOHN P. MAHAN, M.D., HOWARD J. LEE, M.D., RICHARD D. SHUSTERMAN, M.D.

Sleep Disorders, Internal Medicine
St. Mary Medical Bldg., Suite 401, 1205
Langhorne-Newtown Rd., Langhorne, PA
19047; (215)757-1414 *and* Nazareth
Physicians Office Bldg., Suite 203, 2701
Holme Ave., Philadelphia, PA 19152;
(215)332-9095.
Board-certified in internal medicine, pul-
monary disease (asthma, lung disease), and
sleep disorders (apnea, insomnia). Providing
compassionate quality care. Medicare, Blue
Shield and HMO participating.

PENN JERSEY PULMONARY ASSOCIATES

Critical Care
One Penn Blvd., Philadelphia, PA 19144;
(215)951-8740 *and* 509 N. Broad St.,
Woodbury, NJ 08096; (609)853-2025.
Charles R. Egoville, M.D., F.C.C.P., Eric V.
Finkenstadt, M.D., F.C.C.P., Scott B.
Rosenberg, M.D., F.C.C.P. This board-certi-
fied practice provides full-service pulmonary
and critical-care diagnosis and treatment
together with sleep apnea evaluation in
Pennsylvania and southern New Jersey.

RADIOLOGY

DOYLESTOWN MRI CENTER, INC.

MRI

800 W. State St., Suite 205, Doylestown, PA 18901; (215)345-4568.

At Doylestown MRI, a modern wide-open design reduces feelings of confinement. Problems of patient size and claustrophobia are virtually eliminated. Hours: weekdays, evenings, Saturdays.

REHABILITATION

JEFFERSON REHABILITATION MEDICINE, JOHN F. DITUNNO JR., M.D., CHAIRMAN, GERALD J. HERBISON, M.D., FRANK NASO, M.D., STANLEY R. JACOBS, M.D., RALPH J. MARINO, M.D., KELLEY C. CROZIER, M.D., VIRGINIA GRAZIANI, M.D.

Physical Medicine and Rehabilitation (Physiatry)

125 S. 9th St., Suite 600, Philadelphia, PA 19107; (215)955-1202.

Board-certified physical medicine and rehabilitation specialists treat spinal cord injuries, strokes, amputations, burns, arthritis, osteoporosis, sports injuries and back pain, and perform EMG studies.

REPRODUCTIVE ENDOCRINOLOGY

MICHAEL D. BIRNBAUM, M.D.

Gynecologist

8118 Old York Rd., Elkins Park, PA 19117; (215)635-0545 *and* 115 Bloomingdale Ave., Wayne, PA 19087;

Fully trained reproductive endocrinologist; expertise–all aspects of infertility; ovulation induction; intra-uterine insemination; special expertise in operative/laser laparoscopy for endometriosis, pelvic adhesions, tubal disease. Foreign language spoken: Spanish.

JEROME H. CHECK, M.D.

Reproductive and Medical Endocrine Associates, P.C., 7447 Old York Rd., Melrose Park, PA 19126; (215)635-1567 *and* Cooper Center for Reproductive Endocrinology, P.C., 8002E Greentree Commons, Marlton, NJ 08053; (609)751-5575 *and* Delaware

Center for Infertility & Gynecologic Endocrinology, P.A., 620 Stanton-Christiana Rd., Suite 202, Newark, DE 19713; (302)633-0500.

Dr. Check is world-renowned for achieving successful pregnancies using various forms of infertility treatment, including ovulation induction, artificial insemination and hormonal therapy. He specializes in the use of all forms of assisted reproductive technologies, including in-vitro fertilization, micromanipulation, GIFT, ZIFT and ET. A dedicated, caring and knowledgeable staff. Hours and locations convenient for patients.

STEPHEN L. CORSON, M.D., FRANCES R. BATZER, M.D., BENJAMIN GOCIAL, M.D., MAUREEN KELLY, M.D., JACQUELINE N. GUTMANN, M.D.

815 Locust St., Philadelphia, PA 19107; (215)922-2206 *and* Suburban: 5217 Militia Hill Rd., Plymouth Meeting, PA 19462; (610)834-1230.

Philadelphia Fertility Institute. Care from puberty through menopause, focus on infertility, endocrinology, menopause, IVF and reproductive surgery.

SOUTH JERSEY FERTILITY AND IN-VITRO FERTILIZATION CENTER, ROBERT A. SKAF, M.D.

Specialty Office for Infertility and Reproductive Endocrinology

512 Lippincott Dr., Marlton, NJ 08053; (609)596-2233.

Comprehensive Infertility Center including in-house In-Vitro Fertilization Program, GIFT, ZIFT and embryo cryopreservation. Center is equipped to handle all aspects of infertility treatment, including ovulation induction, inseminations, laser surgery, tubal reconstructive surgery. On-site ultrasounds and laboratory.

RESTORATIVE DENTISTRY

JEFFERSON DENTAL ASSOCIATES, NILES NICOLO, D.D.S., LAWRENCE J. GORDON, D.D.S.

Dental Implants, Cosmetic Dentistry

Ben Franklin House, Suite 415, 834 Chestnut St., Philadelphia, PA 19107; (215)955-6666. Multi-specialty group practice emphasizing dental implants, crowns and bridges, cosmetic dentistry. Also comprehensive general dental care. Strict infection control procedures. Thomas Jefferson University Hospital Affiliation. Foreign language spoken: Italian.

RHEUMATOLOGY

JEFFERSON RHEUMATOLOGY ASSOCIATES
111 S. 11th St., Philadelphia, PA 19147; (215)955-8430 *and* Ford Rd. Campus, 3905 Ford Rd., Philadelphia; (215)955-8430 *and* The Jefferson Osteoporosis Center, Ford Rd. Campus; (215)578-3433.
Board-certified physicians provide special programs for lupus, scleroderma, arthritis; treatment of connective tissue diseases, localized and systemic musculoskeletal problems. Osteoporosis Center–evaluation, treatment, DEXA scanning.

SERVICES FOR THE AGING

FRIENDS SERVICES FOR THE AGING
Retirement Residences/Retirement Communities
6834 Anderson St., Philadelphia, PA 19119-1422; (215)849-4428.
Information on 15 area Quaker organizations. Includes assisted living, continuing care retirement communities, in-home services, adult day programs, nursing homes, mental health services. People of all faiths and races welcome.

SPORTS MEDICINE

JEFFERSON SPORTS MEDICINE CENTER, PHILLIP J. MARONE, M.D., DIRECTOR
Department of Orthopaedic Surgery, Thomas Jefferson University, 130 S. 9th St., Suite 106, Philadelphia, PA 19107; (215)955-2001.
Board-certified specialists in the diagnosis and treatment of sports-related injuries, with extensive experience in adolescent and adult,

amateur and professional sports medicine.

SURGERY

HERBERT E. COHN, M.D.
Thoracic and General Surgery
Thomas Jefferson University Hospital, Suite G8290, 111 S. 11th St., Philadelphia, PA 19107; (215)955-6602.
Extensive experience in the diagnosis and treatment of malignant and benign disorders of the lung, esophagus, breast, thyroid and parathyroid gland; experienced in thoracoscopic and laparoscopic surgery.

MATT L. KIRKLAND, M.D., FACS
301 S. 8th St., 2L., Philadelphia, PA 19106; (215)829-3697.
Board-certified surgeon practicing the full spectrum of general surgery including an extensive experience with laparoscopic cholecystectomy and other laparoscopic procedures.

R.B.W. SURGICAL GROUP, P.C., ELIZABETH ROBISON, M.D., F.A.C.S, M. HASSAN BUDEIR, M.D., BARBARA J. WALTER, M.D.
Surgical Critical Care
Brandywine Professional Bldg., Suite 27, 213 Reeceville Rd., Coatesville, PA 19320; (610)384-0580.
Board-certified general surgeons with special added interest in breast, laparoscopic, thoracic, trauma and vascular surgery. Office procedures include minor excisions and venous sclerotherapy. Foreign languages spoken: Arabic, French.

SURGICAL ONCOLOGY

THOMAS G. FRAZIER, M.D.
Breast
101 Bryn Mawr Ave., Suite 201, Bryn Mawr, PA 19010; (610)520-0700.
Dr. Frazier specializes in breast disease and breast-related problems. Please call (610)520-0700 for appointments.

ONCOLOGY ASSOCIATES, LTD. HARVEY J. LERNER, M.D., ELIHU J.

LEDESMA, M.D.
General Surgery
Germantown Hospital, One Penn Blvd., Philadelphia, PA 19144; (215)951-8014.
Board-certified practice with extensive experience in treatment of malignant and benign diseases of the breast, colon, lung and other tumors. Foreign languages spoken: Spanish, Ukranian.

UROLOGY

RICHARD H. CHARNEY, M.D., BOARD-CERTIFIED IN UROLOGIC SURGERY
Warminster Medical Office Bldg., 205 Newtown Rd., Suite 101, Warminster, PA 18974; (215)674-0301.
Emphasizing non-surgical treatment of male/female incontinence, prostate disease, kidney stones and impotence. Extensive experience in treating prostate and bladder cancer, cystitis, vasectomy. Sensitive, concerned staff.

DR. PHILLIP C. GINSBERG
Urology and Urologic Surgery
Albert Einstein Medical Center, Klein Professional Bldg., Suite 204A, 5401 Old York Rd., Philadelphia, PA 19141; (215)456-1177.
Board-certified, emphasis on non-surgical treatment for prostate enlargement. Laser surgery, including kidney stones; urologic problems of the elderly and comprehensive urologic cancer management.

UROLOGIC ASSOCIATES OF JEFFERSON, THOMAS JEFFERSON UNIVERSITY, S. GRANT MULHOLLAND, M.D., CHAIRMAN, DEMETRIUS H. BAGLEY, M.D., MICHAEL B. CHANCELLOR, M.D., LEONARD G. GOMELLA, M.D., IRVIN H. HIRSH, M.D., DAVID A. RIVAS, M.D.
111 S. 11th St., Philadelphia, PA 19107; (215)955-6963.
Board-certified faculty specializing in endoscopy, incontinence, infertility, oncology, prostate problems, sexual dysfunction, urinary stones, urologic cancer and voiding dysfunction.

VALLEY FORGE UROLOGICAL ASSOC.
Urologic Oncology and Cancer
750 S. Main St., Suite 203, Phoenixville, PA 19460; (215)933-1133 *and* Sunset Office Plaza, 1503 Sunset Dr., Suite 2, Pottstown, PA 19464; (215)327-0953.
A full-service practice in the suburbs treating urological cancer, including prostate cryosurgery ("freezing"), urinary stone disease, male fertility and infertility and urinary infections.

KRISTENE E. WHITMORE, M.D. PHILADELPHIA UROSURGICAL ASSOCIATION
1 Graduate Plaza, 606 Pepper Pavilion, Philadelphia, PA 19146; (215)546-2280.
Female urology: bladder disorders, cystitis, interstitial cystitis, incontinence, prostate problems, bladder cancer.

WOMEN'S HEALTH

THE RENFREW CENTER, LARRY MILLER, M.D., WILLIAM DAVIS, PH.D., NANCY LOGUE, PH.D., WENDY CRAMER, M.ED.
475 Spring Lane, Philadelphia, PA 19128; (800)RENFREW.
Provides individual and group therapy, intensive outpatient, day, residential and educational programs for women struggling with eating disorders, depression, anxiety and abuse.

KARYN L. SCHER, PH.D., LISA K. ROONEY, PH.D.
111 Presidential Blvd., Suite 244, Bala Cynwyd, PA 19004; (610)668-9189, (610)660-9416.
Caring support for women's health-care needs. Group/individual psychotherapy for eating disorders, interpersonal/marital issues (K.L.S.). Psychotherapy/support for cancer, chronic and terminal illnesses. Caretaker support/life changes/bereavement (L.K.R.).

Index

NOTES

NOTES

NOTES

NOTES

NOTES

NOTES